THE abc OF
BRITISH RAILWAYS
LOCOMOTIVES

COMBINED VOLUME

PARTS 1—4

Nos. 1-99999

ALSO DIESEL AND ELECTRIC
MULTIPLE UNITS

SUMMER
1958
EDITION

LONDON :

Ian Allan Ltd

NOTES ON THE USE OF THIS BOOK

THE following notes are a guide to the system of reference marks and other details given in the lists of dimensions shown for each class in the alphabetical list of classes.

1. Many of the classes listed are sub-divided by reason of mechanical or constructional differences (on the Eastern and North Eastern Regions the sub-divisions are denoted in some cases by "Parts," shown thus : D16/3). At the head of each class will be found a list of such sub-divisions, if any, usually arranged in order of introduction. Each part is given there a reference mark by which its relevant dimensions, if differing from those of other parts, and the locomotives included in this sub-division, or part, may be identified. Any other differences between locomotives are also indicated, with reference marks, below the details of the class's introduction.

2. The lists of dimensions at the head of each class show locomotives fitted with two inside cylinders, Stephenson valve gear and slide valves, unless otherwise stated, e.g. (O) = two outside cylinders, P.V. = piston valves.

3. The following method is used to denote superheated locomotives, the letters being inserted, where applicable, after the boiler pressure details : Su = All engines superheated.

SS = Some engines superheated.

4. The date on which the first locomotive of a class was built or modified is denoted by " Introduced."

5. S. denotes Service (Departmental) locomotive still carrying B.R. number. This reference letter is introduced only for the reader's guidance and is not borne by the locomotive concerned.

Note :

(a) On the Southern Region the letters " DS " preceding a number indicate a Service Locomotive. On the S.R. (only) this marking appears on the locomotive.

(b) The Eastern and North Eastern Regions number their departmental locomotives in a separate series, as shown in Part IV.

6. Full details of the following will be found in the book named :—

- Electric and Gas turbine locomotives in Part 2 (Nos. 10000–39999).

- Diesel locomotives and multiple-units in *ABC of British Railways Diesels.*

- Electric train units in *ABC of British Electric Trains.*

TRACTIVE EFFORT

THE tractive effort of a locomotive is the propulsive force exerted by the driving wheel at its point of contact with the rail, and is calculated for a steam locomotive from the formula :

$$\text{T.E.} = \frac{d^2 \times s \times p \times 85}{w \times 100}$$

where T.E. = tractive effort in lb., d = diameter of cylinder in inches, s = piston stroke in inches, p = working pressure in lb. per sq. inch and w = diameter of driving wheel in inches. The answer represents the tractive effort at 85 per cent. of the working pressure, a commonly accepted proportion for the average pressure in a cylinder during the complete stroke, resulting from the fact that the steam supply is necessarily cut off before the piston has traversed its full stroke.

The answer must be multiplied by 1½ for three-cylinder simple engines and by 2 for four-cylinder simple engines. For a compound engine, it is usual to base calculations on the dimensions of the low pressure cylinder at 80 per cent. of the boiler pressure.

It should be emphasised that tractive effort is largely a theoretical figure and that comparison of tractive efforts between types of locomotive is not necessarily a guide to their respective hauling powers, to determine which, numerous other factors must be taken into account.

DESCRIBING DIESEL AND ELECTRIC LOCOS.

THE well-known Whyte notation for the description of steam locomotive wheel arrangements is unsatisfactory for the description of other types of locomotive, since it makes no provision for the differences in power arrangements or chassis layout which often occur on non-steam locomotives with apparently identical groupings of wheels.

Wheel arrangements of non-steam locomotives are therefore described by a development of the Continental notation. This :

(i) calculates by axles and not by wheels ;

(ii) uses letters instead of numerals to denote driving axles ("A" = 1, "B" = 2, "C" = 3, etc.) and numerals only for non-powered axles. Thus a 4-6-2 under the Whyte notation is described as a 2-C-1 under this system.

As with the Whyte notation, an indication of the grouping of axles is given, but with non-steam locomotives, powered and non-powered axles may be found in the same group. Thus British Railways' gas-turbine electric locomotive No. 18000 is described as an A1A-A1A, indicating that it is mounted on two six-wheel bogies, each of which has a non-powered axle in the centre and two motored axles at either end. The Fell diesel-mechanical locomotive No. 10100, on the other hand, is a 2-D-2, showing that the two non-motored four-wheel bogies at each end of it are independent of the eight-wheel powered unit in the centre. Groups of axles are separated by a hyphen if they are quite independent of each other, but by a "plus" sign in cases where powered bogies are linked by an articulated joint to take certain stresses.

If all axles on a bogie or frame unit are individually powered a suffix letter "o" is added to the descriptive letter. Thus B.R. diesel-electrics Nos. 10201-3 are shown as 1Co-Co1, indicating that they have a carrying axle at the outer end of the two eight-wheel bogies and the remaining three axles each have their own traction motors. But a standard B.R. diesel-electric six-wheeled shunter, should technically be shown as a 0-C-0, since only one of its three driving axles is motored, the power being transmitted to the others by coupling rods. Engines of this type however are usually described by the Whyte notation of 0-6-0.

BRITISH RAILWAYS LOCOMOTIVE
SHEDS AND SHED CODES

(THESE LISTS INCLUDE ALTERATIONS BROUGHT ABOUT OR
PROPOSED BY THE REGIONAL BOUNDARY CHANGES OF FEBRUARY 1,
1958, AS FAR AS AT PRESENT KNOWN AND ARE SUBJECT TO
AMENDMENT)

ALL B.R. LOCOMOTIVES CARRY THE CODE OF THEIR HOME DEPOT
ON A SMALL PLATE AFFIXED TO THE SMOKEBOX DOOR.

LONDON MIDLAND REGION

1A	**Willesden**	8F	Springs Branch (Wigan)
1B	Camden	8G	Sutton Oak
1C	Watford		
1D	Devons Road (Bow)	9A	**Longsight**
1E	Bletchley	9B	Stockport (Edgeley)
	Leighton Buzzard	9C	Macclesfield
		9D	Buxton
2A	**Rugby**	9E	Trafford Park
2B	Nuneaton	9F	Heaton Mersey
2C	Warwick (W.R.)	9H	Gorton
2D	Coventry		Dinting
2E	Northampton		
2F	Woodford Halse	11A	**Barrow**
		11B	Workington
3A	**Bescot**	11C	Oxenholme
3B	Bushbury	11D	Tebay
3C	Walsall		
3D	Aston	12A	**Carlisle (Kingmoor)**
3E	Monument Lane	12B	Carlisle (Upperby)
			Penrith
5A	**Crewe North**	12C	Carlisle (Canal)
	Whitchurch	12D	Kirkby Stephen
5B	Crewe South		
5C	Stafford	14A	**Cricklewood**
5D	Stoke	14B	Kentish Town
5E	Alsager	14C	St. Albans
5F	Uttoxeter	14D	Neasden
			Aylesbury
6A	**Chester**		Chesham
6B	Mold Junction		Marylebone
6C	Birkenhead		Rickmansworth
6D	Chester (Northgate)	14E	Bedford
6E	Chester (ex-W.R.)		
6F	Bidston	15A	**Wellingborough**
6G	Llandudno Junction	15B	Kettering
6H	Bangor	15C	Leicester
6J	Holyhead	15D	Coalville
6K	Rhyl	15E	Leicester (G.C.)
		15F	Market Harborough
8A	**Edge Hill**		Seaton
8B	Warrington		
	Warrington (Arpley)	16A	**Nottingham**
8C	Speke Junction	16B	Kirkby
8D	Widnes	16C	Mansfield
8E	Northwich	16D	Annesley

4

17A	**Derby**		24F	Fleetwood
17B	Burton		24G	Skipton
	Horninglow		24H	Hellifield
	Overseal		24J	Lancaster
17D	Rowsley		24K	Preston
	Cromford		24L	Carnforth
	Middleton			
	Sheep Pasture			
			26A	**Newton Heath**
				Kenyon Junction
18A	**Toton**		26B	Agecroft
18B	Westhouses		26C	Bolton
18C	Hasland		26D	Bury
			26E	Lees
			26F	Patricroft
21A	**Saltley**			
21B	Bournville			
			27A	**Bank Hall**
			27B	Aintree
24A	**Accrington**		27C	Southport
24B	Rose Grove		27D	Wigan (L. & Y.)
24C	Lostock Hall		27E	Walton
24D	Lower Darwen		27F	Brunswick (Liverpool)
24E	Blackpool			Warrington (C.L.C.)
	Blackpool North			

EASTERN REGION

30A	**Stratford**		32B	Ipswich
	Brentwood			Felixstowe Town
	Chelmsford			Stowmarket
	Enfield Town		32C	Lowestoft
	Epping		32D	Yarmouth (South Town)
	Ilford		32E	Yarmouth (Vauxhall)
	Southend (Victoria)		32F	Yarmouth Beach
	Wood St. (Walthamstow)		32G	Melton Constable
30B	Hertford East			Norwich City
	Buntingford			
	Ware			
30C	Bishops Stortford		33A	**Plaistow**
30E	Colchester		33B	Tilbury
	Braintree		33C	Shoeburyness
	Clacton			
	Maldon			
	Walton-on-Naze		34A	**Kings Cross**
30F	Parkeston		34B	Hornsey
			34C	Hatfield
			34D	Hitchin
31A	**Cambridge**		34E	New England
	Ely		34F	Grantham
	Huntingdon East			
	Saffron Walden			
31B	March		36A	**Doncaster**
	Peterborough (Spital)		36C	Frodingham
	Wisbech		36E	Retford
31C	Kings Lynn			Newark
	Hunstanton			
31D	South Lynn			
31E	Bury St. Edmunds		40A	**Lincoln**
	Sudbury (Suffolk)			Lincoln (St. Marks)
31F	Peterborough (Spital Brge.)		40B	Immingham
				Grimsby
				New Holland
32A	**Norwich**		40E	Colwick
	Cromer Beach		40F	Boston
	Dereham			Sleaford
	Wymondham			Spalding

5

41A	Sheffield (Darnall)	41F	Mexborough
41B	Sheffield (Grimesthorpe)		Wath
41C	Millhouses	41G	Barnsley
41D	Canklow	41H	Staveley (ex-G.C.)
41E	Staveley (Barrow Hill)	41J	Langwith Junction
		41K	Tuxford

NORTH EASTERN REGION

50A	**York**	52F	North Blyth
50B	Leeds (Neville Hill)		South Blyth
50C	Selby		
50D	Starbeck	53A	**Hull (Dairycoates)**
50E	Scarborough	53B	Hull (Botanic Gardens)
50F	Malton	53C	Hull (Springhead)
	Pickering		Alexandra Dock
50G	Whitby	53D	Bridlington
		53E	Goole
51A	**Darlington**	54A	**Sunderland**
	Middleton-in-Teesdale		Durham
51B	Newport (Yorks)	54B	Tyne Dock
51C	West Hartlepool		Pelton Level
51D	Middlesbrough	54C	Borough Gardens
51E	Stockton	54D	Consett
51F	West Auckland		
51G	Haverton Hill	55A	**Leeds (Holbeck)**
51J	Northallerton	55B	Stourton
51K	Saltburn	55C	Farnley Junction
		55D	Royston
		55E	Normanton
52A	**Gateshead**	55F	Manningham
	Bowes Bridge	55G	Huddersfield
52B	Heaton		
52C	Blaydon	56A	**Wakefield**
	Alston	56B	Ardsley
	Hexham	56C	Copley Hill
52D	Tweedmouth	56D	Mirfield
	Alnmouth	56E	Sowerby Bridge
52E	Percy Main	56F	Low Moor
		56G	Bradford

SCOTTISH REGION

60A	**Inverness**	62A	**Thornton**
	Dingwall		Anstruther
	Kyle of Lochalsh		Burntisland
60B	Aviemore		Ladybank
	Boat of Garten		Methil
60C	Helmsdale	62B	Dundee (Tay Bridge)
	Dornoch		Arbroath
	Tain		Dundee West
60D	Wick		Montrose
	Thurso		St. Andrews
60E	Forres	62C	Dunfermline
			Alloa
61A	**Kittybrewster**	63A	**Perth South**
	Ballater		Aberfeldy
	Fraserburgh		Blair Atholl
	Inverurie		Crieff
	Peterhead	63B	Stirling South
61B	Aberdeen (Ferryhill)		Kiliin
61C	Keith	63C	Forfar
	Banff	63D	Oban
	Elgin		Ballachulish

64A	**St. Margarets**		65F	Grangemouth
		(Edinburgh)	65G	Yoker
	Dunbar		65H	Helensburgh
	Galashiels		65I	Balloch
	Longniddry		65J	Fort William
	North Berwick			Mallaig
	Seafield			
	South Leith		66A	**Polmadie (Glasgow)**
64B	Haymarket		66B	Motherwell
64C	Dalry Road		66C	Hamilton
64D	Carstairs		66D	Greenock (Ladyburn)
64E	Polmont			Greenock (Princes Pier)
64F	Bathgate			
64G	Hawick		67A	**Corkerhill (Glasgow)**
	Riccarton		67B	Hurlford
	St. Boswells			Beith
				Muirkirk
65A	**Eastfield (Glasgow)**		67C	Ayr
	Arrochar		67D	Ardrossan
65B	St. Rollox			
65C	Parkhead		68B	Dumfries
65D	Dawsholm		68C	Stranraer
	Dumbarton			Newton Stewart
65E	Kipps		68D	Beattock

SOUTHERN REGION

70A	**Nine Elms**		72B	Salisbury
70B	Feltham		72C	Yeovil
70C	Guildford		72E	Barnstaple Junction
70D	Basingstoke			Ilfracombe
70E	Reading			Torrington
70F	Fratton		72F	Wadebridge
70G	Newport (I.O.W.)			
70H	Ryde (I.O.W.)		73A	**Stewarts Lane**
71A	**Eastleigh**		73B	Bricklayers Arms
	Andover Junction		73C	Hither Green
	Lymington		73D	Gillingham (Kent)
	Winchester		73E	Faversham
71B	Bournemouth			
	Branksome		74A	**Ashford (Kent)**
71G	Weymouth		74B	Ramsgate
	Bridport		74C	Dover
71H	Yeovil (ex-G.W.)			Folkestone
71I	Southampton Docks		74D	Tonbridge
71J	Highbridge		74E	St. Leonards
72A	**Exmouth Junction**		75A	**Brighton**
	Bude		75B	Redhill
	Exmouth		75C	Norwood Junction
	Lyme Regis		75D	Horsham
	Okehampton		75E	Three Bridges
	Seaton		75F	Tunbridge Wells West

WESTERN REGION

2C	**Warwick**		81F	Oxford
				Fairford
81A	**Old Oak Common**			
81B	Slough		82A	**Bristol (Bath Road)**
	Marlow			Bath
81C	Southall			Wells
81D	Reading			Weston-super-Mare
	Henley-on-Thames			Yatton
81E	Didcot		82B	St. Philip's Marsh

82C	Swindon		85E	Gloucester
	Chippenham			Dursley
82D	Westbury			Tewkesbury
	Frome		85F	Bromsgrove
82E	Bristol (Barrow Rd.)			
82F	Bath (ex-S. & D.)		86A	**Newport**
	Radstock			**(Ebbw Junction)**
82G	Templecombe		86B	Newport (Pill)
			86C	Cardiff (Canton)
83A	**Newton Abbot**		86D	Llantrisant
	Ashburton		86E	Severn Tunnel Junction
	Kingsbridge		86F	Tondu
83B	Taunton		86G	Pontypool Road
	Bridgwater			Abergavenny
83C	Exeter		86H	Aberbeeg
	Tiverton Junction		86J	Aberdare
83D	Laira (Plymouth)		86K	Tredegar
	Launceston			
83E	St. Blazey		87A	**Neath**
	Bodmin			Glyn Neath
	Moorswater			Neath (N. & B.)
83F	Truro		87B	Duffryn Yard
83G	Penzance		87C	Danygraig
	Helston		87D	Swansea East Dock
	St. Ives		87E	Landore
83H	Plymouth (Friary)		87F	Llanelly
	Callington			Burry Port
				Pantyfynnon
84A	**Wolverhampton**		87G	Carmarthen
	(Stafford Road)		87H	Neyland
84B	Oxley			Cardigan
84C	Banbury			Milford Haven
84D	Leamington Spa			Pembroke Dock
				Whitland
84E	Tyseley		87J	Goodwick
	Stratford-on-Avon		87K	Swansea (Victoria)
84F	Stourbridge Junction			Gurnos
84G	Shrewsbury			Llandovery
	Builth Road			Upper Bank
	Clee Hill			
	Craven Arms		88A	**Cardiff (Cathays)**
	Knighton			Radyr
84H	Wellington (Salop)		88B	Cardiff East Dock
84J	Croes Newydd		88C	Barry
	Bala		88D	Merthyr
	Penmaenpool			Cae Harris
	Trawsfynydd			Dowlais Central
84K	Wrexham (Rhosddu)			Rhymney
			88E	Abercynon
85A	**Worcester**		88F	Treherbert
	Evesham			Ferndale
	Kingham			
85B	Gloucester		89A	**Oswestry**
	Brimscombe			Llanidloes
	Cheltenham			Moat Lane
	Cirencester		89B	Brecon
	Lydney		89C	Machynlleth
	Tetbury			Aberayron
85C	Hereford			Aberystwyth
	Ledbury			Aberystwyth (V. of R.)
	Leominster			Portmadoc
	Ross			Pwllheli
85D	Kidderminster			

8

Right: Diesel-electric 0-6-0 Service Locomotive No. PWM 650 [*B. K. B. Green*

Below: Ex-Cardiff Rly. 0-4-0ST No. 1338 [*L. King*

Right: 1101 Class 0-4-0T No. 1102 [*R. A. Panting*

Ex-S.H.T. 0-4-0ST No. 1140   [R. J. Buckley

Ex-S.H.T. 0-4-0ST No. 1143   [R. J. Buckley

Ex-S.H.T. 0-4-0ST No. 1144   [R. J. Buckley

Right: Ex-P.M.
0-4-0ST No. 1151
[*R. A. Panting*

Below: 1400 Class
0-4-2T No. 1405
[*H. C. Casserley*

Right: Ex-B.P.G.V.
0-6-0T No. 2198
[*A. W. Martin*

Left: 1361 Class
0-6-0ST No. 1361
[E. J. Dew

Centre: 1500 Class
0-6-0PT No. 1504
[Brian E. Morrison

Bottom: 9400 Class
0-6-0PT No. 9426
[B. K. B. Green

Top: 1366 Class
0-6-0PT No. 1367
[B. K. B. Green

Centre: 1600 Class
0-6-0PT No. 1610
[B. K. B. Green

Right: 5400 Class
0-6-0PT No. 5420
[A. W. Martin

4073 Class 4-6-0 No. 7013 *Bristol Castle*   [G. Wheeler

4073 Class 4-6-0 No. 7018 *Drysllwyn Castle* (fitted with three-row superheater and double chimney)   [C. R. L. Coles

4073 Class 4-6-0 No. 4090 *Dorchester Castle* (fitted with four-row superheater, extended smokebox and double chimney)   [G. Wheeler

Top: 6000 Class 4-6-0
No. 6003 *King George
IV* [G. Wheeler

Centre: 6800 Class
4-6-0 No. 6831 *Bear-
ley Grange*
[D. Penney

Left: 7800 Class 4-6-0
No. 7822 *Foxcote
Manor* [P. H. Wells

LOCOMOTIVE SUPERINTENDENTS AND CHIEF
MECHANICAL ENGINEERS OF THE G.W.R. & W.R.

Sir Daniel Gooch	1837–1864
Joseph Armstrong	{ 1854–1864* { 1864–1877
George Armstrong ... ... *(Bro. of J. Armstrong)*	1864–1896*
William Dean	1877–1902
G. J. Churchward	1902–1921
Charles B. Collett	1922–1941
F. W. Hawksworth	1941–1949

* In charge of standard gauge locomotives at Stafford Road Works, Wolverhampton, with wide powers in design and construction.

G.W.R. DIESEL RAILCARS

Car No.	Date	Engines	Total b.h.p.	Seats	Car No.	Date	Engines	Total b.h.p.	Seats
4*	1934	2	242	44	17‡	1936	2	242	—
5–7	1935	2	242	70	18§	1937	2	242	70
8	1936	2	242	70	19–32	1940	2	210	48
11/12†	1936	2	242	63	33, 38‖	1942	4	420	92
13–16	1936	2	242	70	34‡	1941	2	210	—

* Buffet and lavatory facilities.
† Lavatory facilities.
‡ Parcels cars.
§ Experimentally geared to haul trailer car, became prototype of subsequent designs.

‖ Twin-coach unit with buffet and lavatory facilities. Adjoining statistics apply per 2-car unit. This unit can work as a 3-car set by the addition of an ordinary corridor coach.

4	8	14	18	21	24	27	30	33
5	11	15	19	22	25	28	31	34
6	12	16	20	23	26	29	32	38
7	13	17						

SUMMARY OF WESTERN REGION STEAM LOCOMOTIVE CLASSES
WITH HISTORICAL NOTES AND DIMENSIONS

The Code given in smaller bold type at the head of each Class, e.g. " 6MT " denotes its British Railways power classification.

The numbers of locomotives in service have been checked to January, 25th, 1958.

4-6-0　6MT　**1000 Class**
" County "

Introduced 1945. Hawksworth design.
*Fitted with double chimney.
Weight: Loco.　76 tons 17 cwt.
　　　　　Tender 49 tons 0 cwt.
Pressure: 280 lb. Su.
Cyls.: (O) 18½″ × 30″.
Driving Wheels: 6′ 3″.
T.E.: 32,580 lb.　P.V.

1001–3/5/6/8/10/1/3/5–21/4–6/8/9
*1000/4/7/9/12/4/22/3/7

　　　　　　　　　　　Total 30

4-6-0　7P　**4073 Class**
" Castle "

*Introduced 1923. Collett design, developed from " Star " (4037, 5083–92 converted from " Star ").
†Introduced 1946. Fitted with 3-row superheater.
‡Introduced 1947. Fitted with 4-row superheater.
¶Introduced 1956. Fitted with double chimney.
Weight: Loco.　79 tons 17 cwt.
　　　　　Tender 46 tons 14 cwt.
Pressure: 225 lb. Su.
Cyls.: (4) 16″ × 26″.
Driving Wheels: 6′ 8½″.
T.E.: 31,625 lb.
Inside Walschaerts valve gear and rocking shafts.　P.V.
*4037/73/5–86/9/91/2/4–6/8/9, 5001–25/7–32/4/5/7–42/4–8/51 –6/8–60/2/6–70/3/6/8/80/3–92
†5000/65/72/4/5/7/9/81/2/93/6–9, 7000–3/5–12/4–7/20/1/3/5–8/31 –3/5–7
‡4074/8/87/97,5026/33/6/43/9/50/ 7/61/3/4/71/94/5, 7004/13/9/22/ 4/9/30/4
‡¶4090/3　†¶7018　**Total 166**

4-6-0　5MT　**4900 Class**
" Hall "

*Introduced 1924. Collett rebuild with 6′ 0″ driving wheels of " Saint " (built 1907).
†Introduced 1928. Modified design for new construction, with higher-pitched boiler, modified footplating and detail differences.
Weight: Loco. ⎰72 tons 10 cwt.*
　　　　　　　 ⎱75 tons 0 cwt.†
　　　　　Tender 46 tons 14 cwt.
Pressure: 225 lb. Su.
Cyls.: (O) 18½″ × 30″.
Driving Wheels: 6′ 0″.
T.E.: 27,275 lb.
P.V.

*4900
†4901–10/2–99, 5900–99, 6900–58

　　　　　　　　　　　Total 258

4-6-0　8P　**6000 Class**
" King "

*Introduced 1927. Collett design.
†Introduced 1947. Fitted with 4-row superheater.
‡Introduced 1955. Fitted with double chimney.
Weight: Loco.　89 tons 0 cwt.
　　　　　Tender 46 tons 14 cwt.
Pressure: 250 lb. Su.
Cyls.: (4) 16¼″ × 28″.
Driving Wheels: 6′ 6″.
T.E.: 40,285 lb.
Inside Walschaerts valve gear and rocking shafts.　P.V.

*6026
†6012/8
‡†6000–11/3/5–7/9–25/7–9
‡*6014

　　　　　　　　　　　Total 30

4-6-0   5MT   6800 Class
" Grange "

Introduced 1936. Collett design, variation of " Hall " with smaller wheels, incorporating certain parts of withdrawn 4300 2-6-0 locos.

Weight: Loco.   74 tons 0 cwt.
         Tender   40 tons 0 cwt.
Pressure: 225 lb. Su.
Cyls.: (O) $18\frac{1}{2}'' \times 30''$.
Driving Wheels: 5' 8".
T.E.: 28,875 lb.
P.V.

6800–79   **Total 80**

4-6-0   5MT   6959 Class
" Modified Hall "

Introduced 1944. Hawksworth development of " Hall," with larger superheater, "one-piece" main frames and plate-framed bogie.

Weight: Loco.   75 tons 16 cwt.
         Tender   46 tons 14 cwt.
Pressure: 225 lb. Su.
Cyls.: (O) $18\frac{1}{2}'' \times 30''$.
Driving Wheels: 6' 0".
T.E.: 27,275 lb.
P.V.

6959–99, 7900–29   **Total 71**

4-6-0   5MT   7800 Class
" Manor "

Introduced 1938. Collett design for secondary lines, incorporating certain parts of withdrawn 4300 2-6-0 locos.

Weight: Loco.   68 tons 18 cwt.
         Tender   40 tons 0 cwt.
Pressure: 225 lb. Su.
Cyls.: (O) $18'' \times 30''$.
Driving Wheels: 5' 8".
T.E.: 27,340 lb.
P.V.

7800–29   **Total 30**

4-4-0   " City " Class

Introduced 1903. Churchward design.
Weight: Loco.   55 tons 6 cwt.
         Tender   36 tons 15 cwt.
Pressure: 200 lb. Su.
Cyls.: $18'' \times 26''$.
Driving Wheels: 6' $8\frac{1}{2}''$.
T.E.: 17,790 lb.

3440

                   Total 1

Withdrawn 1931 and preserved in York Museum. Returned to service 1957 for hauling enthusiasts' specials

4-4-0   2P   9000 Class

Introduced 1936. Collett rebuild, incorporating " Duke " type boiler and " Bulldog " frames for light lines.
Weight: Loco.   49 tons 0 cwt.
         Tender $\begin{cases} 40 \text{ tons } 0 \text{ cwt.} \\ 36 \text{ tons } 15 \text{ cwt.} \end{cases}$
Pressure: 180 lb. SS.
Cyls.: $18'' \times 26''$.
Driving Wheels: 5' 8".
T.E.: 18,955 lb.

9004/5/13–5/7/8/21

                   Total 8

2-8-0   8F   2800 Class

*Introduced 1903. Churchward design, earlier locos. subsequently fitted with new boiler and superheater.

†Introduced 1938. Collett locos., with side-window cab and detail alterations.

Weight: Loco. $\begin{cases} 75 \text{ tons } 10 \text{ cwt.}^* \\ 76 \text{ tons } 5 \text{ cwt.}† \end{cases}$
         Tender   40 tons 0 cwt.
Pressure: 225 lb. Su.
Cyls.: (O) $18\frac{1}{2}'' \times 30''$.
Driving Wheels: 4' $7\frac{1}{2}''$.
T.E.: 35,380 lb.
P.V.

*2800–2883

†2884–99, 3800–66

           Total 167

2-8-0 7F R.O.D. Class

Introduced 1911. Robinson G.C. design
(L.N.E.R. O4), built from 1917 for
Railway Operating Division, R.E.,
taken into G.W. stock from 1919 and
subsequently fitted with G.W. boiler
mountings and details.
Weight: Loco.   73 tons 11 cwt.
       Tender 47 tons 6 cwt.
Pressure: 185 lb. Su.
Cyls.: (O) 21″ × 26″.
Driving Wheels: 4′ 8″.
T.E.: 32,200 lb.
P.V.

3011/5/24/36/41   **Total 5**

2-8-0 7F 4700 Class

Introduced 1919. Churchward mixed
traffic design (4700 built with smaller
boiler and later rebuilt).
Weight: Loco.   82 tons 0 cwt.
       Tender 46 tons 14 cwt.
Pressure: 225 lb. Su.
Cyls.: (O) 19″ × 30″.
Driving Wheels: 5′ 8″.
T.E.: 30,460 lb.
P.V.

4700–8   **Total 9**

2-6-0 4MT 4300 Class

*Introduced 1911. Churchward design.
†Introduced 1925. Locos. with detail
alterations affecting weight.
‡Introduced 1932. Locos. with side
window cab and detail alterations.
Weight: Loco. $\begin{cases} 62 \text{ tons } 0 \text{ cwt.*} \\ 64 \text{ tons } 0 \text{ cwt.†} \\ 65 \text{ tons } 6 \text{ cwt.‡} \end{cases}$
      Tender 40 tons 0 cwt.
Pressure: 200 lb. Su.
Cyls.: (O) 18½″ × 30″.
Driving Wheels: 5′ 8″.
T.E.: 25,670 lb.
P.V.

*4358/77, 5306/10–3/5/8/9/ 21–
4/6/8/30–3/5–9/41/4/5/7/50/1
/3/5–8/60–2/7–72/5–82/4–6/8
/90/2–4/6–9, 6300–14/6–20/2
–82/4–99, 7305–21
†7300–4
‡7322–4/9/33/9/40/1, 9303–6/8
–10/2–6   **Total 204**

0-6-0 3MT 2251 Class

Introduced 1930. Collett design.
Weight
  Loco.   43 tons 8 cwt.
  Tender $\begin{cases} 36 \text{ tons } 15 \text{ cwt.} \\ 47 \text{ tons } 6 \text{ cwt. (ex-R.O.D.} \\ \text{tender from 3000 Class} \\ 2\text{-8-0).} \end{cases}$
Pressure: 200 lb. Su.
Cyls.: 17½″ × 24″.
Driving Wheels: 5′ 2″.
T.E.: 20,155 lb.

2200–99, 3200–19   **Total 120**

2-8-2T 8F 7200 Class

Introduced 1934. Collett rebuild, with
extended bunker and trailing wheels,
of Churchward 4200 class 2-8-0T.
Weight: 92 tons 2 cwt.
Pressure: 200 lb. Su.
Cyls.: (O) 19″ × 30″.
Driving Wheels: 4′ 7½″.
T.E.: 33,170 lb.
P.V.

7200–53   **Total 54**

2-8-0T $\begin{Bmatrix} 7F* \\ 8F† \end{Bmatrix}$ 4200 Class

*Introduced 1910. Churchward design.
†5205 class. Introduced 1923. With
enlarged cyls. and detail alterations.
Weight: $\begin{cases} 81 \text{ tons } 12 \text{ cwt.*} \\ 82 \text{ tons } 2 \text{ cwt.†} \end{cases}$
Pressure: 200 lb. Su.
Cyls.: $\begin{cases} (O) 18\frac{1}{2}″ \times 30″*. \\ (O) 19″ \times 30″†. \end{cases}$
Driving Wheels: 4′ 7½″.
T.E.: $\begin{cases} 31,450 \text{ lb.*} \\ 33,170 \text{ lb.†} \end{cases}$
P.V.

*4200/1/3/6–8/11–5/7/8/21–33/5–
8/41–3/6–8/50–99, 5200–4
†5205–64   **Total 151**

2-6-2T 4MT 3100 Class

Introduced 1938. Collett rebuild, with higher pressure and smaller wheels, of Churchward 3150 class (introduced 1906).

Weight: 81 tons 9 cwt.
Pressure: 225 lb. Su.
Cyls.: (O) 18¼″ × 30″.
Driving Wheels: 5′ 3″.
T.E.: 31,170 lb.
P.V.

3102/3   **Total 2**

2-6-2T 4MT 3150 Class

Introduced 1906. Churchward design, developed from his original 3100 class of 1903, but with larger boiler, subsequently fitted with superheater.

Weight: 81 tons 12 cwt.
Pressure: 200 lb. Su.
Cyls.: (O) 18¼″ × 30″.
Driving Wheels: 5′ 8″.
T.E.: 25,670 lb.
P.V.

3170/4/90

    Total 3

2-6-2T 4MT 4500 Class

*Introduced 1906. Churchward design for light branches, developed from 4400 class with larger wheels, earlier locos. subsequently fitted with superheater.
†4575 class. Introduced 1927. With detail alterations and increased weight.
‡Introduced 1953. Push-and-pull fitted.

Weight: { 57 tons 0 cwt.*
         { 61 tons 0 cwt.†‡
Pressure: 200 lb. Su.
Cyls.: (O) 17″ × 24″.
Driving Wheels: 4′ 7½″.
T.E.: 21,250 lb.
P.V.

*4507/8/19/24/36/40/5/7/9–74

†4575–7/9/80/2/4/5/7/8/90–5/9, 5500–4/6–10/4–23/5–8/30–3/6–44/6–54/6–8/61–7/9–71/3

‡4578/81/9, 5511/24/9/34/45/55/9 /60/8/72/4   **Total 125**

2-6-2T 4MT 5100 & 6100 Classes

*5100 class. Introduced 1928. Collett rebuild, with detail alterations and increased weight, of Churchward 3100 class (introduced 1903 and subsequently fitted with superheater).
†5101 class. Introduced 1929. Modified design for new construction.
‡6100 class. Introduced 1931. Locos. for London suburban area with increased boiler pressure.

Weight: { 75 tons 10 cwt*.
        { 78 tons 9 cwt.†‡
Pressure: { 200 lb. Su.*†
         { 225 lb. Su.‡
Cyls.: (O) 18″ × 30″.
Driving Wheels: 5′ 8″.
T.E.: { 24,300 lb.*†
     { 27,340 lb.‡
P.V.

*5148
†4100–79, 5101–6/8/10/50–8/60/2 –99
‡6100–69   **Total 207**

2-6-2T 4MT 8100 Class

Introduced 1938. Collett rebuild, with higher pressure and smaller wheels, of Churchward locos. in 5100 class.

Weight: 76 tons 11 cwt.
Pressure: 225 lb. Su.
Cyls.: (O) 18″ × 30″.
Driving Wheels: 5′ 6″.
T.E.: 28,165 lb.
P.V.

8100–4/6–9   **Total 9**

2-6-2T unclass. V. of R.

*Introduced 1902. Davies and Metcalfe design for V. of R. 1′ 11½″ gauge.
†Introduced 1923. G.W. development of V. of R. design.

Weight: 25 tons 0 cwt.
Gauge: 1′ 11½″.
Pressure: 165 lb.
Cyls.: (O) { 11″ × 17″.*
        { 11½″ × 17″.†
Driving Wheels: 2′ 6″.
T.E.: { 9,615 lb.*
     { 10,510 lb.†
Walschaerts valve gear.

*9   †7/8
    Total 3

0-6-2T   5MT   5600 Class

*Introduced 1924. Collett design for service in Welsh valleys.
†Introduced 1927. Locos. with detail alterations.
Weight: { 68 tons 12 cwt.*
{ 69 tons 7 cwt.†
Pressure: 200 lb. Su.
Cyls.: 18″ × 26″.
Driving Wheels: 4′ 7½″.
T.E.: 25,800 lb.
P.V.

*5600–99
†6600–99   Total 200

0-6-0PT   2F   850 Class

Introduced 1910. Dean saddletanks, subsequently rebuilt with pannier tanks.
Weight: 36 tons 3 cwt.
Pressure: 165 lb.
Cyls.: 16″ × 24″.
Driving Wheels: 4′ 1½″.
T.E.: 17,410 lb.

2008/12   Total 2

0-6-0ST   0F   1361 Class

Introduced 1910. Churchward design for dock shunting.
Weight: 35 tons 4 cwt.
Pressure: 150 lb.
Cyls.: (O) 16″ × 20″.
Driving Wheels: 3′ 8″.
T.E.: 14,835 lb.

1361–5   Total 5

0-6-0PT   1F   1366 Class

Introduced 1934. Collett development of 1361 class, with pannier tanks.
Weight: 35 tons 15 cwt.
Pressure: 165 lb.
Cyls.: (O) '6″ × 20″.
Driving Wheels: 3′ 8″.
T.E.: 16,320 lb.

1366–71   Total 6

0-6-0PT   4F   1500 Class

Introduced 1949. Hawksworth short-wheelbase heavy shunting design.
Weight: 58 tons 4 cwt.
Pressure: 200 lb.
Cyls.: (O) 17½″ × 24″.
Driving Wheels: 4′ 7½″.
T.E.: 22,515 lb.
Walschaerts valve gear. P.V.

1500–9   Total 10

0-6-0PT   2F   1600 Class

Introduced 1949. Hawksworth light branch line and shunting design.
Weight: 41 tons 12 cwt.
Pressure: 165 lb.
Cyls.: 16½″ × 24″.
Driving Wheels: 4′ 1½″.
T.E.: 18,515 lb.

1600–69   Total 70

0-6-0PT   2F   2021 Class

Introduced 1897. Dean saddletank, subsequently rebuilt with pannier tanks.
Weight: 39 tons 15 cwt.
Pressure: 165 lb.
Cyls.: 16½″ × 24″.
Driving Wheels: 4′ 1½″.
T.E.: 18,515 lb.

2069   Total 1

0-6-0PT   1P   5400 Class

Introduced 1931. Collett design for light passenger work, push-and-pull fitted.

Weight: 46 tons 12 cwt.
Pressure: 165 lb.
Cyls.: 16½″ × 24″.
Driving Wheels: 5′ 2″.
T.E.: 14,780 lb.

5400/2/7/9–12/4/6–24

Total 17

0-6-0PT   3F   5700 Class

*Introduced 1929. Collett design for shunting and light goods work developed from 2021 class.
†Introduced 1930. Locos. with steam brake and no A.T.C. fittings, for shunting only.
§Introduced 1933. Locos. with detail alterations, modified cab (except 8700) and increased weight.
‡Introduced 1933. Locos. with condensing apparatus for working over L.T. Metropolitan line.
¶Introduced 1948. Steam brake locos. with increased weight.

Weight: { 47 tons 10 cwt.*†
{ 50 tons 15 cwt.‡
{ 49 tons 0 cwt.§¶
Pressure: 200 lb.
Cyls.: 17½″ × 24″.
Driving Wheels: 4′ 7½″.
T.E.: 22,515 lb.

*5702–9/13/5–22/5–8/30/1/3/4/7–40/2–5 /7–51/3–9/61/3–91/3–9, 7700–10/2–91/3–9, 8701/2/4–49
†6700–2/4/7/11/2/4–21/3–9/31–6/8/9/41–7/9
§3600–3799, 4600–99, 8700/50–4/6–99, 9600–82, 9711–99
‡9700–10
¶6750–79

Total 829

0-6-0PT   2P*   2F†   6400 & 7400 Classes

*6400 class. Introduced 1932. Collett design for light passenger work, variation of 5400 class with smaller wheels, push-and-pull fitted.

†7400 class. Introduced 1936. Non-push-and-pull fitted locos.
Weight: { 45 tons 12 cwt.*
{ 45 tons 9 cwt.†
Pressure: 180 lb.
Cyls.: 16½″ × 24″.
Driving Wheels: 4′ 7½″.
T.E.: 18,010 lb.

*6400–39
†7400–49

Total : 6400 Class 40
7400 Class 50

0-6-0PT   4F   9400 Class

*Introduced 1947. Hawksworth taper boiler design for heavy shunting.
†Introduced 1949. Locos. with non-superheated boiler.
Weight: 55 tons 7 cwt.
Pressure: 200 lb. SS.
Cyls.: 17½″ × 24″.
Driving Wheels: 4′ 7½″.
T.E.: 22,515 lb.

*9400–9
†3400–9, 8400–99, 9410–99

Total 210

0-6-0T   1F   B.P.G.V.

Introduced 1910. Hudswell Clarke design for B.P.G.V., rebuilt by G.W.R.
Weight: 37 tons 15 cwt.
Pressure: 165 lb.
Cyls.: (O) 15″ × 22″.
Driving Wheels: 3′ 9″.
T.E.: 15,430 lb.

2198

Total 1

0-6-0T   Unclass.   W. & L.

(Line closed: locos. stored.)

Introduced 1902. Beyer Peacock design for 2′ 6″ gauge W. & L. Section, Cambrian Railways.
Weight: 19 tons 18 cwt.

23

Gauge: 2′ 6″.
Pressure: 150 lb.
Cyls.: (O) 11½″ × 16″.
Driving Wheels: 2′ 9″.
T.E.: 8,175 lb.
Walschaerts valve gear.

822/3   **Total 2**

0-4-2T   IP
1400 & 5800 Classes

*1400 class introduced 1932. Collett
design for light branch work (originally designated 4800 class). Push-
and-pull fitted.
†5800 class introduced 1933. Non-
push-and-pull fitted locos.
Weight: 41 tons 6 cwt.
Pressure: 165 lb.
Cyls.: 16″ × 24″.
Driving Wheels: 5′ 2″.
T.E.: 13,900 lb.

*1401/5–10/2/7–21/3/4/6–
38/40–2/4–59/61–74
†5800–2/4/5/9/10/5/6/8

         Total 73

0-4-0T   3F   1101 Class

Introduced 1926. Avonside Engine Co.
design to G.W. requirements for
dock shunting.
Weight: 38 tons 4 cwt.
Pressure: 170 lb.
Cyls.: (O) 16″ × 24″.
Driving Wheels: 3′ 9½″.
T.E.: 19,510 lb.
Walschaerts valve gear.

1101–6   **Total 6**

0-4-0ST   OF   Cardiff Rly.

Introduced 1893. Kitson design for
Cardiff Railway.
Weight: 25 tons 10 cwt.
Pressure: 160 lb.
Cyls.: (O) 14″ × 21″.
Driving Wheels: 3′ 2½″.
T.E.: 14,540 lb.
Hawthorn Kitson valve gear.

1338   **Total 1**

0-4-0ST   OF   P. & M.

Introduced 1907. Peckett design for
P. & M.
Weight: 33 tons 10 cwt.
Pressure: 150 lb.
Cyls.: (O) 15″ × 21″.
Driving Wheels: 3′ 7″.
T.E.: 14,010 lb.

1151/2   **Total 2**

0-4-0ST   OF   S.H.T.

Introduced 1905. Barclay design for
S.H.T.
Weight: 28 tons 0 cwt.
Pressure: 160 lb.
Cyls.: (O) 14″ × 22″.
Driving Wheels: 3′ 5″.
T.E.: 14,305 lb.

1140   **Total 1**

Introduced 1906. Peckett design for
S.H.T. (similar to 1151/2).
Weight: 33 tons 10 cwt.
Pressure: 150 lb.
Cyls.: (O) 15″ × 21″.
Driving Wheels: 3′ 7″.
T.E.: 14,010 lb.

1143/5   **Total 2**

Introduced 1909. Hawthorn Leslie
design for S.H.T.
Weight: 26 tons 17 cwt.
Pressure: 150 lb.
Cyls.: (O) 14″ × 22″.
Driving Wheels: 3′ 6″.
T.E.: 13,090 lb.

1144   **Total 1**

Introduced 1911. Hudswell Clarke
design for S.H.T.
Weight: 28 tons 15 cwt.
Pressure: 160 lb.
Cyls.: (O) 15″ × 22″.
Driving Wheels: 3′ 4″.
T.E.: 16,830 lb.

1142   **Total 1**

NUMERICAL LIST OF WESTERN REGION
STEAM LOCOMOTIVES

**Locomotives are of G.W. origin except where
indicated by other initials**

2-6-2T   V. of R.

7	Owain Glyndŵr
8	Llywelyn
9	Prince of Wales

0-6-0T   W. & L.

822   823

(Line closed : locos. stored.)

4-6-0   1000 Class
" County "

1000	County of Middlesex
1001	County of Bucks
1002	County of Berks
1003	County of Wilts
1004	County of Somerset
1005	County of Devon
1006	County of Cornwall
1007	County of Brecknock
1008	County of Cardigan
1009	County of Carmarthen
1010	County of Caernarvon
1011	County of Chester
1012	County of Denbigh
1013	County of Dorset
1014	County of Glamorgan
1015	County of Gloucester
1016	County of Hants
1017	County of Hereford
1018	County of Leicester
1019	County of Merioneth
1020	County of Monmouth
1021	County of Montgomery
1022	County of Northampton
1023	County of Oxford
1024	County of Pembroke
1025	County of Radnor

1026	County of Salop
1027	County of Stafford
1028	County of Warwick
1029	County of Worcester

0-4-0T   1101 Class

| 1101 | 1103 | 1105 |
| 1102 | 1104 | 1106 |

0-4-0ST   S.H.T.

| 1140 | 1143 | 1145 |
| 1142 | 1144 | |

0-4-0ST   P.M.

1151   1152

0-4-0ST   Car. R.

1338

0-6-0ST   1361 Class

| 1361 | 1363 | 1365 |
| 1362 | 1364 | |

0-6-0PT   1366 Class

| 1366 | 1368 | 1370 |
| 1367 | 1369 | 1371 |

0-4-2T   1400 Class

1401	1412	1424	1432
1405	1417	1426	1433
1406	1418	1427	1434
1407	1419	1428	1435
1408	1420	1429	1436
1409	1421	1430	1437
1410	1423	1431	1438

1440	1450	1459	1469
1441	1451	1461	1470
1442	1452	1462	1471
1444	1453	1463	1472
1445	1454	1464	1473
1446	1455	1465	1474
1447	1456	1466	
1448	1457	1467	
1449	1458	1468	

0-6-0PT   1500 Class

1500	1503	1506	1509
1501	1504	1507	
1502	1505	1508	

0-6-0PT   1600 Class

1600	1618	1636	1654
1601	1619	1637	1655
1602	1620	1638	1656
1603	1621	1639	1657
1604	1622	1640	1658
1605	1623	1641	1659
1606	1624	1642	1660
1607	1625	1643	1661
1608	1626	1644	1662
1609	1627	1645	1663
1610	1628	1646	1664
1611	1629	1647	1665
1612	1630	1648	1666
1613	1631	1649	1667
1614	1632	1650	1668
1615	1633	1651	1669
1616	1634	1652	
1617	1635	1653	

0-6-0PT   850 Class

2008   2012

0-6-0PT   2021 Class

2069

0-6-0T   B.P.G.V.

2198

0-6-0   2251 Class

2200	2225	2250	2275
2201	2226	2251	2276
2202	2227	2252	2277
2203	2228	2253	2278
2204	2229	2254	2279
2205	2230	2255	2280
2206	2231	2256	2281
2207	2232	2257	2282
2208	2233	2258	2283
2209	2234	2259	2284
2210	2235	2260	2285
2211	2236	2261	2286
2212	2237	2262	2287
2213	2238	2263	2288
2214	2239	2264	2289
2215	2240	2265	2290
2216	2241	2266	2291
2217	2242	2267	2292
2218	2243	2268	2293
2219	2244	2269	2294
2220	2245	2270	2295
2221	2246	2271	2296
2222	2247	2272	2297
2223	2248	2273	2298
2224	2249	2274	2299

2-8-0   2800 Class

2800	2816	2832	2848
2801	2817	2833	2849
2802	2818	2834	2850
2803	2819	2835	2851
2804	2820	2836	2852
2805	2821	2837	2853
2806	2822	2838	2854
2807	2823	2839	2855
2808	2824	2840	2856
2809	2825	2841	2857
2810	2826	2842	2858
2811	2827	2843	2859
2812	2828	2844	2860
2813	2829	2845	2861
2814	2830	2846	2862
2815	2831	2847	2863

2864	2873	2882	2891
2865	2874	2883	2892
2866	2875	2884	2893
2867	2876	2885	2894
2868	2877	2886	2895
2869	2878	2887	2896
2870	2879	2888	2897
2871	2880	2889	2898
2872	2881	2890	2899

2-8-0   R.O.D. Class

| 3011 | 3024 | 3036 | 3041 |
| 3015 | | | |

2-6-2T   3100 Class

| 3102 | 3103 |

2-6-2T   3150 Class

| 3170 | 3174 | 3190 |

0-6-0   2251 Class

3200	3205	3210	3215
3201	3206	3211	3216
3202	3207	3212	3217
3203	3208	3213	3218
3204	3209	3214	3219

0-6-0PT   9400 Class

3400	3403	3406	3408
3401	3404	3407	3409
3402	3405		

4-4-0   " City " Class

| 3440 | City of Truro |

0-6-0PT   5700 Class

3600	3605	3610	3615
3601	3606	3611	3616
3602	3607	3612	3617
3603	3608	3613	3618
3604	3609	3614	3619

3620	3667	3714	3761
3621	3668	3715	3762
3622	3669	3716	3763
3623	3670	3717	3764
3624	3671	3718	3765
3625	3672	3719	3766
3626	3673	3720	3767
3627	3674	3721	3768
3628	3675	3722	3769
3629	3676	3723	3770
3630	3677	3724	3771
3631	3678	3725	3772
3632	3679	3726	3773
3633	3680	3727	3774
3634	3681	3728	3775
3635	3682	3729	3776
3636	3683	3730	3777
3637	3684	3731	3778
3638	3685	3732	3779
3639	3686	3733	3780
3640	3687	3734	3781
3641	3688	3735	3782
3642	3689	3736	3783
3643	3690	3737	3784
3644	3691	3738	3785
3645	3692	3739	3786
3646	3693	3740	3787
3647	3694	3741	3788
3648	3695	3742	3789
3649	3696	3743	3790
3650	3697	3744	3791
3651	3698	3745	3792
3652	3699	3746	3793
3653	3700	3747	3794
3654	3701	3748	3795
3655	3702	3749	3796
3656	3703	3750	3797
3657	3704	3751	3798
3658	3705	3752	3799
3659	3706	3753	
3660	3707	3754	
3661	3708	3755	
3662	3709	3756	
3663	3710	3757	
3664	3711	3758	
3665	3712	3759	
3666	3713	3760	

2-8-0   2800 Class

3800	3817	3834	3851
3801	3818	3835	3852
3802	3819	3836	3853
3803	3820	3837	3854
3804	3821	3838	3855
3805	3822	3839	3856
3806	3823	3840	3857
3807	3824	3841	3858
3808	3825	3842	3859
3809	3826	3843	3860
3810	3827	3844	3861
3811	3828	3845	3862
3812	3829	3846	3863
3813	3830	3847	3864
3814	3831	3848	3865
3815	3832	3849	3866
3816	3833	3850	

4-6-0   4073 Class
" Castle "

4037	The South Wales Borderers
4073	Caerphilly Castle
4074	Caldicot Castle
4075	Cardiff Castle
4076	Carmarthen Castle
4077	Chepstow Castle
4078	Pembroke Castle
4079	Pendennis Castle
4080	Powderham Castle
4081	Warwick Castle
4082	Windsor Castle
4083	Abbotsbury Castle
4084	Aberystwyth Castle
4085	Berkeley Castle
4086	Builth Castle
4087	Cardigan Castle
4088	Dartmouth Castle
4089	Donnington Castle
4090	Dorchester Castle
4091	Dudley Castle
4092	Dunraven Castle
4093	Dunster Castle

4094	Dynevor Castle
4095	Harlech Castle
4096	Highclere Castle
4097	Kenilworth Castle
4098	Kidwelly Castle
4099	Kilgerran Castle

2-6-2T   5100 Class

4100	4120	4140	4160
4101	4121	4141	4161
4102	4122	4142	4162
4103	4123	4143	4163
4104	4124	4144	4164
4105	4125	4145	4165
4106	4126	4146	4166
4107	4127	4147	4167
4108	4128	4148	4168
4109	4129	4149	4169
4110	4130	4150	4170
4111	4131	4151	4171
4112	4132	4152	4172
4113	4133	4153	4173
4114	4134	4154	4174
4115	4135	4155	4175
4116	4136	4156	4176
4117	4137	4157	4177
4118	4138	4158	4178
4119	4139	4159	4179

2-8-0T   4200 Class

4200	4222	4237	4256
4201	4223	4238	4257
4203	4224	4241	4258
4206	4225	4242	4259
4207	4226	4243	4260
4208	4227	4246	4261
4211	4228	4247	4262
4212	4229	4248	4263
4213	4230	4250	4264
4214	4231	4251	4265
4215	4232	4252	4266
4217	4233	4253	4267
4218	4235	4254	4268
4221	4236	4255	4269

4270	4278	4286	4294
4271	4279	4287	4295
4272	4280	4288	4296
4273	4281	4289	4297
4274	4282	4290	4298
4275	4283	4291	4299
4276	4284	4292	
4277	4285	4293	

2-6-0   4300 Class

4358	4377

2-6-2T   4500 Class

4507	4555	4569	4584
4508	4556	4570	4585
4519	4557	4571	4587
4524	4558	4572	4588
4536	4559	4573	4589
4540	4560	4574	4590
4545	4561	4575	4591
4547	4562	4576	4592
4549	4563	4577	4593
4550	4564	4578	4594
4551	4565	4579	4595
4552	4566	4580	4599
4553	4567	4581	
4554	4568	4582	

0-6-0PT   5700 Class

4600	4609	4618	4627
4601	4610	4619	4628
4602	4611	4620	4629
4603	4612	4621	4630
4604	4613	4622	4631
4605	4614	4623	4632
4606	4615	4624	4633
4607	4616	4625	4634
4608	4617	4626	4635

4300 Class

4636	4652	4668	4684
4637	4653	4669	4685
4638	4654	4670	4686
4639	4655	4671	4687
4640	4656	4672	4688
4641	4657	4673	4689
4642	4658	4674	4690
4643	4659	4675	4691
4644	4660	4676	4692
4645	4661	4677	4693
4646	4662	4678	4694
4647	4663	4679	4695
4648	4664	4680	4696
4649	4665	4681	4697
4650	4666	4682	4698
4651	4667	4683	4699

2-8-0   4700 Class

4700	4703	4705	4707
4701	4704	4706	4708
4702			

4-6-0 " Hall " 4900 Class

4900	Saint Martin
4901	Adderley Hall
4902	Aldenham Hall
4903	Astley Hall
4904	Binnegar Hall
4905	Barton Hall
4906	Bradfield Hall
4907	Broughton Hall
4908	Broome Hall
4909	Blakesley Hall
4910	Blaisdon Hall
4912	Berrington Hall
4913	Baglan Hall
4914	Cranmore Hall
4915	Condover Hall
4916	Crumlin Hall
4917	Crosswood Hall
4918	Dartington Hall
4919	Donnington Hall
4920	Dumbleton Hall
4921	Eaton Hall
4922	Enville Hall

4923	Evenley Hall
4924	Eydon Hall
4925	Eynsham Hall
4926	Fairleigh Hall
4927	Farnborough Hall
4928	Gatacre Hall
4929	Goytrey Hall
4930	Hagley Hall
4931	Hanbury Hall
4932	Hatherton Hall
4933	Himley Hall
4934	Hindlip Hall
4935	Ketley Hall
4936	Kinlet Hall
4937	Lanelay Hall
4938	Liddington Hall
4939	Littleton Hall
4940	Ludford Hall
4941	Llangedwyn Hall
4942	Maindy Hall
4943	Marrington Hall
4944	Middleton Hall
4945	Milligan Hall
4946	Moseley Hall
4947	Nanhoran Hall
4948	Northwick Hall
4949	Packwood Hall
4950	Patshull Hall
4951	Pendeford Hall
4952	Peplow Hall
4953	Pitchford Hall
4954	Plaish Hall
4955	Plaspower Hall
4956	Plowden Hall
4957	Postlip Hall
4958	Priory Hall
4959	Purley Hall
4960	Pyle Hall
4961	Pyrland Hall
4962	Ragley Hall
4963	Rignall Hall
4964	Rodwell Hall
4965	Rood Ashton Hall
4966	Shakenhurst Hall
4967	Shirenewton Hall
4968	Shotton Hall
4969	Shrugborough Hall

4970	Sketty Hall
4971	Stanway Hall
4972	Saint Brides Hall
4973	Sweeney Hall
4974	Talgarth Hall
4975	Umberslade Hall
4976	Warfield Hall
4977	Watcombe Hall
4978	Westwood Hall
4979	Wootton Hall
4980	Wrottesley Hall
4981	Abberley Hall
4982	Acton Hall
4983	Albert Hall
4984	Albrighton Hall
4985	Allesley Hall
4986	Aston Hall
4987	Brockley Hall
4988	Bulwell Hall
4989	Cherwell Hall
4990	Clifton Hall
4991	Cobham Hall
4992	Crosby Hall
4993	Dalton Hall
4994	Downton Hall
4995	Easton Hall
4996	Eden Hall
4997	Elton Hall
4998	Eyton Hall
4999	Gopsal Hall

4-6-0 "Castle" 4073 Class

5000	Launceston Castle
5001	Llandovery Castle
5002	Ludlow Castle
5003	Lulworth Castle
5004	Llanstephan Castle
5005	Manorbier Castle
5006	Tregenna Castle
5007	Rougemont Castle
5008	Raglan Castle
5009	Shrewsbury Castle
5010	Restormel Castle
5011	Tintagel Castle
5012	Berry Pomeroy Castle

5013	Abergavenny Castle	5059	Earl St. Aldwyn
5014	Goodrich Castle	5060	Earl of Berkeley
5015	Kingswear Castle	5061	Earl of Birkenhead
5016	Montgomery Castle	5062	Earl of Shaftesbury
5017	The Gloucestershire Regiment 28th, 61st	5063	Earl Baldwin
		5064	Bishop's Castle
5018	St. Mawes Castle	5065	Newport Castle
5019	Treago Castle	5066	Sir Felix Pole
5020	Trematon Castle	5067	St. Fagans Castle
5021	Whittington Castle	5068	Beverston Castle
5022	Wigmore Castle	5069	Isambard Kingdom Brunel
5023	Brecon Castle	5070	Sir Daniel Gooch
5024	Carew Castle	5071	Spitfire
5025	Chirk Castle	5072	Hurricane
5026	Criccieth Castle	5073	Blenheim
5027	Farleigh Castle	5074	Hampden
5028	Llantilio Castle	5075	Wellington
5029	Nunney Castle	5076	Gladiator
5030	Shirburn Castle	5077	Fairey Battle
5031	Totnes Castle	5078	Beaufort
5032	Usk Castle	5079	Lysander
5033	Broughton Castle	5080	Defiant
5034	Corfe Castle	5081	Lockheed Hudson
5035	Coity Castle	5082	Swordfish
5036	Lyonshall Castle	5083	Bath Abbey
5037	Monmouth Castle	5084	Reading Abbey
5038	Morlais Castle	5085	Evesham Abbey
5039	Rhuddlan Castle	5086	Viscount Horne
5040	Stokesay Castle	5087	Tintern Abbey
5041	Tiverton Castle	5088	Llanthony Abbey
5042	Winchester Castle	5089	Westminster Abbey
5043	Earl of Mount Edgcumbe	5090	Neath Abbey
5044	Earl of Dunraven	5091	Cleeve Abbey
5045	Earl of Dudley	5092	Tresco Abbey
5046	Earl Cawdor	5093	Upton Castle
5047	Earl of Dartmouth	5094	Tretower Castle
5048	Earl of Devon	5095	Barbury Castle
5049	Earl of Plymouth	5096	Bridgwater Castle
5050	Earl of St. Germans	5097	Sarum Castle
5051	Earl Bathurst	5098	Clifford Castle
5052	Earl of Radnor	5099	Compton Castle
5053	Earl Cairns		
5054	Earl of Ducie		
5055	Earl of Eldon		
5056	Earl of Powis		
5057	Earl Waldegrave		
5058	Earl of Clancarty		

2-6-2T   5100 Class

5101	5103	5105	5108
5102	5104	5106	5110

5148	5164	5176	5188		5370	5378	5385	5394
5150	5165	5177	5189		5371	5379	5386	5396
5151	5166	5178	5190		5372	5380	5388	5397
5152	5167	5179	5191		5375	5381	5390	5398
5153	5168	5180	5192		5376	5382	5392	5399
5154	5169	5181	5193		5377	5384	5393	
5155	5170	5182	5194
5156	5171	5183	5195
5157	5172	5184	5196
5158	5173	5185	5197
5160	5174	5186	5198
5162	5175	5187	5199
5163			

0-6-0PT   5400 Class

5400	5411	5418	5423
5402	5412	5419	5424
5407	5414	5420	
5409	5416	5421	
5410	5417	5422	

2-8-0T   4200 Class

5200	5217	5234	5251
5201	5218	5235	5252
5202	5219	5236	5253
5203	5220	5237	5254
5204	5221	5238	5255
5205	5222	5239	5256
5206	5223	5240	5257
5207	5224	5241	5258
5208	5225	5242	5259
5209	5226	5243	5260
5210	5227	5244	5261
5211	5228	5245	5262
5212	5229	5246	5263
5213	5230	5247	5264
5214	5231	5248	
5215	5232	5249	
5216	5233	5250	

2-6-2T   4500 Class

5500	5521	5540	5558
5501	5522	5541	5559
5502	5523	5542	5560
5503	5524	5543	5561
5504	5525	5544	5562
5506	5526	5545	5563
5507	5527	5546	5564
5508	5528	5547	5565
5509	5529	5548	5566
5510	5530	5549	5567
5511	5531	5550	5568
5514	5532	5551	5569
5515	5533	5552	5570
5516	5534	5553	5571
5517	5536	5554	5572
5518	5537	5555	5573
5519	5538	5556	5574
5520	5539	5557	

2-6-0   4300 Class

5306	5323	5337	5355
5310	5324	5338	5356
5311	5326	5339	5357
5312	5328	5341	5358
5313	5330	5344	5360
5315	5331	5345	5361
5318	5332	5347	5362
5319	5333	5350	5367
5321	5335	5351	5368
5322	5336	5353	5369

0-6-2T   5600 Class

5600	5603	5606	5609
5601	5604	5607	5610
5602	5605	5608	5611

5612	5634	5656	5678
5613	5635	5657	5679
5614	5636	5658	5680
5615	5637	5659	5681
5616	5638	5660	5682
5617	5639	5661	5683
5618	5640	5662	5684
5619	5641	5663	5685
5620	5642	5664	5686
5621	5643	5665	5687
5622	5644	5666	5688
5623	5645	5667	5689
5624	5646	5668	5690
5625	5647	5669	5691
5626	5648	5670	5692
5627	5649	5671	5693
5628	5650	5672	5694
5629	5651	5673	5695
5630	5652	5674	5696
5631	5653	5675	5697
5632	5654	5676	5698
5633	5655	5677	5699

5789	5793	5796	5799
5790	5794	5797	
5791	5795	5798	

0-4-2T   5800 Class

5800	5804	5809	5815
5801	5805	5810	5818
5802			

4-6-0   4900 Class
" Hall "

5900	Hinderton Hall
5901	Hazel Hall
5902	Howick Hall
5903	Keele Hall
5904	Kelham Hall
5905	Knowsley Hall
5906	Lawton Hall
5907	Marble Hall
5908	Moreton Hall
5909	Newton Hall
5910	Park Hall
5911	Preston Hall
5912	Queen's Hall
5913	Rushton Hall
5914	Ripon Hall
5915	Trentham Hall
5916	Trinity Hall
5917	Westminster Hall
5918	Walton Hall
5919	Worsley Hall
5920	Wycliffe Hall
5921	Bingley Hall
5922	Caxton Hall
5923	Colston Hall
5924	Dinton Hall
5925	Eastcote Hall
5926	Grotrian Hall
5927	Guild Hall
5928	Haddon Hall
5929	Hanham Hall
5930	Hannington Hall
5931	Hatherley Hall

0-6-0PT   5700 Class

5702	5726	5750	5771
5703	5727	5751	5772
5704	5728	5753	5773
5705	5730	5754	5774
5706	5731	5755	5775
5707	5733	5756	5776
5708	5734	5757	5777
5709	5737	5758	5778
5713	5738	5759	5779
5715	5739	5761	5780
5716	5740	5763	5781
5717	5742	5764	5782
5718	5743	5765	5783
5719	5744	5766	5784
5720	5745	5767	5785
5721	5747	5768	5786
5722	5748	5769	5787
5725	5749	5770	5788

5932	Haydon Hall		5979	Cruckton Hall
5933	Kingsway Hall		5980	Dingley Hall
5934	Kneller Hall		5981	Frensham Hall
5935	Norton Hall		5982	Harrington Hall
5936	Oakley Hall		5983	Henley Hall
5937	Stanford Hall		5984	Linden Hall
5938	Stanley Hall		5985	Mostyn Hall
5939	Tangley Hall		5986	Arbury Hall
5940	Whitbourne Hall		5987	Brocket Hall
5941	Campion Hall		5988	Bostock Hall
5942	Doldowlod Hall		5989	Cransley Hall
5943	Elmdon Hall		5990	Dorford Hall
5944	Ickenham Hall		5991	Gresham Hall
5945	Leckhampton Hall		5992	Horton Hall
5946	Marwell Hall		5993	Kirby Hall
5947	Saint Benet's Hall		5994	Roydon Hall
5948	Siddington Hall		5995	Wick Hall
5949	Trematon Hall		5996	Mytton Hall
5950	Wardley Hall		5997	Sparkford Hall
5951	Clyffe Hall		5998	Trevor Hall
5952	Cogan Hall		5999	Wollaton Hall
5953	Dunley Hall			
5954	Faendre Hall			
5955	Garth Hall		**4-6-0**	**6000 Class**
5956	Horsley Hall			**" King "**
5957	Hutton Hall			
5958	Knolton Hall		6000	King George V
5959	Mawley Hall		6001	King Edward VII
5960	Saint Edmund Hall		6002	King William IV
5961	Toynbee Hall		6003	King George IV
5962	Wantage Hall		6004	King George III
5963	Wimpole Hall		6005	King George II
5964	Wolseley Hall		6006	King George I
5965	Woollas Hall		6007	King William III
5966	Ashford Hall		6008	King James II
5967	Bickmarsh Hall		6009	King Charles II
5968	Cory Hall		6010	King Charles I
5969	Honington Hall		6011	King James I
5970	Hengrave Hall		6012	King Edward VI
5971	Merevale Hall		6013	King Henry VIII
5972	Olton Hall		6014	King Henry VII
5973	Rolleston Hall		6015	King Richard III
5974	Wallsworth Hall		6016	King Edward V
5975	Winslow Hall		6017	King Edward IV
5976	Ashwicke Hall		6018	King Henry VI
5977	Beckford Hall		6019	King Henry V
5978	Bodinnick Hall		6020	King Henry IV

6021	King Richard II
6022	King Edward III
6023	King Edward II
6024	King Edward I
6025	King Henry III
6026	King John
6027	King Richard I
6028	King George VI
6029	King Edward VIII

6354	6366	6378	6391
6355	6367	6379	6392
6356	6368	6380	6393
6357	6369	6381	6394
6358	6370	6382	6395
6359	6371	6384	6396
6360	6372	6385	6397
6361	6373	6386	6398
6362	6374	6387	6399
6363	6375	6388	
6364	6376	6389	
6365	6377	6390	

2-6-2T   6100 Class

6100	6118	6136	6154
6101	6119	6137	6155
6102	6120	6138	6156
6103	6121	6139	6157
6104	6122	6140	6158
6105	6123	6141	6159
6106	6124	6142	6160
6107	6125	6143	6161
6108	6126	6144	6162
6109	6127	6145	6163
6110	6128	6146	6164
6111	6129	6147	6165
6112	6130	6148	6166
6113	6131	6149	6167
6114	6132	6150	6168
6115	6133	6151	6169
6116	6134	6152	
6117	6135	6153	

0-6-0PT   6400 Class

6400	6410	6420	6430
6401	6411	6421	6431
6402	6412	6422	6432
6403	6413	6423	6433
6404	6414	6424	6434
6405	6415	6425	6435
6406	6416	6426	6436
6407	6417	6427	6437
6408	6418	6428	6438
6409	6419	6429	6439

0-6-2T   5600 Class

6600	6620	6640	6660
6601	6621	6641	6661
6602	6622	6642	6662
6603	6623	6643	6663
6604	6624	6644	6664
6605	6625	6645	6665
6606	6626	6646	6666
6607	6627	6647	6667
6608	6628	6648	6668
6609	6629	6649	6669
6610	6630	6650	6670
6611	6631	6651	6671
6612	6632	6652	6672
6613	6633	6653	6673
6614	6634	6654	6674
6615	6635	6655	6675
6616	6636	6656	6676
6617	6637	6657	6677
6618	6638	6658	6678
6619	6639	6659	6679

2-6-0   4300 Class

6300	6313	6328	6341
6301	6314	6329	6342
6302	6316	6330	6343
6303	6317	6331	6344
6304	6318	6332	6345
6305	6319	6333	6346
6306	6320	6334	6347
6307	6322	6335	6348
6308	6323	6336	6349
6309	6324	6337	6350
6310	6325	6338	6351
6311	6326	6339	6352
6312	6327	6340	6353

6680	6685	6690	6695
6681	6686	6691	6696
6682	6687	6692	6697
6683	6688	6693	6698
6684	6689	6694	6699

0-6-0PT   5700 Class

6700	6726	6747	6766
6701	6727	6749	6767
6702	6728	6750	6768
6704	6729	6751	6769
6707	6731	6752	6770
6711	6732	6753	6771
6712	6733	6754	6772
6714	6734	6755	6773
6715	6735	6756	6774
6716	6736	6757	6775
6717	6738	6758	6776
6718	6739	6759	6777
6719	6741	6760	6778
6720	6742	6761	6779
6721	6743	6762	
6723	6744	6763	
6724	6745	6764	
6725	6746	6765	

4-6-0   6800 Class
"Grange"

6800	Arlington Grange
6801	Aylburton Grange
6802	Bampton Grange
6803	Bucklebury Grange
6804	Brockington Grange
6805	Broughton Grange
6806	Blackwell Grange
6807	Birchwood Grange
6808	Beenham Grange
6809	Burghclere Grange
6810	Blakemere Grange
6811	Cranbourne Grange
6812	Chesford Grange
6813	Eastbury Grange
6814	Enborne Grange
6815	Frilford Grange
6816	Frankton Grange
6817	Gwenddwr Grange
6818	Hardwick Grange
6819	Highnam Grange
6820	Kingstone Grange
6821	Leaton Grange
6822	Manton Grange
6823	Oakley Grange
6824	Ashley Grange
6825	Llanvair Grange
6826	Nannerth Grange
6827	Llanfrechfa Grange
6828	Trellech Grange
6829	Burmington Grange
6830	Buckenhill Grange
6831	Bearley Grange
6832	Brockton Grange
6833	Calcot Grange
6834	Dummer Grange
6835	Eastham Grange
6836	Estevarney Grange
6837	Forthampton Grange
6838	Goodmoor Grange
6839	Hewell Grange
6840	Hazeley Grange
6841	Marlas Grange
6842	Nunhold Grange
6843	Poulton Grange
6844	Penhydd Grange
6845	Paviland Grange
6846	Ruckley Grange
6847	Tidmarsh Grange
6848	Toddington Grange
6849	Walton Grange
6850	Cleeve Grange
6851	Hurst Grange
6852	Headbourne Grange
6853	Morehampton Grange
6854	Roundhill Grange
6855	Saighton Grange
6856	Stowe Grange
6857	Tudor Grange
6858	Woolston Grange
6859	Yiewsley Grange
6860	Aberporth Grange

6861	Crynant Grange	6924	Grantley Hall
6862	Derwent Grange	6925	Hackness Hall
6863	Dolhywel Grange	6926	Holkham Hall
6864	Dymock Grange	6927	Lilford Hall
6865	Hopton Grange	6928	Underley Hall
6866	Morfa Grange	6929	Whorlton Hall
6867	Peterston Grange	6930	Aldersey Hall
6868	Penrhos Grange	6931	Aldborough Hall
6869	Resolven Grange	6932	Burwarton Hall
6870	Bodicote Grange	6933	Birtles Hall
6871	Bourton Grange	6934	Beachamwell Hall
6872	Crawley Grange	6935	Browsholme Hall
6873	Caradoc Grange	6936	Breccles Hall
6874	Haughton Grange	6937	Conyngham Hall
6875	Hindford Grange	6938	Corndean Hall
6876	Kingsland Grange	6939	Calveley Hall
6877	Llanfair Grange	6940	Didlington Hall
6878	Longford Grange	6941	Fillongley Hall
6879	Overton Grange	6942	Eshton Hall
		6943	Farnley Hall
		6944	Fledborough Hall

4-6-0　　　　　　4900 Class
" Hall "

		6945	Glasfryn Hall
		6946	Heatherden Hall
6900	Abney Hall	6947	Helmingham Hall
6901	Arley Hall	6948	Holbrooke Hall
6902	Butlers Hall	6949	Haberfield Hall
6903	Belmont Hall	6950	Kingsthorpe Hall
6904	Charfield Hall	6951	Impney Hall
6905	Claughton Hall	6952	Kimberley Hall
6906	Chicheley Hall	6953	Leighton Hall
6907	Davenham Hall	6954	Lotherton Hall
6908	Downham Hall	6955	Lydcott Hall
6909	Frewin Hall	6956	Mottram Hall
6910	Gossington Hall	6957	Norcliffe Hall
6911	Holker Hall	6958	Oxburgh Hall
6912	Helmster Hall		
6913	Levens Hall		

4-6-0　　　　　　6959 Class
" Modified Hall "

6914	Langton Hall		
6915	Mursley Hall	6959	Peatling Hall
6916	Misterton Hall	6960	Raveningham Hall
6917	Oldlands Hall	6961	Stedham Hall
6918	Sandon Hall	6962	Soughton Hall
6919	Tylney Hall	6963	Throwley Hall
6920	Barningham Hall	6964	Thornbridge Hall
6921	Borwick Hall	6965	Thirlestaine Hall
6922	Burton Hall	6966	Witchingham Hall
6923	Croxteth Hall		

37

6967	Willesley Hall
6968	Woodcock Hall
6969	Wraysbury Hall
6970	Whaddon Hall
6971	Athelhampton Hall
6972	Beningbrough Hall
6973	Bricklehampton Hall
6974	Bryngwyn Hall
6975	Capesthorne Hall
6976	Graythwaite Hall
6977	Grundisburgh Hall
6978	Haroldstone Hall
6979	Helperly Hall
6980	Llanrumney Hall
6981	Marbury Hall
6982	Melmerby Hall
6983	Otterington Hall
6984	Owsden Hall
6985	Parwick Hall
6986	Rydal Hall
6987	Shervington Hall
6988	Swithland Hall
6989	Wightwick Hall
6990	Witherslack Hall
6991	Acton Burnell Hall
6992	Arborfield Hall
6993	Arthog Hall
6994	Baggrave Hall
6995	Benthall Hall
6996	Blackwell Hall
6997	Bryn-Ivor Hall
6998	Burton Agnes Hall
6999	Capel Dewi Hall

4-6-0   4073 Class
" Castle "

7000	Viscount Portal
7001	Sir James Milne
7002	Devizes Castle
7003	Elmley Castle
7004	Eastnor Castle
7005	Sir Edward Elgar
7006	Lydford Castle
7007	Great Western
7008	Swansea Castle

7009	Athelney Castle
7010	Avondale Castle
7011	Banbury Castle
7012	Barry Castle
7013	Bristol Castle
7014	Caerhays Castle
7015	Carn Brea Castle
7016	Chester Castle
7017	G. J. Churchward
7018	Drysllwyn Castle
7019	Fowey Castle
7020	Gloucester Castle
7021	Haverfordwest Castle
7022	Hereford Castle
7023	Penrice Castle
7024	Powis Castle
7025	Sudeley Castle
7026	Tenby Castle
7027	Thornbury Castle
7028	Cadbury Castle
7029	Clun Castle
7030	Cranbrook Castle
7031	Cromwell's Castle
7032	Denbigh Castle
7033	Hartlebury Castle
7034	Ince Castle
7035	Ogmore Castle
7036	Taunton Castle
7037	Swindon

2-8-2T   7200 Class

7200	7214	7228	7242
7201	7215	7229	7243
7202	7216	7230	7244
7203	7217	7231	7245
7204	7218	7232	7246
7205	7219	7233	7247
7206	7220	7234	7248
7207	7221	7235	7249
7208	7222	7236	7250
7209	7223	7237	7251
7210	7224	7238	7252
7211	7225	7239	7253
7212	7226	7240	
7213	7227	7241	

2-6-0   4300 Class

7300	7308	7316	7324
7301	7309	7317	7329
7302	7310	7318	7333
7303	7311	7319	7339
7304	7312	7320	7340
7305	7313	7321	7341
7306	7314	7322	
7307	7315	7323	

0-6-0PT   7400 Class

7400	7413	7426	7438
7401	7414	7427	7439
7402	7415	7428	7440
7403	7416	7429	7441
7404	7417	7430	7442
7405	7418	7431	7443
7406	7419	7432	7444
7407	7420	7433	7445
7408	7421	7434	7446
7409	7422	7435	7447
7410	7423	7436	7448
7411	7424	7437	7449
7412	7425		

0-6-0PT   5700 Class

7700	7721	7741	7761
7701	7722	7742	7762
7702	7723	7743	7763
7703	7724	7744	7764
7704	7725	7745	7765
7705	7726	7746	7766
7706	7727	7747	7767
7707	7728	7748	7768
7708	7729	7749	7769
7709	7730	7750	7770
7710	7731	7751	7771
7712	7732	7752	7772
7713	7733	7753	7773
7714	7734	7754	7774
7715	7735	7755	7775
7716	7736	7756	7776
7717	7737	7757	7777
7718	7738	7758	7778
7719	7739	7759	7779
7720	7740	7760	7780

7781	7786	7791	7797
7782	7787	7793	7798
7783	7788	7794	7799
7784	7789	7795	
7785	7790	7796	

4-6-0   7800 Class
" Manor "

7800	Torquay Manor
7801	Anthony Manor
7802	Bradley Manor
7803	Barcote Manor
7804	Baydon Manor
7805	Broome Manor
7806	Cockington Manor
7807	Compton Manor
7808	Cookham Manor
7809	Childrey Manor
7810	Draycott Manor
7811	Dunley Manor
7812	Erlestoke Manor
7813	Freshford Manor
7814	Fringford Manor
7815	Fritwell Manor
7816	Frilsham Manor
7817	Garsington Manor
7818	Granville Manor
7819	Hinton Manor
7820	Dinmore Manor
7821	Ditcheat Manor
7822	Foxcote Manor
7823	Hook Norton Manor
7824	Iford Manor
7825	Lechlade Manor
7826	Longworth Manor
7827	Lydham Manor
7828	Odney Manor
7829	Ramsbury Manor

4-6-0   6959 Class
" Modified Hall "

7900	Saint Peter's Hall
7901	Dodington Hall
7902	Eaton Mascot Hall
7903	Foremarke Hall
7904	Fountains Hall

7905	Fowey Hall
7906	Fron Hall
7907	Hart Hall
7908	Henshall Hall
7909	Heveningham Hall
7910	Hown Hall
7911	Lady Margaret Hall
7912	Little Linford Hall
7913	Little Wyrley Hall
7914	Lleweni Hall
7915	Mere Hall
7916	Mobberley Hall
7917	North Aston Hall
7918	Rhose Wood Hall
7919	Runter Hall
7920	Coney Hall
7921	Edstone Hall
7922	Salford Hall
7923	Speke Hall
7924	Thornycroft Hall
7925	Westol Hall
7926	Willey Hall
7927	Willington Hall
7928	Wolf Hall
7929	Wyke Hall

2-6-2T 8100 Class

8100	8103	8106	8108
8101	8104	8107	8109
8102			

0-6-0PT 9400 Class

8400	8414	8428	8442
8401	8415	8429	8443
8402	8416	8430	8444
8403	8417	8431	8445
8404	8418	8432	8446
8405	8419	8433	8447
8406	8420	8434	8448
8407	8421	8435	8449
8408	8422	8436	8450
8409	8423	8437	8451
8410	8424	8438	8452
8411	8425	8439	8453
8412	8426	8440	8454
8413	8427	8441	8455

8456	8467	8478	8489
8457	8468	8479	8490
8458	8469	8480	8491
8459	8470	8481	8492
8460	8471	8482	8493
8461	8472	8483	8494
8462	8473	8484	8495
8463	8474	8485	8496
8464	8475	8486	8497
8465	8476	8487	8498
8466	8477	8488	8499

0-6-0PT 5700 Class

8700	8726	8751	8777
8701	8727	8752	8778
8702	8728	8753	8779
8704	8729	8754	8780
8705	8730	8756	8781
8706	8731	8757	8782
8707	8732	8758	8783
8708	8733	8759	8784
8709	8734	8760	8785
8710	8735	8761	8786
8711	8736	8762	8787
8712	8737	8763	8788
8713	8738	8764	8789
8714	8739	8765	8790
8715	8740	8766	8791
8716	8741	8767	8792
8717	8742	8768	8793
8718	8743	8769	8794
8719	8744	8770	8795
8720	8745	8771	8796
8721	8746	8772	8797
8722	8747	8773	8798
8723	8748	8774	8799
8724	8749	8775	
8725	8750	8776	

4-4-0 9000 Class

9004	9013	9015	9018
9005	9014	9017	9021

2-6-0   4300 Class

9303	9306	9310	9314
9304	9308	9312	9315
9305	9309	9313	9316

0-6-0PT   9400 Class

9400	9425	9450	9475
9401	9426	9451	9476
9402	9427	9452	9477
9403	9428	9453	9478
9404	9429	9454	9479
9405	9430	9455	9480
9406	9431	9456	9481
9407	9432	9457	9482
9408	9433	9458	9483
9409	9434	9459	9484
9410	9435	9460	9485
9411	9436	9461	9486
9412	9437	9462	9487
9413	9438	9463	9488
9414	9439	9464	9489
9415	9440	9465	9490
9416	9441	9466	9491
9417	9442	9467	9492
9418	9443	9468	9493
9419	9444	9469	9494
9420	9445	9470	9495
9421	9446	9471	9496
9422	9447	9472	9497
9423	9448	9473	9498
9424	9449	9474	9499

0-6-0PT   5700 Class

9600	9610	9620	9630
9601	9611	9621	9631
9602	9612	9622	9632
9603	9613	9623	9633
9604	9614	9624	9634
9605	9615	9625	9635
9606	9616	9626	9636
9607	9617	9627	9637
9608	9618	9628	9638
9609	9619	9629	9639

9640	9676	9729	9765
9641	9677	9730	9766
9642	9678	9731	9767
9643	9679	9732	9768
9644	9680	9733	9769
9645	9681	9734	9770
9646	9682	9735	9771
9647	9700	9736	9772
9648	9701	9737	9773
9649	9702	9738	9774
9650	9703	9739	9775
9651	9704	9740	9776
9652	9705	9741	9777
9653	9706	9742	9778
9654	9707	9743	9779
9655	9708	9744	9780
9656	9709	9745	9781
9657	9710	9746	9782
9658	9711	9747	9783
9659	9712	9748	9784
9660	9713	9749	9785
9661	9714	9750	9786
9662	9715	9751	9787
9663	9716	9752	9788
9664	9717	9753	9789
9665	9718	9754	9790
9666	9719	9755	9791
9667	9720	9756	9792
9668	9721	9757	9793
9669	9722	9758	9794
9670	9723	9759	9795
9671	9724	9760	9796
9672	9725	9761	9797
9673	9726	9762	9798
9674	9727	9763	9799
9675	9728	9764	

SERVICE LOCOMOTIVES

Diesel Mechanical

20
PWM 650   **Total 2**

Petrol

22   24   27

                           Total 3

POWER AND WEIGHT CLASSIFICATION

Since 1920 Western Region locomotives have been classified for power and weight by a letter on a coloured disc on the cab side. The letter represents the power of the locomotive, and is approximately proportional to the tractive effort as under :

Power class	Tractive effort lb.	Power class	Tractive effort lb.
Special	Over 38,000	B	18,501–20,500
E	33,001–38,000	A	16,500–18,500
D	25,001–33,000	Un-	
C	20,501–25,000	grouped	Below 16,500

The colour of the circle represents the routes over which the engine may work. Red engines are limited to the main lines and lines capable of carrying the heaviest locomotives ; blue engines are allowed over additional routes, yellow engines over nearly the whole system and uncoloured engines are more or less unrestricted. The double red circles on the " King " class represent special restrictions for these engines.

Class	Power Class	Route Restriction Colour	Class	Power Class	Route Restriction Colour
4-6-0			**0-6-2T**		
1000	D	Red	5600	D	Red
4073	D	Red			
4900	D	Red	**0-6-0T**		
6000	Special	Double Red	850	—	—
6800	D	Red	1361	—	—
6959	D	Red	1366	—	—
7800	D	Blue	1500	C	Red
4-4-0			1600	A	—
9000	B	Yellow	2021	A	—
2-8-0			5400	—	Yellow
2800	E	Blue	5700	C	Yellow
R.O.D.	D	Blue	9700–10	C	Blue
4700	D	Red	6400	A	Yellow
2-6-0			7400	A	Yellow
4300	D	Blue	9400	C	Red
9304	D	Red	(2198)	—	—
0-6-0			**0-4-2T**		
2251	B	Yellow	1400	—	—
2-8-2T			5800	—	—
7200	E	Red			
2-8-0T			**0-4-0T**		
4200	E	Red	1101	B	Red
2-6-2T			(1338)	—	—
3100	D	Red	(1151)	—	—
4500	C	Yellow	(1140)	—	—
5100	D	Blue	(1143)	—	Blue
6100	D	Blue	(1144)	—	Yellow
8100	D	Blue	(1142)	A	Yellow
(7)	—	—			

WESTERN REGION PASSENGER TRAIN REPORTING NUMBERS

SUMMER

CERTAIN passenger trains, and any relief trains run thereto, bear a number for identification purposes for the whole or part of the journey over the Western Region, as shown in the following list. In a few instances through trains to and from the Southern Region carry the identification number during their journey over that Region also.

The number allotted to each train is displayed in a metal frame carried on the smokebox door of the engine.

The numbers shown in this list refer to ordinary and regular relief trains only: those carried by occasional relief or duplicate trains are shown only in the Western Region's official working notices, as required, and do not appear in this list.

Train No.	Time	From	To
038	10.50 a.m.‡‡	Manchester (L.R.)	Cardiff
100	5.30 a.m.•	Paddington	Penzance
102	5.30 a.m.†	"	Minehead
103	6.55 a.m.†	"	Penzance
105	7. 0 a.m.†	"	Kingswear
	7. 5 a.m.†	"	Penzance
107	7.25 a.m.†	Ealing Broadway	Paignton
	7.30 a.m.§	Paddington	"
108	7.40 a.m.†	"	"
110	8.10 a.m.†	"	Weymouth
113	8.20 a.m.†	"	Penzance
114	8.25 a.m.†	"	Weymouth
115	8.20 a.m.•	"	Weymouth
116	8.30 a.m.†	"	Bristol
117	8.45 a.m.†	"	Paignton
119	8.50 a.m.†	"	Bristol
120	9. 5 a.m.§	"	Durston
122	9.15 a.m.†	"	Newquay
	9.30 a.m.•	"	Falmouth
123	9.30 a.m.†	"	Minehead
125	9.35 a.m.†	"	Paignton
128	9.40 a.m.†	"	Kingswear
130	10.20 a.m.§	"	Penzance
131	10.30 a.m.†	"	"
133	10.35 a.m.§	"	Paignton
135	10.35 a.m.•	"	"
136	10.40 a.m.†	Swindon	Sheffield
138	11. 0 a.m.†	Paddington	Penzance

§ **Every weekday.**   • **Sats. exc.**   † **Sats. only.**   ‡ **Fris. only.**   ¶ **Sats. & Suns.**   ‖ **Tues. to Sats. or Suns. incl. only.**   ** **Weekdays and Suns.**   †† **Mons. only.**   ‡‡ **Suns. only.**

Train No.	Time	From	To
010	9.50 p.m.‡	Paddington	Penzance
011	10.12 p.m.†	"	"
012	10.35 p.m.†	"	"
015	10.50 p.m.‡	"	Newquay
016	11.35 p.m.‡‡	"	Penzance
018	11.50 p.m.‡	"	"
	12.30 a.m.†	"	"
019	12.35 a.m.† (News)	"	"

Left table:

Train No.	Time	From	To
140	11. 5 a.m.†	Paddington	Penzance
142	11.15 a.m.§	"	Weston-s-Mare
144	11.30 a.m.*	"	Penzance
146	11.30 a.m.†	"	Minehead
147	12. 0 nn.§	"	Kingswear
149	12. 5 p.m.	"	Plymouth
150	1.25 p.m.	"	Kingswear
151	1.35 p.m.	"	Penzance
152	3.20 p.m.§	"	Penzance
153	3.30 p.m.	"	Kingswear
154	4.15 p.m.	"	Penzance
155	5. 5 p.m.§	Bournemouth	Weston-s-Mare
156	5. 5 p.m.§	Paddington	Plymouth
157	5.30 p.m.§	"	Sheffield
158	6.15 p.m.	"	Bristol
159	7.55 a.m.‡‡	"	Weston-s-Mare
161	8.50 a.m.§	"	Carmarthen
162	8.40 a.m.*	"	Pembroke Dock
163	8.55 a.m.§	"	"
164	9.55 a.m.†	"	"
165	9.55 a.m.*	"	Swansea
166	10.55 a.m.§	"	Neyland
167	11.35 a.m.†	"	Pembroke Dock
168	11.55 a.m.†	"	Neyland
169	1.50 p.m.†	"	Pembroke Dock
170	1.55 p.m.§	"	Carmarthen
171	3.45 p.m.§	"	Pembroke Dock
172	3.55 p.m.†	"	Fishguard Harbour
173	4.55 p.m.§	"	Cheltenham
174	4.45 p.m.§	"	Carmarthen
175	5.50 p.m.§	"	Swansea
176	6.35 p.m.§	"	Cheltenham

Right table:

Train No.	Time	From	To
178	6.55 p.m.§	Paddington	Fishguard Harbour
179	7.15 p.m.‡‡	"	"
180	9. 0 a.m.*	"	Birkenhead
181	9.10 a.m.	"	Wolverhampton
183	10.10 a.m.†	"	Pwllheli
185	11.45 a.m.§	"	Aberystwyth
186	1.45 p.m.	"	Hereford
187	4.10 p.m.§	"	Birkenhead
189	4.45 p.m.	"	Hereford
192	5.10 p.m.	"	Wolverhampton
195	6.10 p.m.§	"	Birkenhead
198	6.45 p.m.§	"	Hereford
201	10.22 p.m.†	"	Swindon
202	11.35 p.m.‡	York	Penzance
204	11.16 a.m.†	Liverpool	Newcastle
205	8.10 a.m.§	Bournemouth	Crewe
206	8. 5 a.m.†	Penzance	Newcastle
208	9.15 a.m.†	Bournemouth	Plymouth
"	10.40 a.m.‡‡	Liverpool	York
210	9.40 p.m.§	Swindon	Swansea
212	9.25 a.m.§	Manchester (L.R.)	Paignton
214	9.10 a.m.†	Glasgow	Plymouth
215	5.30 p.m.†	Cardiff	Liverpool
216	12. 5 a.m.**	Birkenhead	Plymouth
217	9. 5 a.m.†	Bristol	Manchester (L.R.)
221	12.10 a.m.‡‡	Penzance	"
223	4.45 p.m.§	Penzance	" (V)
	7. 5 p.m.†	"	
	9. 0 a.m.†	Exmouth	" (L.R.)

Train No.	Time	From	To
227	8.20 a.m.†	Cardiff...	Manchester (May.)
228	11.55 a.m.§	Manchester (L.R.)	Plymouth
230	12.15 a.m.†	"	Paignton
232	12.40 p.m.‡‡	Cardiff...	Manchester (Ex.)
234	3. 0 p.m.*	Liverpool	Cardiff
239	3. 5 p.m.‡‡	Bradford (Exch.)	Poole
240	10.15 a.m.†	Manchester (L.R.)	Plymouth
	3.10 p.m.‡‡	"	Bristol
	3.15 p.m.†	"	Manchester (L.R.)
241	8.55 a.m.§	Cardiff...	Bournemouth
243	10.25 a.m.†	Derby	Manchester (Ex.)
244	8.25 a.m.†	Ilfracombe	Cardiff
246	8.33 p.m.§	Crewe...	Bristol
248	8.20 p.m.†	"	Newquay
252	9.25 p.m.†	Manchester (L.R.)	Manchester (L.R.)
257	4.40 p.m.†	Cardiff...	Paignton
258	10.35 p.m.†	Manchester (V.)	Plymouth
262	12.35 a.m.§	Manchester (L.R.)	"
263	1.40 a.m.‡‡	Crewe...	Crewe
	8. 0 a.m.†	Plymouth	"
265	8.45 a.m.¶	Cardiff...	Manchester (L.R.)
	12.40 p.m.‡‡	"	"
	11.15 a.m.†	Swansea	"
268	11.50 a.m.*	Manchester (V.)	Paignton
273	11.15 p.m.†	Penzance	Crewe
280	7.30 a.m.	Newquay	Manchester (L.R.)
	7.50 a.m.†	Crewe...	Liverpool
283	1.25 a.m.**	Bristol	Manchester (L.R.)
	8.15 a.m.†	Liverpool	Manchester (L.R.)
284	8.45 a.m.†	Penzance	Penzance
285	10. 5 a.m.§	Cardiff...	Liverpool
289	6. 5 p.m.‡‡	Manchester (L.R.)	Crewe
292	11.15 p.m.†		Penzance

Train No.	Time	From	To
297	7.35 a.m.†	Cardiff...	Blackpool
300	9.15 a.m.†	Blackpool	Cardiff
301	5.40 p.m.‡‡	Penzance	Crewe
305	8. 0 p.m.†	Manchester (L.R.)	Manchester (V.)
314	12. 0 nn.†	Penzance	Manchester (L.R.)
329	4.40 p.m.†	Manchester (V.)	Cardiff
334	9.10 p.m.†	"	Paignton
341	9. 8 p.m.†	Penzance	Penzance
350	4.40 p.m.†	"	Manchester (L.R.)
353	6.45 a.m.§	Wolverhampton	Paddington
355	7.30 a.m.†	Shrewsbury	"
360	6.35 a.m.§	Hereford	"
363	8.19 a.m.§	Kidderminster	"
365	7.25 a.m.*	Wolverhampton	"
370	11.15 a.m.*	Aberystwyth	"
375	4.35 p.m.†	Wolverhampton	"
376	2.40 p.m.§	Birkenhead...	"
380	5.20 p.m.†	Wolverhampton	"
383	9.25 a.m.†	Weymouth...	Wolverhampton
384	10. 0 a.m.†	"	Birmingham
385	10.20 a.m.†	"	Wolverhampton
387	11.12 a.m.†	"	Paddington
388	3.40 p.m.§	"	
389	4.10 p.m.	"	Cardiff
390	4.18 p.m.†	Bournemouth	Swansea
391	9. 0 a.m.†	New Milton	Cardiff
392	8.50 a.m.†	Portsmouth	"
395	9. 0 a.m.†	"	"
396	9.33 a.m.†	"	"
397	10.34 a.m.†	Brighton	Penzance
399	11.37 a.m.†	Newcastle	
400	11. 0 a.m.†	Sheffield	Penzance
403	3.57 p.m.‡‡		Newquay

Train No.	Time	From	To
405	1. 5 a.m.†	Bristol	Penzance
408	9.12 p.m.†	Nottingham	Paignton
410	10. 0 p.m.†		"
413	10.20 p.m.†	Sheffield	"
415	8.50 p.m.†	Bradford	"
417	10.10 p.m.†	Hull	"
418	9. 5 p.m.†	Newcastle	Plymouth
419	6.25 a.m.†	Bristol	Penzance
420	7. 0 a.m.†	Swindon	Weymouth
422	8.30 a.m.†	Weston-s-Mare	Kingswear
423	9.35 a.m.†	Bristol	Paignton
425	6.35 a.m.†	Walsall	Penzance
430	6.40 a.m.†	Leicester	Plymouth
433	7.43 a.m.†	Nottingham	Kingswear
435	8. 6 a.m.†	Sheffield	Plymouth
438	1.45 a.m.†	Bristol	Paignton
440	7.30 a.m.†	Newcastle	Penzance
442	9.30 a.m.†	Leeds	Paignton
444	9.25 a.m.†	Bradford	Paddington
446	7. 0 a.m.§	Weston-s-Mare	"
450	8.20 a.m.†	"	"
455	10.42 a.m.§	"	"
457	11. 5 a.m.†	Weston-s-Mare	"
460	11.45 a.m.†	Bristol	"
462	1.50 p.m.†	Weston-s-Mare	"
463	1.58 p.m.†	Bristol	"
465	4.15 p.m.†	"	"
470	4.30 p.m.*	Weston-s-Mare	"
473	4.35 p.m.	"	Birmingham
475	4.41 p.m.†	"	Swansea
480	2. 5 p.m.	"	Sheffield
490	1.50 p.m.†	Swindon	Paddington
493	7.30 p.m.†	Kingswear	"
500	7. 0 a.m.†		"

Train No.	Time	From	To
503	10.30 p.m.†	Paignton	Nottingham
505	8. 0 a.m.†	Kingswear	Kingswear
508	9. 5 a.m.†	Minehead	Paddington
510	9.45 a.m.†	Churston	"
512	10.40 a.m.†	Minehead	"
513	6. 5 a.m.†	Paignton	L.M.R.
515	10.35 a.m.†	Torquay	Paddington
517	11.50 p.m.†	Paignton	Wolverhampton
518	6.30 a.m.†	"	L.M.R.
520	11.20 a.m.*	Kingswear	Paddington
522	11.25 a.m.†	"	"
523	11.55 a.m.†	Minehead	Bradford
525	6.55 a.m.†	Paignton	Paddington
527	11.30 a.m.†	Torquay	Birmingham
528	10. — a.m.†	"	L.M.R.
529	7.10 a.m.†	Paignton	Paddington
530	12.18 p.m.†	Newton Abbot	"
533	1.30 p.m.†	Paignton	Newcastle
535	7.45 a.m.†	"	Paddington
537	1.40 p.m.†	Kingswear	Wolverhampton
540	10.35 a.m.†	Paignton	Paddington
542	1.45 p.m.†	"	"
543	2.15 p.m.†	Minehead	Nottingham
545	8.40 a.m.†	Paignton	Paddington
550	2.45 p.m.†	"	"
552	4.15 p.m.†	Teignmouth	Bradford
553	10.15 a.m.†	Paignton	Sheffield
555	8.52 a.m.†	Kingswear	Paddington
557	4.35 p.m.†	"	Wolverhampton
560	12.15 p.m.†	Ilfracombe	"
563	10.55 a.m.†	Kingswear	Bradford
565	8.45 a.m.†	Paignton	Manchester (L.R.)
567	1.55 p.m.†	"	Wolverhampton

Table A (upper)

Train No.	Time	From	To
663	10.20 a.m.†	Penzance	Cardiff
666	3.35 p.m.‡	Plymouth	Stapleton Road
670	7.40 a.m.†	St. Austell	Birmingham
672	7.30 a.m.†	Penzance	Wolverhampton
675	10.35 a.m.*	Penzance	"
678	11.10 a.m.†	"	"
683	11.15 a.m.†	Newquay	Newcastle
685	8. 5 a.m.†	"	York
688	11. 0 a.m.†	"	Sheffield
700	10.45 a.m.†	Penzance	Paignton
703	6.15 a.m.†	Cardiff...	Kingswear
704	8.10 a.m.†	Newport	"
705	8. 5 a.m.†	Cardiff...	"
708	9. 5 a.m.†	Swansea	"
710	8.17 a.m.†	Carmarthen	Penzance
711	3.35 a.m.‡‡	Fishguard Harbour	Paddington
712	4. 5 a.m.‡‡	"	"
	3.55 a.m.‡‡	"	"
715	4.35 a.m.‡‡	"	"
716	4.25 a.m.‡‡	"	"
718	5. 5 a.m.‡‡	"	"
719	6.30 a.m.§	Swansea	"
720	7.43 a.m.†	Cardiff...	"
722	7.50 a.m.*	Swansea	"
724	4.55 a.m.‖	Fishguard Harbour	"
725	8.15 a.m.††	Cardiff...	"
730	8.20 a.m.†	Swansea	"
733	9.45 a.m.*	Cardiff...	"
	7.30 a.m.§	Carmarthen	"
	9.55 a.m.†	Cardiff...	"
	7. 5 a.m.§	Cardiff...	"
	8. 0 a.m.§	Cheltenham	"
	11.45 a.m.†		"
	7.30 a.m.†	Pembroke Dock	"

Table B (lower)

Train No.	Time	From	To
568	6.40 a.m.†	Paignton	Stockport
570	7.45 a.m.†	Newton Abbot	Swansea
573	10.58 a.m.†	Paignton	Nottingham
577	2.55 p.m.†	"	Wolverhampton
578	8. 5 a.m.†	"	Manchester (Y.) (L.R.)
579	9. 5 a.m.†	"	"
580	9. 5 a.m.†	Kingswear	Swansea
583	2.25 p.m.†	Paignton	Sheffield
585	10.10 a.m.†	"	Cardiff
587	9.25 a.m.†	Ilfracombe	"
	3.10 p.m.†	Paignton	Wolverhampton
588	10.20 a.m.†	Kingswear	Crewe
590	12. 5 p.m.†	Paignton	Cardiff
593	5.15 p.m.†	"	Nottingham
594	12.30 p.m.†	"	Manchester (L.R.)
595	3.20 p.m.†	Kingswear	Manchester
597	10.30 p.m.†	Paignton	Cardiff
600	7. 0 a.m.†	Plymouth	Paddington
	7.15 a.m.†	"	"
603	7.25 a.m.†	"	"
605	8.30 a.m.†	Truro	"
608	7.30 a.m.†	Perranporth	"
610	8.15 a.m.†	Falmouth	"
615	8.35 a.m.†	Plymouth	"
620	11.15 a.m.†	Falmouth	"
623	9.40 a.m.†	Penzance	"
625	8.20 a.m.†	St. Ives	"
630	9.20 a.m.†	Penzance	"
635	10. 0 a.m.§	Penzance	"
638	10. 0 a.m.†	Newquay	"
640	12.30 p.m.†	Penzance	"
645	7. 5 a.m.†	Newquay	"
447	11.50 a.m.†	Penzance	"
449	1.20 p.m.†	Penzance	"

Train No.	Time	From	To
735	8. 0 a.m.†	Neyland	Paddington
736	9.25 a.m.†	Carmarthen	"
739	10.20 a.m.†	Pembroke Dock	"
740	11.10 a.m.†	Milford Haven	"
745	12. 0 nn.		"
750	12. 5 p.m.§	Pembroke Dock	"
753	1.10 p.m.	Neyland	"
755	2.35 p.m.	Swansea	"
758	4.35 p.m.*	Cardiff	"
760	9. 0 a.m.†		Portsmouth
765	9.28 a.m.†		New Milton
770	10. 8 a.m.†		Portsmouth
775	10.30 a.m.†		"
780	9.20 a.m.†	Swansea	Bournemouth
783	12.53 p.m.†	Cardiff	Portsmouth
785	1. 0 p.m.†		Brighton
790	9.50 p.m.‡	Swansea	York
805	10.40 p.m.	Wolverhampton	Penzance
808	7. 0 a.m.†		Paignton
810	7.30 a.m.†	Birmingham	Penzance
812	6.55 a.m.†	Wolverhampton	Paignton
815	8.30 a.m.†	Birmingham	Weston-s-Mare
818	8.55 a.m.†	Wolverhampton	Penzance
820	10.55 a.m.†	Birmingham	Paignton
823	9. 0 a.m.†	Wolverhampton	Penzance
825	9. 0 a.m.*†		Paignton
826	9.10 a.m.*	"	Kingswear
827	10.35 a.m.†		Paignton
830	10.50 a.m.†	Birmingham	Minehead
848	7.50 a.m.†		Weymouth
850	8. 0 a.m.†	Wolverhampton	Paignton
855	9.10 a.m.†		Weymouth
865	11. 5 a.m.†	Wolverhampton	Paignton
873	9.10 a.m.†	Birmingham	Pembroke Dock

Train No.	Time	From	To
875	6.30 p.m.†	York	Swindon
877	3.45 p.m.§	Birmingham	Swansea
881	9.42 p.m.§	Newcastle	Bournemouth
887	8.37 a.m.†		Cardiff
891	1.36 p.m.†	Sheffield	Swansea
893	10.15 a.m.†	Newcastle	Portsmouth
900	12.30 a.m.†	Birmingham	Bournemouth
903	6. 5 a.m.†		Hastings
905	7.28 a.m.†	Wolverhampton	Portsmouth
908	8.40 a.m.†	Birmingham	"
910	9. 5 a.m.†		"
913	8.40 a.m.†	Wolverhampton	Margate
915	10.10 a.m.†	Birmingham	"
918	10.20 a.m.†		"
920	10.40 a.m.†		Hastings
923	7.35 a.m.†	Birkenhead...	Ramsgate
925	12.15 p.m.†	Birmingham	Bournemouth
927	9.20 a.m.†	Birkenhead...	"
929	9.30 a.m.†		"
953	8.50 a.m.†	Portsmouth	Birmingham
955	9.11 a.m.†		Wolverhampton
958	8.55 a.m.†	Margate	Birmingham
960	9.32 a.m.†	Bournemouth	Wolverhampton
963	8.48 a.m.†	Hastings	Birmingham
965	9.30 a.m.†	Bournemouth	Birkenhead
968	9.10 a.m.†	Margate	Wolverhampton
970	8.56 a.m.†	Ramsgate	Birkenhead
973	11.50 a.m.†	Bournemouth	Birmingham
975	1.11 p.m.†	Portsmouth	"
978	1.30 p.m.†		"
980	12.18 p.m.†	Hastings	"
983	2.38 p.m.†	Portsmouth	Wolverhampton
985	3.30 p.m.†		"
993	10.25 a.m.†	Poole...	Bradford (Exch.)

Right: 1000 Class 4-6-0 No. 1014 *County of Glamorgan*
[R. A. Panting

Centre: 4900 Class 4-6-0 No. 6925 *Hackness Hall*
[G. Wheeler

Bottom: 6959 Class 4-6-0 No. 7918 *Rhose Wood Hall*
[J. Hodge

2800 Class 2-8-0 No. 2812

[A. W. Martin

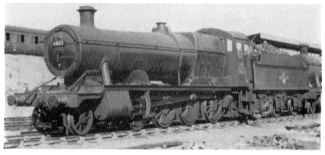

2800 Class 2-8-0 No. 3803 (with side-window cab)

[G. W. Morrison

4700 Class 2-8-0 No. 4700

G. Wheeler

R.O.D. Class 2-8-0 No. 3015   [*Brian E. Morrison*

4300 Class 2-6-0 No. 6304   [*A. E. Brown*

4300 Class 2-6-0 No. 7341 (with side-window cab)   [*G. Wheeler*

5101 Class 2-6-2T No. 4115

[*G. Wheeler*

3100 Class 2-6-2T No. 3103

[*G. Wheeler*

4500 Class 2-6-2T No. 4508

Above: 4575 Class
2-6-2T No. 5569
[G. Wheeler

Right: 7200 Class
2-8-2T No. 7235
[A. W. Martin

Below: 7200 Class
2-8-2T No. 7228
(with raised foot-
plating over cylin-
ders) [G. Wheeler

Above: 4200 Class
2-8-0T No. 4289
[Brian E. Morrison

Left: 5600 Class
0-6-2T No. 6639
[J. Hodge

Below: 2251 Class
0-6-0 No. 2243
[F. J. Saunders

Class 5 4-6-0 No. 73059   [J. R. Paterson

Class 5 4-6-0 No. 73146 (fitted with Caprotti valve gear)   [R. E. Vincent

Class 4 2-6-0 No. 76053

[B. K. B. Green

Class 2 2-6-0 No. 78006

[G. Wheeler

Class 3 2-6-2T No. 82022

[David A. Anderson

Rebuilt Class MN 4-6-2 No. 35017 *Belgian Marine*

[R. K. Evans

Class WC 4-6-2 No. 34101 *Hartland*

[Brian E. Morrison

Rebuilt Class WC 4-6-2 No. 34005 *Barnstaple*

[G. Wheeler

Class LN 4-6-0 No. 30863 *Lord Rodney*

[L. King

Class N15 4-6-0 No. 30448 *Sir Tristram*

[L. Elsey

Class H15 4-6-0 No. 30335 (Urie rebuild of Drummond E14)

C. P. Boocock

Class H15 4-6-0 (Maunsell) No. 30475　　　　　　　　[R. J. Buckley

Class S15 (Urie) 4-6-0 No. 30515　　　　　　　　[B. K. B. Green

Class S15 (Maunsell) 4-6-0 No. 30828　　　　　　　　[B. K. B. Green

Class V 4-4-0 No. 30929 *Malvern* [R. C. Riley

Class T9 4-4-0 No. 30729 (with six-wheel tender) [A. R. Carpenter

Class T9 4-4-0 No. 30338 with wider cab and splashers) R. K. Evans

Class L 4-4-0 No. 31770   [*Brian E. Morrison*

Class L1 4-4-0 No. 31785   [*D. Marriott*

Class D1 4-4-0 No. 31489   [*A. Trickett*

Class N 2-6-0 No. 31815

[K. R. Pirt

Class U 2-6-0 No. 31624

[Brian E. Morrison

Class U1 2-6-0 No. 31893

[B. K. B. Green

Class K 2-6-0 No. 32349 [A. A. Cameron

Class Q1 0-6-0 No. 33003 [R. J. Buckley

Class Q 0-6-0 No. 30541 [R. J. Buckley

Class 0395 0-6-0 No. 30567   [Brian E. Morrison

Class 700 0-6-0 No. 30317   [R. H. Tunstall

Class O1 0-6-0 No. 31064   [P. H. Wells

BRITISH RAILWAYS NON-STEAM
LOCOMOTIVE CLASSES
INTERNAL COMBUSTION LOCOMOTIVES

In future, diesel locomotives will be numbered in a separate series commencing at D1. New construction will bear these numbers at the outset and existing locomotives numbered in the 11100 and 13000 series will be renumbered.

Owing to the large number of deisel locomotives in service and under construction, it is not now possible to show diesel locomotive particulars in this publication for space reasons. Full details may be found in the ABC British Railways Diesels.

ICo-Col 4 Diesel Electric

D1	D4	D7	D9
D2	D5	D8	D10
D3	D6		

ICo-Col 4 Diesel Electric

D200	D203	D206	D208
D201	D204	D207	D209
D202	D205		

AIA-AIA 4 Diesel Hydraulic

D600	Active
D601	Ark Royal
D602	Bulldog
D603	Conquest
D604	Cossack

Bo-Bo 4 Diesel Hydraulic

D800	D809	D817	D825
D801	D810	D818	D826
D802	D811	D819	D827
D803	D812	D820	D828
D804	D813	D821	D829
D805	D814	D822	D830
D806	D815	D823	D831
D807	D816	D824	D832
D808			

0-6-0 Diesel Mechanical

D2000	D2030	D2060	D2200
D2001	D2031	D2061	D2201
D2002	D2032	D2062	D2202
D2003	D2033	D2063	D2203
D2004	D2034	D2064	D2204
D2005	D2035	D2065	D2205
D2006	D2036	D2066	D2206
D2007	D2037	D2067	D2207
D2008	D2038	D2068	D2208
D2009	D2039	D2069	D2209
D2010	D2040	D2070	D2210
D2011	D2041	D2071	D2211
D2012	D2042	D2072	D2212
D2013	D2043	D2073	D2213
D2014	D2044	D2074	D2214
D2015	D2045	D2075	D2215
D2016	D2046	D2076	D2216
D2017	D2047	D2077	D2217
D2018	D2048	D2078	D2218
D2019	D2049	D2079	D2219
D2020	D2050	D2080	D2220
D2021	D2051	D2081	D2221
D2022	D2052	D2082	D2222
D2023	D2053	D2083	D2223
D2024	D2054	D2084	D2224
D2025	D2055	D2085	D2225
D2026	D2056	D2086	D2226
D2027	D2057	D2087	D2227
D2028	D2058	D2088	D2228
D2029	D2059		D2229

D2230	D2260	D2415	D2558
D2231	D2261	D2416	D2559
D2232	D2262	D2417	D2560
D2233	D2263	D2418	D2561
D2234	D2264	D2419	D2562
D2235	D2265	D2420	D2563
D2236	D2266	D2421	D2564
D2237	D2267	D2422	D2565
D2238	D2268	D2423	D2566
D2239	D2269	D2424	D2567
D2240	D2270		D2568
D2241	D2271	D2500	D2569
D2242	D2272	D2501	D2570
D2243	D2273	D2502	D2571
D2244		D2503	D2572
D2245	D2400	D2504	D2573
D2246	D2401	D2505	D2574
D2247	D2402	D2506	D2575
D2248	D2403	D2507	D2576
D2249	D2404	D2508	D2577
D2250	D2405	D2509	D2578
D2251	D2406		D2579
D2252	D2407	D2550	D2580
D2253	D2408	D2551	D2581
D2254	D2409	D2552	D2582
D2255	D2410	D2553	D2583
D2256	D2411	D2554	D2584
D2257	D2412	D2555	D2585
D2258	D2413	D2556	
D2259	D2414	D2557	

200 h.p. Diesel Hydraulic

0-4-0

D2700	D2712	D2723	D2734
D2701	D2713	D2724	D2735
D2702	D2714	D2725	D2736
D2703	D2715	D2726	D2737
D2704	D2716	D2727	D2738
D2705	D2717	D2728	D2739
D2706	D2718	D2729	D2740
D2707	D2719	D2730	D2741
D2708	D2720	D2731	D2742
D2709	D2721	D2732	D2743
D2710	D2722	D2733	D2744
D2711			

300 h.p. Diesel Hydraulic

0-4-0

D2900	D2903	D2906	D2909
D2901	D2904	D2907	D2910
D2902	D2905	D2908	

0-4-0 Diesel Mechanical

D2950	D2953	D2955	D2957
D2951	D2954	D2956	D2958
D2952			

0-6-0 Diesel Electric

D3000	D3033	D3066	D3099
D3001	D3034	D3067	D3100
D3002	D3035	D3068	D3101
D3003	D3036	D3069	D3102
D3004	D3037	D3070	D3103
D3005	D3038	D3071	D3104
D3006	D3039	D3072	D3105
D3007	D3040	D3073	D3106
D3008	D3041	D3074	D3107
D3009	D3042	D3075	D3108
D3010	D3043	D3076	D3109
D3011	D3044	D3077	D3110
D3012	D3045	D3078	D3111
D3013	D3046	D3079	D3112
D3014	D3047	D3080	D3113
D3015	D3048	D3081	D3114
D3016	D3049	D3082	D3115
D3017	D3050	D3083	D3116
D3018	D3051	D3084	D3117
D3019	D3052	D3085	D3118
D3020	D3053	D3086	D3119
D3021	D3054	D3087	D3120
D3022	D3055	D3088	D3121
D3023	D3056	D3089	D3122
D3024	D3057	D3090	D3123
D3025	D3058	D3091	D3124
D3026	D3059	D3092	D3125
D3027	D3060	D3093	D3126
D3028	D3061	D3094	D3127
D3029	D3062	D3095	D3128
D3030	D3063	D3096	D3129
D3031	D3064	D3097	D3130
D3032	D3065	D3098	D3131

D3132	D3179	D3226	D3273	D3320	D3367	D3414	D3471
D3133	D3180	D3227	D3274	D3321	D3368	D3415	D3472
D3134	D3181	D3228	D3275	D3322	D3369	D3416	D3473
D3135	D3182	D3229	D3276	D3323	D3370	D3417	D3474
D3136	D3183	D3230	D3277	D3324	D3371	D3418	D3475
D3137	D3184	D3231	D3278	D3325	D3372	D3419	D3476
D3138	D3185	D3232	D3279	D3326	D3373	D3420	D3477
D3139	D3186	D3233	D3280	D3327	D3374	D3421	D3478
D3140	D3187	D3234	D3281	D3328	D3375	D3422	D3479
D3141	D3188	D3235	D3282	D3329	D3376	D3423	D3480
D3142	D3189	D3236	D3283	D3330	D3377	D3424	D3481
D3143	D3190	D3237	D3284	D3331	D3378	D3425	D3482
D3144	D3191	D3238	D3285	D3332	D3379	D3426	D3483
D3145	D3192	D3239	D3286	D3333	D3380	D3427	D3484
D3146	D3193	D3240	D3287	D3334	D3381	D3428	D3485
D3147	D3194	D3241	D3288	D3335	D3382	D3439	D3486
D3148	D3195	D3242	D3289	D3336	D3383	D3440	D3487
D3149	D3196	D3243	D3290	D3337	D3384	D3441	D3488
D3150	D3197	D3244	D3291	D3338	D3385	D3442	D3489
D3151	D3198	D3245	D3292	D3339	D3386	D3443	D3490
D3152	D3199	D3246	D3293	D3340	D3387	D3444	D3491
D3153	D3200	D3247	D3294	D3341	D3388	D3445	D3492
D3154	D3201	D3248	D3295	D3342	D3389	D3446	D3493
D3155	D3202	D3249	D3296	D3343	D3390	D3447	D3494
D3156	D3203	D3250	D3297	D3344	D3391	D3448	D3495
D3157	D3204	D3251	D3298	D3345	D3392	D3449	D3496
D3158	D3205	D3252	D3299	D3346	D3393	D3450	D3497
D3159	D3206	D3253	D3300	D3347	D3394	D3451	D3498
D3160	D3207	D3254	D3301	D3348	D3395	D3452	D3499
D3161	D3208	D3255	D3302	D3349	D3396	D3453	D3500
D3162	D3209	D3256	D3303	D3350	D3397	D3454	D3501
D3163	D3210	D3257	D3304	D3351	D3398	D3455	D3502
D3164	D3211	D3258	D3305	D3352	D3399	D3456	D3503
D3165	D3212	D3259	D3306	D3353	D3400	D3457	D3504
D3166	D3213	D3260	D3307	D3354	D3401	D3458	D3505
D3167	D3214	D3261	D3308	D3355	D3402	D3459	D3506
D3168	D3215	D3262	D3309	D3356	D3403	D3460	D3507
D3169	D3216	D3263	D3310	D3357	D3404	D3461	D3508
D3170	D3217	D3264	D3311	D3358	D3405	D3462	D3509
D3171	D3218	D3265	D3312	D3359	D3406	D3463	D3510
D3172	D3219	D3266	D3313	D3360	D3407	D3464	D3511
D3173	D3220	D3267	D3314	D3361	D3408	D3465	D3512
D3174	D3221	D3268	D3315	D3362	D3409	D3466	D3513
D3175	D3222	D3269	D3316	D3363	D3410	D3467	D3514
D3176	D3223	D3270	D3317	D3364	D3411	D3468	D3515
D3177	D3224	D3271	D3318	D3365	D3412	D3469	D3516
D3178	D3225	D3272	D3319	D3366	D3413	D3470	D3517

D3518	D3557	D3596	D3635
D3519	D3558	D3597	D3636
D3520	D3559	D3598	D3637
D3521	D3560	D3599	D3638
D3522	D3561	D3600	D3639
D3523	D3562	D3601	D3640
D3524	D3563	D3602	D3641
D3525	D3564	D3603	D3642
D3526	D3565	D3604	D3643
D3527	D3566	D3605	D3644
D3528	D3567	D3606	D3645
D3529	D3568	D3607	D3646
D3530	D3569	D3608	D3647
D3531	D3570	D3609	D3648
D3532	D3571	D3610	D3649
D3533	D3572	D3611	D3650
D3534	D3573	D3612	D3651
D3535	D3574	D3613	D3652
D3536	D3575	D3614	D3653
D3537	D3576	D3615	D3654
D3538	D3577	D3616	D3655
D3539	D3578	D3617	D3656
D3540	D3579	D3618	D3657
D3541	D3580	D3619	D3658
D3542	D3581	D3620	D3659
D3543	D3582	D3621	D3660
D3544	D3583	D3622	D3661
D3545	D3584	D3623	D3662
D3546	D3585	D3624	D3663
D3547	D3586	D3625	D3664
D3548	D3587	D3626	D3665
D3549	D3588	D3627	D3666
D3550	D3589	D3628	D3667
D3551	D3590	D3629	D3668
D3552	D3591	D3630	D3669
D3553	D3592	D3631	D3670
D3554	D3593	D3632	D3671
D3555	D3594	D3633	
D3556	D3595	D3634	

1,160 h.p. Diesel
Bo-Bo 2 Electric

D5000	D5005	D5010	D5015
D5001	D5006	D5011	D5016
D5002	D5007	D5012	D5017
D5003	D5008	D5013	D5018
D5004	D5009	D5014	D5019

1,160 h.p. Diesel
Bo-Bo 2 Electric

D5300	D5305	D5310	D5315
D5301	D5306	D5311	D5316
D5302	D5307	D5312	D5317
D5303	D5308	D5313	D5318
D5304	D5309	D5314	D5319

Diesel
AlA-AlA 2 Electric

D5500	D5505	D5510	D5515
D5501	D5506	D5511	D5516
D5502	D5507	D5512	D5517
D5503	D5508	D5513	D5518
D5504	D5509	D5514	D5519

Diesel
Co-Bo 2 Electric

D5700	D5705	D5710	D5715
D5701	D5706	D5711	D5716
D5702	D5707	D5712	D5717
D5703	D5708	D5713	D5718
D5704	D5709	D5714	D5719

1,100 h.p. Diesel
Bo-Bo 2 Electric

D5900	D5903	D5906	D5908
D5901	D5904	D5907	D5909
D5902	D5905		

1,000 h.p. Diesel
Bo-Bo 2 Electric

D6100	D6103	D6106	D6108
D6101	D6104	D6107	D6109
D6102	D6105		

Diesel
B-B 2 Hydraulic

D6300	D6302	D6304	D6305
D6301	D6303		

1,550 h.p. Diesel
Bo-Bo 3 Electric

D6500	D6512	D6523	D6534
D6501	D6513	D6524	D6535
D6502	D6514	D6525	D6536
D6503	D6515	D6526	D6537
D6504	D6516	D6527	D6538
D6505	D6517	D6528	D6539
D6506	D6518	D6529	D6540
D6507	D6519	D6530	D6541
D6508	D6520	D6531	D6542
D6509	D6521	D6532	D6543
D6510	D6522	D6533	D6544
D6511			

1,000 h.p. Diesel
Bo-Bo 1 Electric

D8000	D8005	D8010	D8015
D8001	D8006	D8011	D8016
D8002	D8007	D8012	D8017
D8003	D8008	D8013	D8018
D8004	D8009	D8014	D8019

800 h.p. Diesel
Bo-Bo 1 Electric

D8200	D8203	D8206	D8208
D8201	D8204	D8207	D8209
D8202	D8205		

800 h.p. Diesel
Bo-Bo 1 Electric

D8400	D8403	D8406	D8408
D8401	D8404	D8407	D8409
D8402	D8405		

Diesel
Co-Co 6P/5F Electric

10000	10001	Total 2

Diesel
2-D-2 6P/5F Mechanical

10100	Total 1

Diesel
1Co-Co1 {10201/2 5P/5F / 10203 6P/6F} **Elec.**

10201	10202	10203	Total 3

Diesel
Bo-Bo 3P/3F Electric

10800	Total 1

0-6-0 Diesel Mechanical

11001	Total 1

0-6-0 Diesel Electric

12000	12036	12071	12106
12001	12037	12072	12107
12002	12038	12073	12108
12003	12039	12074	12109
12004	12040	12075	12110
12005	12041	12076	12111
12006	12042	12077	12112
12007	12043	12078	12113
12008	12044	12079	12114
12009	12045	12080	12115
12010	12046	12081	12116
12011	12047	12082	12117
12012	12048	12083	12118
12013	12049	12084	12119
12014	12050	12085	12120
12015	12051	12086	12121
12016	12052	12087	12122
12017	12053	12088	12123
12018	12054	12089	12124
12019	12055	12090	12125
12020	12056	12091	12126
12021	12057	12092	12127
12022	12058	12093	12128
12023	12059	12094	12129
12024	12060	12095	12130
12025	12061	12096	12131
12026	12062	12097	12132
12027	12063	12098	12133
12028	12064	12099	12134
12029	12065	12100	12135
12030	12066	12101	12136
12031	12067	12102	12137
12032	12068	12103	12138
12033	12069	12104	
12034	12070	12105	
12035			Total 138

0-6-0   Diesel Electric

15000	15106	15217	15228
15001	15107	15218	15229
15002	15201	15219	15230
15003	15202	15220	15231
15004	15203	15221	15232
15100	15211	15222	15233
15101	15212	15223	15234
15102	15213	15224	15235
15103	15214	15225	15236
15104	15215	15226	
15105	15216	15227	

AIA-AIA   Gas Turbine

Introduced 1949. Brown Boveri (Switzerland) design for G.W.R.

Weight: 115 tons.

Driving Wheels: 4' 0½".

T.E.: 31,500 lb. at 21 m.p.h.

Engine: 2,500 h.p. gas turbine.

Motors: Four independently mounted electric traction motors with spring drive.

18000   Total 1

Co-Co   Gas Turbine

Introduced 1951.

Metropolitan-Vickers and Hawksworth design for G.W.R.

Weight: 129 tons 10 cwt.

Driving Wheels: 3' 8".

T.E.: maximum 60,000 lb. Continuous rating: 30,000 lb.

Motors: Six nose-suspended electric traction motors with single reduction gear drive.

18100   Total 1

ELECTRIC LOCOMOTIVES

Co-Co 7P/5F Class CC

*Introduced 1941. Raworth & Bulleid design for S.R.

†Introduced 1948. Later design with detail differences.

Weight: $\begin{cases} 99 \text{ tons } 14 \text{ cwt.*} \\ 104 \text{ tons } 14 \text{ cwt.†} \end{cases}$

Driving Wheels: 3′ 7″.

T.E.: $\begin{cases} 40,000 \text{ lb.*} \\ 45,000 \text{ lb.†} \end{cases}$

Voltage: 660 D.C.

Current Collection: Overhead and third rail, with flywheel-driven generator for gaps in third rail.

20001*	20002*	20003†
		Total 3

Bo-Bo Class EM1

*Introduced 1941. Metropolitan-Vickers and Gresley design for L.N.E.R.

Remainder. Introduced 1950. Production design with detail alterations.

Weight: 87 tons 18 cwt.

Driving Wheels: 4′ 2″.

T.E.: 45,000 lb.   Voltage: 1,500 D.C.

Current Collection: Overhead.

26000*	26011	26022	26033
26001	26012	26023	26034
26002	26013	26024	26035
26003	26014	26025	26036
26004	26015	26026	26037
26005	26016	26027	26038
26006	26017	26028	26039
26007	26018	26029	26040
26008	26019	26030	26041
26009	26020	26031	26042
26010	26021	26032	26043
26044	26048	26052	26056
26045	26049	26053	26057
26046	26050	26054	**Total**
26047	26051	26055	**58**

*26000 named *Tommy*.

Bo-Bo Class ES1

Built 1902. Brush & Thomson-Houston shunting design for N.E.R.

Weight: 46 tons.

Voltage: 600 D.C.   T.E.: 25,000 lb.

Current collection: Overhead and third rail.

26500	26501	**Total 2**

Bo-Bo Class EB1

Introduced 1946. L.N.E.R. rebuild of N.E.R. Raven freight design (introduced 1914) originally for banking work on Manchester–Wath line.

Weight: 74 tons 8 cwt.

Driving Wheels: 4′ 0″.

T.E.: 37,600 lb.   Voltage: 1,500 D.C.

Current Collection: Overhead.

26510	**Total 1**

Co-Co Class EM2

Introduced 1954. Metropolitan-Vickers and L.N.E.R. design, development of EM1 with six axles and higher speed range.

Weight: 102 tons.

Driving Wheels: 4′ 2″.

T.E.: 45,000 lb.   Voltage: 1,500 D.C.

Current Collection: Overhead.

27000	27002	27004	27006
27001	27003	27005	
			Total 7

SUMMARY OF SOUTHERN REGION STEAM LOCOMOTIVE CLASSES

IN ALPHABETICAL ORDER
WITH HISTORICAL NOTES AND DIMENSIONS

The code given in smaller bold type at the head of each Class,
e.g. " 2F " denotes its British Railways power Classification.
The numbers of locomotives in service have been checked to January 14th, 1958.

Classes

0-6-0T 0P A1 & A1X

*A1. Introduced 1872. Stroudley L.B.S.C. " Terrier," later fitted with Marsh boiler, retaining original type smokebox.

†A1X. Introduced 1911. Rebuild of A1 with Marsh boiler and extended smokebox.

‡A1X. Loco. with increased cylinder diameter.

Weight: { 27 tons 10 cwt.*
{ 28 tons 5 cwt.††

Pressure: 150 lb.

Cyls.: { 12″ × 20″.*†
{ 14⅜″ × 20″.‡

Driving Wheels: 4′ 0″.

T.E.: { 7,650 lb.*†
{ 10,695 lb.‡

*DS680
†DS377 DS681, 32640/6/50/5/61/2/70/7/8
‡32636

Total A1 1
AIX 12

0-4-0T 1F Class B4

*Introduced 1891. Adams L.S.W. design for dock shunting.

†Introduced 1908. Drummond K14 locos., with smaller boiler and detail alterations.

Weight: { 33 tons 9 cwt.*
{ 32 tons 18 cwt.†

Pressure: 140 lb. Cyls. (O): 16″ × 22″.

Driving Wheels: 3′ 9¾″.

T.E.: 14,650 lb.

*30086–9/93/6, 30102
†30083/4 Total 9

0-6-0 2F Class C

Introduced 1900. Wainwright S.E.C. design.

Weight: Loco. 43 tons 16 cwt.
Pressure: 160 lb.
Cyls.: 18½″ × 26″.
Driving Wheels: 5′ 2″.
T.E.: 19,520 lb.

31004/18/33/7/54/9/61/8/71/86, 31102/12/3/50/91, 31218/9/21/3/7/9/42–5/52/3/5/6/67/8/70–2/80/7/93/7/8, 31317, 31461/80/1/95/8,31510/73/5/6/8/9/81–5/8–90/2/3, 31681–4/6/8–95, 31714–7/9–25 Total 85

0-6-0 2F Class C2X

Introduced 1908. Marsh rebuild of R. J. Billinton L.B.S.C. C2 with larger C3-type boiler, extended smokebox, etc.
Weight: Loco. 45 tons 5 cwt.
Pressure: 170 lb.
Cyls.: 17½″ × 26″.
Driving Wheels: 5′ 0″.
T.E.: 19,175 lb.

32437/8/40–51, 32521–9/32/4–6/8–41/3–54 Total 43

0-4-0T 0P Class C14

Introduced 1923. Urie rebuild as shunting locos. of Drummond L.S.W. motor-train 2-2-0T (originally introduced 1906).
Weight: 25 tons 15 cwt.
Pressure: 150 lb.
Cyls.: (O) 14″ × 14″.
Driving Wheels: 3′ 0″.
T.E.: 9,720 lb.
Walschaerts valve gear.

DS77 Total 1

4-4-0 3P Class D1

Introduced 1921. Maunsell rebuild of Wainwright D, with larger super-heated boiler, Belpaire firebox and long-travel piston valves.

Weight: Loco. 52 tons 4 cwt.

Pressure: 180 lb. Su.

Cyls.: 19″ × 26″.

Driving Wheels: 6′ 8″.

T.E.: 17,950 lb.

31145, 31246/7, 31470/87/9/92/4, 31505/9/45, 31727/35/9/41/3/9

Total 17

4-4-0 3P Class E1

Introduced 1919. Maunsell rebuild of Wainwright E, with larger super-heated boiler, Belpaire firebox and long-travel piston valves.

Weight: Loco. 53 tons 9 cwt.

Pressure: 180 lb.

Cyls.: 19″ × 26″.

Driving Wheels: 6′ 6″.

T.E.: 18,410 lb.

31019/67,   31165,   31497, 31504/6/7

Total 7

0-6-0T 2F Class E1

Introduced 1874. Stroudley L.B.S.C. design, reboiled by Marsh.

Weight: 44 tons 3 cwt.

Pressure: 170 lb.

Cyls.: 17″ × 24″.

Driving Wheels: 4′ 6″.

T.E.: 18,560 lb.

3/4,   32113/39/51,   32689/94

Total 7

0-6-2T 1P2F Class E1/R

Introduced 1927. Maunsell rebuild of Stroudley E1, with radial trailing axle and larger bunker for passenger service in West of England.

Weight: 50 tons 5 cwt.

Pressure: 170 lb.

Cyls.: 17″ × 24″.

Driving Wheels: 4′ 6″.

T.E.: 18,560 lb.

32124/35, 32697

Total 3

0-6-0T 3F Class E2

*Introduced 1913. L. B. Billinton L.B.S.C. design.

†Introduced 1915. Later locos. with tanks extended further forward.

Weight: $\begin{cases} 52 \text{ tons } 15 \text{ cwt.*} \\ 53 \text{ tons } 10 \text{ cwt.†} \end{cases}$

Pressure: 170 lb.

Cyls.: 17½″ × 26″.

Driving Wheels: 4′ 6″.

T.E.: 21,305 lb.

*32100–4

†32105–9

Total 10

0-6-2T 2F Class E3

Introduced 1894. R. J. Billinton L.B.S.C. design, development of Stroudley " West Brighton " (introduced 1891), reboiled and fitted with extended smokebox, 1918 onwards; cylinder diameter reduced from 18″ by S.R.

Weight: 56 tons 10 cwt.

Pressure: 170 lb.

Cyls.: 17½″ × 26″.

Driving Wheels: 4′ 6″.

T.E.: 21,305 lb.

32165/6, 32454–6

Total 5

Classes
0-6-2T 2P2F E4 & E4X

*E4. Introduced 1897. R. J. Billinton L.B.S.C. design, development of E3 with larger wheels, reboilered with Marsh boiler and extended smokebox, cylinder diameter reduced from 18″ by S.R.
†E4X. Introduced 1909. E4 reboilered with larger I2 4-4-2T type boiler.

Weight: $\begin{cases} 57 \text{ tons } 10 \text{ cwt.*} \\ 59 \text{ tons } 5 \text{ cwt.†} \end{cases}$
Pressure: 170 lb.
Cyls.: 17½″ × 26″.
Driving Wheels: 5′ 0″.
T.E.: 19,175 lb.

*32463/7–75/9–81/4/6/7/91/3–5/7/8, 32500/2–10/2/5/7/9/56/7/9/60/2–6/77–81

†32466/77

	Total	E4 50
		E4X 2

Classes
0-6-2T 3F E6 & E6X

*‡E6. Introduced 1904. R. J. Billinton L.B.S.C. design, development of E5 with smaller wheels, some with higher pressure.
†E6X. Introduced 1911. E6 reboilered with larger C3-type boiler.

Weight: $\begin{cases} 61 \text{ tons.*‡} \\ 63 \text{ tons.†} \end{cases}$
Pressure: $\begin{cases} 160 \text{ lb.*} \\ 175 \text{ lb.‡} \\ 170 \text{ lb.†} \end{cases}$
Cyls.: 18″ × 26″.
Driving Wheels: 4′ 6″.
T.E.: $\begin{cases} 21,215 \text{ lb.*} \\ 23,205 \text{ lb.‡} \\ 22,540 \text{ lb.†} \end{cases}$
*‡32408/10/3–8   †32411

	Total	E6 8
		E6X 1

0-6-0T 2F Class G6

*Introduced 1894. Adams L.S.W. design, later additions by Drummond, but with Adams type boiler.
†Introduced 1925. Fitted with Drummond type boiler.
Weight: 47 tons 13 cwt.
Pressure: 160 lb.
Cyls.: 17½″ × 24″.
Driving Wheels: 4′ 10″.
T.E.: 17,235 lb.

*30162, 30238/58/60/6/70/7, 30349, DS3152

†30160, 30274

	Total 11

4-8-0T 8F Class G16

Introduced 1921. Urie L.S.W. " Hump " loco.
Weight: 95 tons 2 cwt.
Pressure: 180 lb. Su.
Cyls.: (O) 22″ × 28″.
Driving Wheels: 5′ 1″.
T.E.: 33,990 lb.
Walschaerts valve gear. P.V.

30492–5   Total 4

0-4-4T IP Class H

Introduced 1904. Wainwright S.E.C. design.
*Introduced 1949. Fitted for push-and-pull working.
Weight: 54 tons 8 cwt.
Pressure: 160 lb.
Cyls.: 18″ × 26″.
Driving Wheels: 5′ 6″.
T.E.: 17,360 lb.

31005, 31259/61/3/5/6, 31305–7/24/6/8, 31500/3/33/40/2/50–3

*31161/2/4/77/84/93, 31239/69/76/8/9/95, 31308/10/9/22/7/9, 31512/7–23/30/43/4/8/54

	Total 52

4-4-2 4P Class H2

Introduced 1911. Marsh L.B.S.C.
design, superheated development of
H1 with larger cylinders.
Weight: Loco. 68 tons 5 cwt.
Pressure: 200 lb. Su.
Cyls.: (O) 21″ × 26″.
Driving Wheels: 6′ 7½″.
T.E.: 24,520 lb.
P.V.

32424   Total 1

4-6-0 4P5F Class H15

*Introduced 1914. Urie L.S.W. design,
fitted with " Maunsell " superheater
from 1927, replacing earlier types.
†Introduced 1915. Urie rebuild with
two outside cylinders of Drummond
E14 4-cyl. 4-6-0 introduced 1907,
retaining original boiler retubed and
fitted with superheater.
‡Introduced 1924. Maunsell locos.
with N15-type boiler and smaller
tender.
§Introduced 1924. Maunsell rebuild of
Drummond F13 4-cyl. 4-6-0 introduced 1905, with detail differences
from rebuild of E14.
¶Introduced 1927. Urie loco. (built
1914 saturated), rebuilt with later
N15-type boiler, with smaller firebox.

Weight: Loco. $\begin{cases} 81 \text{ tons} & 5 \text{ cwt.*} \\ 82 \text{ tons} & 1 \text{ cwt.†} \\ 79 \text{ tons} & 19 \text{ cwt.‡¶} \\ 80 \text{ tons} & 11 \text{ cwt.§} \end{cases}$

Pressure: $\begin{cases} 180 \text{ lb. Su.*‡¶} \\ 175 \text{ lb. Su.†§} \end{cases}$

Cyls.: (O) 21″ × 28″.
Driving Wheels: 6′ 0″.
T.E.: $\begin{cases} 26,240 \text{ lb.*‡¶} \\ 25,510 \text{ lb.†§} \end{cases}$

Walschaerts valve gear. P.V.

*30482/4/6/8/9   †30335
‡30473-8, 30521-4   §30331/3/4
¶30491   Total 20

4-6-2T 6F Class H16

Introduced 1921. Urie L.S.W. design
for heavy freight traffic.
Weight: 96 tons 8 cwt.
Pressure: 180 lb. Su.
Cyls.: (O) 21″ × 28″.
Driving Wheels: 5′ 7″.
T.E.: 28,200 lb.
Walschaerts valve gear. P.V.

30516-20   Total 5

2-6-0 4P5F Class K

Introduced 1913. L. B. Billinton
L.B.S.C. design.
Weight: Loco. 63 tons 15 cwt.
Pressure: 180 lb. Su.
Cyls.: (O) 21″ × 26″.
Driving Wheels: 5′ 6″.
T.E.: 26,580 lb.
P.V.

32337-53   Total 17

4-4-0 3P Class L

Introduced 1914. Wainwright S.E.C.
design, with detail alterations by
Maunsell.
Weight: Loco. 57 tons 9 cwt.
Pressure: 160 lb. Su.
Cyls.: 20½″ × 26″.
Driving Wheels: 6′ 8″.
T.E.: 18,575 lb.
P.V.

31760/2-8/70-81   Total 20

4-4-0 3P Class L1

Introduced 1926. Post-grouping devel-
opment of L, with long-travel valves,
side window cab and detail alterations.
Weight: Loco. 57 tons 16 cwt.
Pressure: 180 lb. Su.
Cyls.: 19½″ × 26″.
Driving Wheels: 6′ 8″.
T.E.: 18,910 lb.
P.V.

31753-9/82-9   Total 15

Classes LN-N & NI

4-6-0   7P   Class LN

*Introduced 1926. Maunsell design, cylinders and tender modified by Bulleid from 1938, and fitted with multiple-jet blastpipe and large-diameter chimney.

†Introduced 1929. Loco. fitted experimentally with smaller driving wheels.

‡Introduced 1929. Loco. fitted experimentally with longer boiler.

Weight: Loco. $\begin{cases} 83 \text{ tons } 10 \text{ cwt.}*† \\ 84 \text{ tons } 16 \text{ cwt.}‡ \end{cases}$

Pressure: 220 :b. Su.

Cyls.: (4) $16\frac{1}{2}'' \times 26''$.

Driving Wheels: $\begin{cases} 6' 7''.*‡ \\ 6' 3''.† \end{cases}$

T.E.: $\begin{cases} 33,510 \text{ lb.}*‡ \\ 35,300 \text{ lb.}† \end{cases}$

Walschaerts valve gear. P.V.

*30850–8/61–5

†30859   ‡30860

Total 16

4-6-2   8P   Class MN

*Introduced 1941. Bulleid design originally with 280 lb. pressure, multiple-jet blastpipe and Bulleid valve gear.

†Introduced 1956. Rebuilt with Walschaerts valve gear, modified details and air-smoothed casing removed.

Weight: Loco. $\begin{cases} 94 \text{ tons } 15 \text{ cwt.}* \\ 97 \text{ tons } 18 \text{ cwt.}† \end{cases}$

Pressure: 250 lb.

Cyls.: (3) $18'' \times 24''$.

Driving Wheels: 6' 2''.

T.E.: 33,495 lb.

P.V.

*35001–8/11/5/9/21/4/8–30

†35009/10/2–4/6–8/20/2/3/5–7

Total 30

0-4-4T   2P   Class M7

*Introduced 1897. Drummond L.S.W. M7 design.

†Introduced 1903. Drummond X14 design, with increased front overhang, steam reverser and detail alterations, now classified M7 (30254 originally M7).

‡Introduced 1925. X14 design fitted for push-and-pull working.

Weight: $\begin{cases} 60 \text{ tons } 4 \text{ cwt.}* \\ 60 \text{ tons } 3 \text{ cwt.}† \\ 62 \text{ tons } 0 \text{ cwt.}‡ \end{cases}$

Pressure: 175 lb.

Cyls.: $18\frac{1}{2}'' \times 26''$.

Driving Wheels: 5' 7''.

T.E.: 19,755 lb.

*30022–6/31–40/3/4,30112, 30241–3/5–9/51–3/5/6, 30318–24/56/7,30667–71/3–6

†30030, 30123/4/7/30/2/3, 30254, 30374–8, 30479

‡30021/7/8/9/45–60, 30104–11/25/8/9/31, 30328/79, 30480/1

Total 99

2-6-0   4P5F   Classes N & NI

*N. Introduced 1917. Maunsell S.E.C mixed traffic design.

†NI. Introduced 1922. 3-cylinder development of N.

Weight: Loco. $\begin{cases} 61 \text{ tons } 4 \text{ cwt.}* \\ 64 \text{ tons } 5 \text{ cwt.}† \end{cases}$

Pressure: 200 lb. Su.

Cyls.: $\begin{cases} (O) 19'' \times 28''.* \\ (3) 16'' \times 28''.† \end{cases}$

Driving Wheels: 5' 6''.

T.E.: $\begin{cases} 26,035 \text{ lb.}* \\ 27,695 \text{ lb.}† \end{cases}$

Walschaerts valve gear. P.V.

*31400–14, 31810–21/3–75

†31822/76–80

Total   Class N   80

Class NI   6

4-6-0 5P Class N15

*Introduced 1928. Urie L.S.W. locos. (1918 design) modified with cylinders of reduced diameter.

†Introduced 1925. Maunsell locos. with long-travel valves, increased boiler pressure, smaller fireboxes, and tenders from Drummond G14 4-6-0's.

‡Introduced 1925. Later locos. with detail alterations and increased weight.

§Introduced 1925. Locos. with modified cabs to suit Eastern Section, and new bogie tenders.

¶Introduced 1926. Locos. with detail alterations and six-wheeled tenders for Central Section.

Weight: Loco. $\begin{cases} 80 \text{ tons } 7 \text{ cwt.*} \\ 79 \text{ tons } 18 \text{ cwt.†} \\ 80 \text{ tons } 19 \text{ cwt.‡§} \\ 81 \text{ tons } 17 \text{ cwt.¶} \end{cases}$

Pressure: $\begin{cases} 180 \text{ lb. Su.*} \\ 200 \text{ lb. Su.†‡§¶} \end{cases}$

Cyls.: $\begin{cases} (O) 21'' \times 28''.* \\ (O) 20\frac{1}{2}'' \times 28''.†‡§¶ \end{cases}$

Driving Wheels: 6' 7".

T.E.: $\begin{cases} 23,915 \text{ lb.*} \\ 25,320 \text{ lb.†‡§¶} \end{cases}$

Walschaerts valve gear. P.V.

*30738   †30453–7
‡30448–52   §30763–92
¶30793–30806

Total 55

0-6-0 2F Class O1

*Introduced 1903. Wainwright rebuild with domed boiler and new cab of Stirling S.E. Class O 0-6-0 (introduced 1878).

†Introduced 1903. Loco. with smaller driving wheels.

Weight: Loco. 41 tons 1 cwt.
Pressure: 150 lb.
Cyls.: 18" × 26".
Driving Wheels: $\begin{cases} 5' 2''.* \\ 5' 1''.† \end{cases}$
T.E.: $\begin{cases} 17,325 \text{ lb.*} \\ 17,610 \text{ lb.†} \end{cases}$

*31064/5, 31258, 31370, 31425/30/4
†31048

Total 8

0-4-4T 0P Class O2

*Introduced 1889. Adams L.S.W. design.

†Introduced 1923. Fitted with Westinghouse brake for I.O.W. Bunkers enlarged from 1932.

‡Fitted with Drummond-type boiler.

§Fitted for push-and-pull working.

Weight: $\begin{cases} 46 \text{ tons } 18 \text{ cwt.*‡} \\ 48 \text{ tons } 8 \text{ cwt.†} \end{cases}$
Pressure: 160 lb.
Cyls.: $17\frac{1}{2}'' \times 24''$.
Driving Wheels: 4' 10".
T.E.: 17,235 lb.

*30177/9/92/3/9, 30200/12/24/5/ 9/32/6
†14/6–8/20–2/4–33
†§35/6
‡30223/33   ‡§30182/3

Total 35

0-6-0T Unclass Class P

Introduced 1909. Wainwright S.E.C. design for push-and-pull work, now used for shunting.

Weight: 28 tons 10 cwt.
Pressure: 160 lb.
Cyls.: 12" × 18".
Driving Wheels: 3' 9¼".
T.E.: 7,810 lb.

31027, 31178, 31323/5, 31556/8

Total 6

0-6-0   4F   **Class Q**

Introduced 1938. Maunsell design, later
   fitted with multiple-jet blastpipe and
   large-diameter chimney.
Weight: Loco. 49 tons 10 cwt.
Pressure: 200 lb. Su.
Cyls.: 19″ × 26″.
Driving Wheels: 5′ 1″.
T.E.: 26,160 lb.
P.V.

30530–49   **Total 20**

0-6-0   5F   **Class Q1**

Introduced 1942. Bulleid "Austerity"
   design.
Weight: Loco. 51 tons 5 cwt.
Pressure: 230 lb. Su.
Cyls.: 19″ × 26″.
Driving Wheels: 5′ 1″.
T.E.: 30,080 lb.
P.V.

33001–40   **Total 40**

0-6-0T   2F   **Class R1**

*Introduced 1888. Stirling S.E. design
   later rebuilt with domed boiler.
†Introduced 1938. Fitted with Urie
   type short chimney for Whitstable
   branch and fitted with or retaining
   original Stirling-type cab.
‡Introduced 1952. Rebuilt with
   domed boiler but retaining Stirling
   cab.
Weight: $\begin{cases} 46 \text{ tons 15 cwt.*} \\ 46 \text{ tons 8 cwt.†‡} \end{cases}$
Pressure: 160 lb.
Cyls.: 18″ × 26″.
Driving Wheels: $\begin{cases} 5′ 2″.* \\ 5′ 1″.†‡ \end{cases}$
T.E.: $\begin{cases} 18,480 \text{ lb.*} \\ 18,780 \text{ lb.†‡} \end{cases}$

*31047, 31107/28/74, 31337/40
†31010, 31147, 31339
‡31069   **Total 10**

4-6-0   6F   **Class S15**

*Introduced 1920. Urie L.S.W. design,
   development of N15 for mixed traffic
   work.
†Introduced 1927. Maunsell design,
   with higher pressure, smaller grate,
   modified footplating and other detail
   differences. 30833–7 with 6-wheel
   tenders for Central Section.
‡Introduced 1936. Later locos. with
   detail differences and reduced weight.
Weight: Loco. $\begin{cases} 79 \text{ tons 16 cwt.*} \\ 80 \text{ tons 14 cwt.†} \\ 79 \text{ tons 5 cwt.‡} \end{cases}$
Pressure: $\begin{cases} 180 \text{ lb. Su.*} \\ 200 \text{ lb. Su.†‡} \end{cases}$
Cyls.: $\begin{cases} (O) 21″ × 28″.* \\ (O) 20\frac{1}{2}″ × 28″.†‡ \end{cases}$
Driving Wheels: 5′ 7″.
T.E.: $\begin{cases} 28,200 \text{ lb.*} \\ 29,855 \text{ lb.†‡} \end{cases}$
Walschaerts valve gear. P.V.

*30496–30515   †30823–37
‡30838–47

                        Total 45

4-4-0   3P   **Class T9**

*Introduced 1899. Drummond L.S.W.
   design, fitted with superheater and
   larger cylinders by Urie from 1922.
†Introduced 1899. Locos. with detail
   differences (originally fitted with
   firebox watertubes).
‡Introduced 1900. Locos. with wider
   cab and splashers, without coupling
   rod splashers and originally fitted
   with firebox watertubes.
Weight: Loco. $\begin{cases} 51 \text{ tons 18 cwt.*} \\ 51 \text{ tons 16 cwt.†} \\ 51 \text{ tons 7 cwt.‡} \end{cases}$
Pressure: 175 lb. Su.
Cyls.: 19″ × 26″.
Driving Wheels: 6′ 7″.
T.E.: 17,675 lb.

*30117/20, 30284/5/7–9
†30702/6/7/9–12/5/7–9/24/6/7/
   9/32
‡30300/1/10/3/37/8

                        Total 29

Classes
2-6-0   4P3F   U & UI

*U. Introduced 1928. Rebuild of Maunsell S.E.C. Class K (" River ") 2-6-4T (introduced 1917).
†U. Introduced 1928. Locos. built as Class U, with smaller splashers and detail alterations.
‡UI. Introduced 1928. 3-cylinder development of Class U (prototype 31890, rebuilt from 2-6-4T, originally built 1925).

Weight: Loco. { 63 tons.*
{ 62 tons 6 cwt.†
{ 65 tons 6 cwt.‡

Pressure: 200 lb. Su.
Cyls.: { (O) 19″ × 28″.*†
{ (3) 16″ × 28″.‡
Driving Wheels: 6′ 0″.
T.E.: { 23,865 lb.*†
{ 25,385 lb.‡
Walschaerts valve gear. P.V.

*31790–31809   †31610–39
‡31890–31910

Total Class U 50
Class UI 21

0-6-0T   3F   Class USA

Introduced 1942. U.S. Army Transportation Corps design, purchased by S.R. 1946, and fitted with modified cab and bunker and other detail alterations.
Weight: 46 tons 10 cwt.
Pressure: 210 lb.
Cyls.: (O) 16½″ × 24″.
Driving Wheels: 4′ 6″.
T.E.: 21,600 lb.
Walschaerts valve gear. P.V.

30061–74   **Total 14**

4-4-0   5P   Class V

*Introduced 1930. Maunsell design.
†Introduced 1938. Fitted with multiple-jet blastpipe and large-diameter chimney by Bulleid.
Weight: Loco. 67 tons 2 cwt.
Pressure: 220 lb. Su.
Cyls.: (3) 16½″ × 26″.
Driving Wheels: 6′ 7″.
T.E.: 25,135 lb.
Walschaerts valve gear. P.V.

Classes U & UI-Z

*30902–6/8/10–2/6/22/3/5–8/ 32/5/6
†30900/1/7/9/13–5/7–21/4/29–31/ 3/4/7–9   **Total 40**

2-6-4T   6F   Class W

Introduced 1931. Maunsell design, developed from Class N1 2-6-0.
Weight: 90 tons 14 cwt.
Pressure: 200 lb. Su.
Cyls.: (3) 16½″ × 28″.
Driving Wheels: 5′ 6″.
T.E.: 29,450 lb.
Walschaerts valve gear. P.V.

31911–25   **Total 15**

Classes
4-6-2   7P5F   WC & BB

*Introduced 1945. Bulleid "West Country " Class, with Bulleid valve gear.
†Introduced 1946. Bulleid "Battle of Britain " Class, with Bulleid valve gear.
‡Introduced 1948. Locos. with larger tenders.
§Introduced 1957. Rebuilt with Walschaerts valve gear, modified details and air-smoothed casing removed.
Weight: Loco. { 86 tons 0 cwt.*†‡
{ 90 tons 1 cwt.§
Pressure: 250 lb. Su.
Cyls.: (3) 16⅜″ × 24″.
Driving Wheels: 6′ 2″.
T.E.: 27,715 lb.
Bulleid valve gear   P.V.

*34002/6–11/5/8–20/3/4/8–36/8– 48   †34049–70
†‡34071–90, 34109/10
*‡34091–34108   §34001/3–5/12– 4/6/7/21/2/5–7/37

Total 110

0-8-0T   6F   Class Z

Introduced 1929. Maunsell design for heavy shunting.
Weight: 71 tons 12 cwt.
Pressure 180 lb.
Cyls.: (3) 16″ × 28″.
Driving Wheels: 4′ 8″.
T.E.: 29,375 lb.
Walschaerts valve gear. P.V.

30950–7   **Total 8**

0-6-0   3F   Class 700

Introduced 1897. Drummond L.S.W. design, superheated from 1921.

Weight: Loco. 46 tons 14 cwt.

Pressure: 180 lb. Su.

Cyls.: 19″ × 26″.

Driving Wheels: 5′ 1″.

T.E.: 23,540 lb.

30306/8/9/15–7/25–7/39/46/50/2/5/68, 30687/9–30701

Total 29

0-6-0   2F   Class 0395

*Introduced 1881. Adams L.S.W. design.

†Introduced 1885. Adams " 496 " class with longer front overhang.

‡Introduced 1928. Reboilered with ex-L.C. & D. Class M3 4-4-0 boiler.

Weight: Loco. $\begin{cases} 37 \text{ tons } 12 \text{ cwt.}^{*\ddagger} \\ 38 \text{ tons } 14 \text{ cwt.}^{\dagger\ddagger} \end{cases}$

Pressure: $\begin{cases} 140 \text{ lb.}^{*\dagger} \\ 150 \text{ lb.}^{\ddagger} \end{cases}$

Driving Wheels: 5′ 1″.

T.E.: $\begin{cases} 15,535 \text{ lb.}^{*\dagger} \\ 16,645 \text{ lb.}^{\ddagger} \end{cases}$

*30568/75	†30566
*‡30567	††‡30564

Total 5

2-4-0WT   0P   Class 0298

Introduced 1874. Beattie L.S.W. design, rebuilt by Adams (1884–92), Urie (1921–2) and Maunsell (1931–5).

Weight: 37 tons 16 cwt.

Pressure: 160 lb.

Cyls.: (O) 16½″ × 20″.

Driving Wheels: 5′ 7″.

T.E.: 11,050 lb.

30585–7

Total 3

4-4-2T   1P   Class 0415

Introduced 1882. Adams L.S.W. design, later reboilered.

Weight: 55 tons 2 cwt.

Pressure: 160 lb.

Cyls.: (O) 17½″ × 24″.

Driving Wheels: 5′ 7″.

T.E.: 14,920 lb.

30582–4

Total 3

SOUTHERN REGION SERVICE LOCOMOTIVES

No.	Old No.	Class	Station
DS 49	—	—	Broad Clyst
*DS 74		Bo-Bo	Durnsford Road Power Station
*DS 75	—	Bo	Waterloo & City
DS 77	0745	C14	Redbridge Sleeper Depot
†DS 377	2635	A1X	Brighton Works
DS 600	—	0-4-0 Diesel	Eastleigh Carriage Works
DS 680	{ L.B.S.C. 654 / S.E.C. 751 / L.B.S.C. 659 }	A1	Lancing Carriage Works
DS 681		A1X	Lancing Carriage Works
DS 1169	—		Folkestone Warren
DS 1173	2217	0-6-0 Diesel	Engineer's Department
DS 3152	30272	G6	Meldon Quarry

* Electric.   † Repainted 1947 in Stroudley livery.

BRITISH RAILWAYS LOCOMOTIVES
Nos. 30021-35030, 3-36

Named Engines are indicated by an asterisk (*)

No.	Class	No.	Class	No.	Class	No.	Class
30021	M7	30059	M7	30123	M7	30249	M7
30022	M7	30060	M7	30124	M7	30251	M7
30023	M7	30061	U.S.A.	30125	M7	30252	M7
30024	M7	30062	U.S.A.	30127	M7	30253	M7
30025	M7	30063	U.S.A.	30128	M7	30254	M7
30026	M7	30064	U.S.A.	30129	M7	30255	M7
30027	M7	30065	U.S.A.	30130	M7	30256	M7
30028	M7	30066	U.S.A.	30131	M7	30258	G6
30029	M7	30067	U.S.A.	30132	M7	30260	G6
30030	M7	30068	U.S.A.	30133	M7	30266	G6
30031	M7	30069	U.S.A.	30160	G6	30270	G6
30032	M7	30070	U.S.A.	30162	G6	30274	G6
30033	M7	30071	U.S.A.	30177	O2	30277	G6
30034	M7	30072	U.S.A.	30179	O2	30284	T9
30035	M7	30073	U.S.A.	30182	O2	30285	T9
30036	M7	30074	U.S.A.	30183	O2	30287	T9
30037	M7	30083	B4	30192	O2	30288	T9
30038	M7	30084	B4	30193	O2	30289	T9
30039	M7	30086	B4	30199	O2	30300	T9
30040	M7	30087	B4	30200	O2	30301	T9
30043	M7	30088	B4	30212	O2	30306	700
30044	M7	30089	B4	30223	O2	30308	700
30045	M7	30093	B4	30224	O2	30309	700
30046	M7	30096	B4	30225	O2	30310	T9
30047	M7	30102	B4	30229	O2	30313	T9
30048	M7	30104	M7	30232	O2	30315	700
30049	M7	30105	M7	30233	O2	30316	700
30050	M7	30106	M7	30236	O2	30317	700
30051	M7	30107	M7	30238	G6	30318	M7
30052	M7	30108	M7	30241	M7	30319	M7
30053	M7	30109	M7	30242	M7	30320	M7
30054	M7	30110	M7	30243	M7	30321	M7
30055	M7	30111	M7	30245	M7	30322	M7
30056	M7	30112	M7	30246	M7	30323	M7
30057	M7	30117	T9	30247	M7	30324	M7
30058	M7	30120	T9	30248	M7	30325	700

No.	Class	No.	Class	No.	Class	No.	Class
30326	700	30486	H15	30538	Q	30701	700
30327	700	30488	H15	30539	Q	30702	T9
30328	M7	30489	H15	30540	Q	30706	T9
30331	H15	30491	H15	30541	Q	30707	T9
30333	H15	30492	G16	30542	Q	30709	T9
30334	H15	30493	G16	30543	Q	30710	T9
30335	H15	30494	G16	30544	Q	30711	T9
30337	T9	30495	G16	30545	Q	30712	T9
30338	T9	30496	S15	30546	Q	30715	T9
30339	700	30497	S15	30547	Q	30717	T9
30346	700	30498	S15	30548	Q	30718	T9
30349	G6	30499	S15	30549	Q	30719	T9
30350	700	30500	S15	30564	0395	30724	T9
30352	700	30501	S15	30566	0395	30726	T9
30355	700	30502	S15	30567	0395	30727	T9
30356	M7	30503	S15	30568	0395	30729	T9
30357	M7	30504	S15	30575	0395	30732	T9
30368	700	30505	S15	30582	0415	30738*	N15
30374	M7	30506	S15	30583	0415	30763*	N15
30375	M7	30507	S15	30584	0415	30764*	N15
30376	M7	30508	S15	30585	0298	30765*	N15
30377	M7	30509	S15	30586	0298	30766*	N15
30378	M7	30510	S15	30587	0298	30767*	N15
30379	M7	30511	S15	30667	M7	30768*	N15
30448*	N15	30512	S15	30668	M7	30769*	N15
30449*	N15	30513	S15	30669	M7	30770*	N15
30450*	N15	30514	S15	30670	M7	30771*	N15
30451*	N15	30515	S15	30671	M7	30772*	N15
30452*	N15	30516	H16	30673	M7	30773*	N15
30453*	N15	30517	H16	30674	M7	30774*	N15
30454*	N15	30518	H16	30675	M7	30775*	N15
30455*	N15	30519	H16	30676	M7	30776*	N15
30456*	N15	30520	H16	30687	700	30777*	N15
30457*	N15	30521	H15	30689	700	30778*	N15
30473	H15	30522	H15	30690	700	30779*	N15
30474	H15	30523	H15	30691	700	30780*	N15
30475	H15	30524	H15	30692	700	30781*	N15
30476	H15	30530	Q	30693	700	30782*	N15
30477	H15	30531	Q	30694	700	30783*	N15
30478	H15	30532	Q	30695	700	30784*	N15
30479	M7	30533	Q	30696	700	30785*	N15
30480	M7	30534	Q	30697	700	30786*	N15
30481	M7	30535	Q	30698	700	30787*	N15
30482	H15	30536	Q	30699	700	30788*	N15
30484	H15	30537	Q	30700	700	30789*	N15

No.	Class	No.	Class	No.	Class	No.	Class
30790*	N15	30853*	LN	30932*	V	31162	H
30791*	N15	30854*	LN	30933*	V	31164	H
30792*	N15	30855*	LN	30934*	V	31165	EI
30793*	N15	30856*	LN	30935*	V	31174	RI
30794*	N15	30857*	LN	30936*	V	31177	H
30795*	N15	30858*	LN	30937*	V	31178	P
30796*	N15	30859*	LN	30938*	V	31184	H
30797*	N15	30860*	LN	30939*	V	31191	C
30798*	N15	30861*	LN	30950	Z	31193	H
30799*	N15	30862*	LN	30951	Z	31218	C
30800*	N15	30863*	LN	30952	Z	31219	C
30801*	N15	30864*	LN	30953	Z	31221	C
30802*	N15	30865*	LN	30954	Z	31223	C
30803*	N15	30900*	V	30955	Z	31227	C
30804*	N15	30901*	V	30956	Z	31229	C
30805*	N15	30902*	V	30957	Z	31239	H
30806*	N15	30903*	V	31004	C	31242	C
30823	S15	30904*	V	31005	H	31243	C
30824	S15	30905*	V	31010	RI	31244	C
30825	S15	30906*	V	31018	C	31245	C
30826	S15	30907*	V	31019	EI	31246	DI
30827	S15	30908*	V	31027	P	31247	DI
30828	S15	30909*	V	31033	C	31252	C
30829	S15	30910*	V	31037	C	31253	C
30830	S15	30911*	V	31047	RI	31255	C
30831	S15	30912*	V	31048	OI	31256	C
30832	S15	30913*	V	31054	C	31258	OI
30833	S15	30914*	V	31059	C	31259	H
30834	S15	30915*	V	31061	C	31261	H
30835	S15	30916*	V	31064	OI	31263	H
30836	S15	30917*	V	31065	OI	31265	H
30837	S15	30918*	V	31067	EI	31266	H
30838	S15	30919*	V	31068	C	31267	C
30839	S15	30920*	V	31069	RI	31268	C
30840	S15	30921*	V	31071	C	31269	H
30841	S15	30922*	V	31086	C	31270	C
30842	S15	30923*	V	31102	C	31271	C
30843	S15	30924*	V	31107	RI	31272	C
30844	S15	30925*	V	31112	C	31276	H
30845	S15	30926*	V	31113	C	31278	H
30846	S15	30927*	V	31128	RI	31279	H
30847	S15	30928*	V	31145	DI	31280	C
30850*	LN	30929*	V	31147	RI	31287	C
30851*	LN	30930*	V	31150	C	31293	C
30852*	LN	30931*	V	31161	H	31295	H

No.	Class	No.	Class	No.	Class	No.	Class
31297	C	31492	DI	31585	C	31692	C
31298	C	31494	DI	31588	C	31693	C
31305	H	31495	C	31589	C	31694	C
31306	H	31497	EI	31590	C	31695	C
31307	H	31498	C	31592	C	31714	C
31308	H	31500	H	31593	C	31715	C
31310	H	31503	H	31610	U	31716	C
31317	C	31504	EI	31611	U	31717	C
31319	H	31505	DI	31612	U	31719	C
31322	H	31506	EI	31613	U	31720	C
31323	P	31507	EI	31614	U	31721	C
31324	H	31509	DI	31615	U	31722	C
31325	P	31510	C	31616	U	31723	C
31326	H	31512	H	31617	U	31724	C
31327	H	31517	H	31618	U	31725	C
31328	H	31518	H	31619	U	31727	DI
31329	H	31519	H	31620	U	31735	DI
31337	RI	31520	H	31621	U	31739	DI
31339	RI	31521	H	31622	U	31741	DI
31340	RI	31522	H	31623	U	31743	DI
31370	OI	31523	H	31624	U	31749	DI
31400	N	31530	H	31625	U	31753	LI
31401	N	31533	H	31626	U	31754	LI
31402	N	31540	H	31627	U	31755	LI
31403	N	31542	H	31628	U	31756	LI
31404	N	31543	H	31629	U	31757	LI
31405	N	31544	H	31630	U	31758	LI
31406	N	31545	DI	31631	U	31759	LI
31407	N	31548	H	31632	U	31760	L
31408	N	31550	H	31633	U	31762	L
31409	N	31551	H	31634	U	31763	L
31410	N	31552	H	31635	U	31764	L
31411	N	31553	H	31636	U	31765	L
31412	N	31554	H	31637	U	31766	L
31413	N	31556	P	31638	U	31767	L
31414	N	31558	P	31639	U	31768	L
31425	OI	31573	C	31681	C	31770	L
31430	OI	31575	C	31682	C	31771	L
31434	OI	31576	C	31683	C	31772	L
31461	C	31578	C	31684	C	31773	L
31470	DI	31579	C	31686	C	31774	L
31480	C	31581	C	31688	C	31775	L
31481	C	31582	C	31689	C	31776	L
31487	DI	31583	C	31690	C	31777	L
31489	DI	31584	C	31691	C	31778	L

No.	Class	No.	Class	No.	Class	No.	Class
31779	L	31824	N	31869	N	31923	W
31780	L	31825	N	31870	N	31924	W
31781	L	31826	N	31871	N	31925	W
31782	LI	31827	N	31872	N	32100	E2
31783	LI	31828	N	31873	N	32101	E2
31784	LI	31829	N	31874	N	32102	E2
31785	LI	31830	N	31875	N	32103	E2
31786	LI	31831	N	31876	NI	32104	E2
31787	LI	31832	N	31877	NI	32105	E2
31788	LI	31833	N	31878	NI	32106	E2
31789	LI	31834	N	31879	NI	32107	E2
31790	U	31835	N	31880	NI	32108	E2
31791	U	31836	N	31890	UI	32109	E2
31792	U	31837	N	31891	UI	32113	EI
31793	U	31838	N	31892	UI	32124	EI/R
31794	U	31839	N	31893	UI	32135	EI/R
31795	U	31840	N	31894	UI	32139	EI
31796	U	31841	N	31895	UI	32151	EI
31797	U	31842	N	31896	UI	32165	E3
31798	U	31843	N	31897	UI	32166	E3
31799	U	31844	N	31898	UI	32337	K
31800	U	31845	N	31899	UI	32338	K
31801	U	31846	N	31900	UI	32339	K
31802	U	31847	N	31901	UI	32340	K
31803	U	31848	N	31902	UI	32341	K
31804	U	31849	N	31903	UI	32342	K
31805	U	31850	N	31904	UI	32343	K
31806	U	31851	N	31905	UI	32344	K
31807	U	31852	N	31906	UI	32345	K
31808	U	31853	N	31907	UI	32346	K
31809	U	31854	N	31908	UI	32347	K
31810	N	31855	N	31909	UI	32348	K
31811	N	31856	N	31910	UI	32349	K
31812	N	31857	N	31911	W	32350	K
31813	N	31858	N	31912	W	32351	K
31814	N	31859	N	31913	W	32352	K
31815	N	31860	N	31914	W	32353	K
31816	N	31861	N	31915	W	32408	E6
31817	N	31862	N	31916	W	32410	E6
31818	N	31863	N	31917	W	32411	E6X
31819	N	31864	N	31918	W	32413	E6
31820	N	31865	N	31919	W	32414	E6
31821	N	31866	N	31920	W	32415	E6
31822	NI	31867	N	31921	W	32416	E6
31823	N	31868	N	31922	W	32417	E6

No.	Class	No.	Class	No.	Class	No.	Class
32418	E6	32503	E4	32562	E4	33023	Q1
32424*	H2	32504	E4	32563	E4	33024	Q1
32437	C2X	32505	E4	32564	E4	33025	Q1
32438	C2X	32506	E4	32565	E4	33026	Q1
32440	C2X	32507	E4	32566	E4	33027	Q1
32441	C2X	32508	E4	32577	E4	33028	Q1
32442	C2X	32509	E4	32578	E4	33029	Q1
32443	C2X	32510	E4	32579	E4	33030	Q1
32444	C2X	32512	E4	32580	E4	33031	Q1
32445	C2X	32515	E4	32581	E4	33032	Q1
32446	C2X	32517	E4	32636	A1X	33033	Q1
32447	C2X	32519	E4	32640	A1X	33034	Q1
32448	C2X	32521	C2X	32646	A1X	33035	Q1
32449	C2X	32522	C2X	32650	A1X	33036	Q1
32450	C2X	32523	C2X	32655	A1X	33037	Q1
32451	C2X	32524	C2X	32661	A1X	33038	Q1
32454	E3	32525	C2X	32662	A1X	33039	Q1
32455	E3	32526	C2X	32670	A1X	33040	Q1
32456	E3	32527	C2X	32677	A1X	34001*	WC
32463	E4	32528	C2X	32678	A1X	34002*	WC
32466	E4X	32529	C2X	32689	E1	34003*	WC
32467	E4	32532	C2X	32694	E1	34004*	WC
32468	E4	32534	C2X	32697	E1/R	34005*	WC
32469	E4	32535	C2X	33001	Q1	34006*	WC
32470	E4	32536	C2X	33002	Q1	34007*	WC
32471	E4	32538	C2X	33003	Q1	34008*	WC
32472	E4	32539	C2X	33004	Q1	34009*	WC
32473	E4	32540	C2X	33005	Q1	34010*	WC
32474	E4	32541	C2X	33006	Q1	34011*	WC
32475	E4	32543	C2X	33007	Q1	34012*	WC
32477	E4X	32544	C2X	33008	Q1	34013*	WC
32479	E4	32545	C2X	33009	Q1	34014*	WC
32480	E4	32546	C2X	33010	Q1	34015*	WC
32481	E4	32547	C2X	33011	Q1	34016*	WC
32484	E4	32548	C2X	33012	Q1	34017*	WC
32486	E4	32549	C2X	33013	Q1	34018*	WC
32487	E4	32550	C2X	33014	Q1	34019*	WC
32491	E4	32551	C2X	33015	Q1	34020*	WC
32493	E4	32552	C2X	33016	Q1	34021*	WC
32494	E4	32553	C2X	33017	Q1	34022*	WC
32495	E4	32554	C2X	33018	Q1	34023*	WC
32497	E4	32556	E4	33019	Q1	34024*	WC
32498	E4	32557	E4	33020	Q1	34025*	WC
32500	E4	32559	E4	33021	Q1	34026*	WC
32502	E4	32560	E4	33022	Q1	34027*	WC

No.	Class	No.	Class	No.	Class	No.	Class
34028*	WC	34073*	BB	35008*	MN	35020*	MN
34029*	WC	34074*	BB	35009*	MN	35021*	MN
34030*	WC	34075*	BB	35010*	MN	35022*	MN
34031*	WC	34076*	BB	35011*	MN	35023*	MN
34032*	WC	34077*	BB	35012*	MN	35024*	MN
34033*	WC	34078*	BB	35013*	MN	35025*	MN
34034*	WC	34079*	BB	35014*	MN	35026*	MN
34035*	WC	34080*	BB	35015*	MN	35027*	MN
34036*	WC	34081*	BB	35016*	MN	35028*	MN
34037*	WC	34082*	BB	35017*	MN	35029*	MN
34038*	WC	34083*	BB	35018*	MN	35030*	MN
34039*	WC	34084*	BB	35019*	MN		
34040*	WC	34085*	BB				
34041*	WC	34086*	BB				
34042*	WC	34087*	BB				
34043*	WC	34088*	BB				
34044*	WC	34089*	BB				
34045*	WC	34090*	BB				
34046*	WC	34091*	WC				
34047*	WC	34092*	WC				
34048*	WC	34093*	WC				
34049*	BB	34094*	WC				
34050*	BB	34095*	WC				
34051*	BB	34096*	WC				
34052*	BB	34097*	WC				
34053*	BB	34098*	WC				
34054*	BB	34099*	WC				
34055*	BB	34100*	WC				
34056*	BB	34101*	WC				
34057*	BB	34102*	WC				
34058*	BB	34103*	WC				
34059*	BB	34104*	WC				
34060*	BB	34105*	WC				
34061*	BB	34106*	WC				
34062*	BB	34107*	WC				
34063*	BB	34108*	WC				
34064*	BB	34109*	BB				
34065*	BB	34110*	BB				
34066*	BB	35001*	MN				
34067*	BB	35002*	MN				
34068*	BB	35003*	MN				
34069*	BB	35004*	MN				
34070*	BB	35005*	MN				
34071*	BB	35006*	MN				
34072*	BB	35007*	MN				

Isle of Wight Locomotives

No.	Class	No.	Class
3*	E1	26*	O2
4*	E1	27*	O2
14*	O2	28*	O2
16*	O2	29*	O2
17*	O2	30*	O2
18*	O2	31*	O2
20*	O2	32*	O2
21*	O2	33*	O2
22*	O2	35*	O2
24*	O2	36*	O2
25*	O2		

BRITISH RAILWAYS LOCOMOTIVES
Nos. 26000-35030 and 3-36

NAMED LOCOMOTIVES

CLASS EM1 BO-BO ELECTRIC

26000 Tommy

CLASS N15 " KING ARTHUR " 4-6-0

30448	Sir Tristram		30780	Sir Persant
30449	Sir Torre		30781	Sir Aglovale
30450	Sir Kay		30782	Sir Brian
30451	Sir Lamorak		30783	Sir Gillemere
30452	Sir Meliagrance		30784	Sir Nerovens
30453	King Arthur		30785	Sir Mador de la Porte
30454	Queen Guinevere		30786	Sir Lionel
30455	Sir Launcelot		30787	Sir Menadeuke
30456	Sir Galahad		30788	Sir Urre of the Mount
30457	Sir Bedivere		30789	Sir Guy
30738	King Pellinore		30790	Sir Villiars
30763	Sir Bors de Ganis		30791	Sir Uwaine
30764	Sir Gawain		30792	Sir Hervis de Revel
30765	Sir Gareth		30793	Sir Ontzlake
30766	Sir Geraint		30794	Sir Ector de Maris
30767	Sir Valence		30795	Sir Dinadan
30768	Sir Balin		30796	Sir Dodinas le Savage
30769	Sir Balan		30797	Sir Blamor de Ganis
30770	Sir Prianius		30798	Sir Hectimere
30771	Sir Sagramore		30799	Sir Ironside
30772	Sir Percivale		30800	Sir Meleaus de Lile
30773	Sir Lavaine		30801	Sir Meliot de Logres
30774	Sir Gaheris		30802	Sir Durnore
30775	Sir Agravaine		30803	Sir Harry le Fise Lake
30776	Sir Galagars		30804	Sir Cador of Cornwall
30777	Sir Lamiel		30805	Sir Constantine
30778	Sir Pelleas		30806	Sir Galleron
30779	Sir Colgrevance			

CLASS LN "LORD NELSON" 4-6-0

30850	Lord Nelson	30858	Lord Duncan
30851	Sir Francis Drake	30859	Lord Hood
30852	Sir Walter Raleigh	30860	Lord Hawke
30853	Sir Richard Grenville	30861	Lord Anson
30854	Howard of Effingham	30862	Lord Collingwood
30855	Robert Blake	30863	Lord Rodney
30856	Lord St. Vincent	30864	Sir Martin Frobisher
30857	Lord Howe	30865	Sir John Hawkins

CLASS V "SCHOOLS" 4-4-0

30900	Eton	30920	Rugby
30901	Winchester	30921	Shrewsbury
30902	Wellington	30922	Marlborough
30903	Charterhouse	30923	Bradfield
30904	Lancing	30924	Haileybury
30905	Tonbridge	30925	Cheltenham
30906	Sherborne	30926	Repton
30907	Dulwich	30927	Clifton
30908	Westminster	30928	Stowe
30909	St. Paul's	30929	Malvern
30910	Merchant Taylors	30930	Radley
30911	Dover	30931	King's Wimbledon
30912	Downside	30932	Blundells
30913	Christ's Hospital	30933	King's Canterbury
30914	Eastbourne	30934	St. Lawrence
30915	Brighton	30935	Sevenoaks
30916	Whitgift	30936	Cranleigh
30917	Ardingly	30937	Epsom
30918	Hurstpierpoint	30938	St. Olave's
30919	Harrow	30939	Leatherhead

CLASS H2 4-4-2

32424	Beachy Head

CLASSES WC & BB 4–6–2

"WEST COUNTRY" and "BATTLE OF BRITAIN"

34001	Exeter		34036	Westward Ho
34002	Salisbury		34037	Clovelly
34003	Plymouth		34038	Lynton
34004	Yeovil		34039	Boscastle
34005	Barnstaple		34040	Crewkerne
34006	Bude		34041	Wilton
34007	Wadebridge		34042	Dorchester
34008	Padstow		34043	Combe Martin
34009	Lyme Regis		34044	Woolacombe
34010	Sidmouth		34045	Ottery St. Mary
34011	Tavistock		34046	Braunton
34012	Launceston		34047	Callington
34013	Okehampton		34048	Crediton
34014	Budleigh Salterton		34049	Anti-Aircraft Command
34015	Exmouth		34050	Royal Observer Corps
34016	Bodmin		34051	Winston Churchill
34017	Ilfracombe		34052	Lord Dowding
34018	Axminster		34053	Sir Keith Park
34019	Bideford		34054	Lord Beaverbrook
34020	Seaton		34055	Fighter Pilot
34021	Dartmoor		34056	Croydon
34022	Exmoor		34057	Biggin Hill
34023	Blackmore Vale		34058	Sir Frederick Pile
34024	Tamar Valley		34059	Sir Archibald Sinclair
34025	Whimple		34060	25 Squadron
34026	Yes Tor		34061	73 Squadron
34027	Taw Valley		34062	17 Squadron
34028	Eddystone		34063	229 Squadron
34029	Lundy		34064	Fighter Command
34030	Watersmeet		34065	Hurricane
34031	Torrington		34066	Spitfire
34032	Camelford		34067	Tangmere
34033	Chard		34068	Kenley
34034	Honiton		34069	Hawkinge
34035	Shaftesbury		34070	Manston

NAMED LOCOMOTIVES—contd.

34071	601 Squadron	34091	Weymouth
34072	257 Squadron	34092	City of Wells
34073	249 Squadron	34093	Saunton
34074	46 Squadron	34094	Mortehoe
34075	264 Squadron	34095	Brentor
34076	41 Squadron	34096	Trevone
34077	603 Squadron	34097	Holsworthy
34078	222 Squadron	34098	Templecombe
34079	141 Squadron	34099	Lynmouth
34080	74 Squadron	34100	Appledore
34081	92 Squadron	34101	Hartland
34082	615 Squadron	34102	Lapford
34083	605 Squadron	34103	Calstock
34084	253 Squadron	34104	Bere Alston
34085	501 Squadron	34105	Swanage
34086	219 Squadron	34106	Lydford
34087	145 Squadron	34107	Blandford Forum
34088	213 Squadron	34108	Wincanton
34089	602 Squadron	34109	Sir Trafford
34090	Sir Eustace Missenden,		Leigh-Mallory
	Southern Railway	34110	66 Squadron

CLASS MN "MERCHANT NAVY" 4-6-2

35001	Channel Packet	35015	Rotterdam Lloyd
35002	Union Castle	35016	Elders Fyffes
35003	Royal Mail	35017	Belgian Marine
35004	Cunard White Star	35018	British India Line
35005	Canadian Pacific	35019	French Line CGT
35006	Peninsular & Oriental	35020	Bibby Line
	S.N. Co.	35021	New Zealand Line
35007	Aberdeen	35022	Holland-America Line
	Commonwealth	35023	Holland-Afrika Line
35008	Orient Line	35024	East Asiatic Company
35009	Shaw Savill	35025	Brocklebank Line
35010	Blue Star	35026	Lamport & Holt Line
35011	General Steam	35027	Port Line
	Navigation	35028	Clan Line
35012	United States Line	35029	Ellerman Lines
35013	Blue Funnel	35030	Elder Dempster Lines
35014	Nederland Line		

NAMED LOCOMOTIVES—*cont.*

CLASS E1 0-6-0T

3 Ryde	4 Wroxall

CLASS O2 0-4-4T

14	Fishbourne	27	Merstone
16	Ventnor	28	Ashey
17	Seaview	29	Alverstone
18	Ningwood	30	Shorwell
20	Shanklin	31	Chale
21	Sandown	32	Bonchurch
22	Brading	33	Bembridge
24	Calbourne	35	Freshwater
25	Godshill	36	Carisbrooke
26	Whitwell		

SOUTHERN RAILWAY LOCOMOTIVE SUPERINTENDENTS AND CHIEF MECHANICAL ENGINEERS OF CONSTITUENT COMPANIES

LONDON & SOUTH WESTERN RAILWAY

J. Woods ...	...	...	1835–1841
J. V. Gooch	...	...	1841–1850
J. Beattie ...	...	...	1850–1871
W. G. Beattie	...	...	1871–1878
W. Adams ...	...	...	1878–1895
D. Drummond	...	...	1895–1912
R. W. Urie...	...	...	1912–1922

LONDON BRIGHTON AND SOUTH COAST RAILWAY

—. Statham	...	...	? –1845
J. Gray ...	...	...	1845–1847
S. Kirtley ...	...	...	1847
J. C. Craven	...	...	1847–1869
W. Stroudley	...	...	1870–1889
R. J. Billinton	...	...	1890–1904
D. Earle Marsh	...	...	1905–1911
L. B. Billinton	...	...	1911–1922

SOUTH EASTERN RAILWAY

B. Cubitt ...	...	...	? –1845
J. Cudworth	...	...	1845–1876
A. M. Watkin	...	...	1876
R. Mansell ...	...	...	1877–1878
J. Stirling ...	...	...	1878–1898

LONDON, CHATHAM AND DOVER RAILWAY

W. Cubitt ...	...	...	? –1860
W. Martley ...	...	...	1860–1874
W. Kirtley ...	...	...	1874–1898

SOUTH EASTERN AND CHATHAM RAILWAY

| H. S. Wainwright ... | ... | 1899–1913 |
| R. E. L. Maunsell ... | ... | 1913–1922 |

SOUTHERN RAILWAY

| R. E. L. Maunsell ... | ... | 1923–1937 |
| O. V. Bulleid | ... | ... | 1937–1949 |

SOME S.R. LOCOMOTIVE HEADCODES

This list is not complete and gives only the principal one, two and three disc (or lamp) codes.

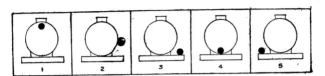

NO. 1

    Victoria and Dover via Chatham
    Victoria and Norwood Yard via Selhurst
    Loughborough Sidings to Holborn
    Ashford and Hastings
    Reading and Margate via Redhill
    Eastleigh and Bulford via Chandlers Ford and Andover
    Southampton Terminus and Brockenhurst and Weymouth via Wimborne
    Plymouth Friary and Tavistock
    Woking and Reading via Virginia Water West Curve
    Exeter Central and Ilfracombe
    Bodmin and Wadebridge
    Exeter Central and Exmouth

NO. 2

    Victoria or Clapham Junction and Holborn (L.L.)
    London Bridge or Bricklayers' Arms and Portsmouth via Quarry line and
        Horsham
    Via Mid Kent Line and Beckenham Junction
    Ashford and Eastbourne direct
    Waterloo or Nine Elms and Southampton Terminus, direct (not boat trains)
    Willesden and Feltham Yard via Gunnersbury
    Waterloo or Nine Elms and Windsor via Twickenham
    Southampton Central to Lymington
    Yeovil Junction and Yeovil Town
    Seaton Junction and Seaton
    Barnstaple Junction and Torrington
    Halwill and Bude

NO. 3

    Victoria or Clapham Junction and Holborn
    London Bridge or Bricklayers' Arms and Brighton via Quarry Line
    Tonbridge and Brighton via Eridge
    Hastings via Mid Kent Line, Oxted, Crowhurst Junction and Tonbridge
    Dunton Green and Westerham
    Ashford and Margate via Canterbury West
    Lydd Branch
    Folkestone Junction and Folkestone Harbour
    Crowhurst and Bexhill West
    Swanley Junction and Gravesend West
    Sittingbourne and Sheerness
    Deal and Kearsney
    Gravesend Central and Allhallows-on-Sea or Port Victoria
    All stations to Feltham (except via Mortlake)

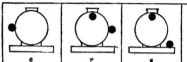

Weymouth and Portland and Easton (goods trains)
Bournemouth West and Brockenhurst via Wimborne

NO. 4

Victoria or Battersea Yard and Brighton via Redhill
Oxted and Eastbourne via Eridge
London Bridge and New Cross via Bricklayers' Arms Junction
Horsham and Brighton
Alton and Fareham
Bentley and Bordon
Salisbury and Bulford
Axminster and Lyme Regis
Tipton St. John's and Exmouth
Wareham and Swanage
Brockenhurst and Lymington Pier
Bere Alston and Callington

NO. 5

Victoria or Stewarts Lane and Clapham Junction
Oxted and Tunbridge Wells West via East Grinstead (H.L.)
Pulborough, Midhurst and Chichester
Havant and Hayling Island
London Bridge and Bricklayers' Arms
Tonbridge and Maidstone West
Ashford (Kent) and Dover via Minster and Deal
Stewarts Lane to Victoria
Southampton Docks and Nine Elms via main line (market goods, fruit or potato train)

NO. 6

London Bridge or Bricklayers' Arms and Dover or Ramsgate via East Croydon Oxted and Tonbridge
Tonbridge and Hawkhurst
Battersea Yard and Kensington
Waterloo or Nine Elms and Reading via Twickenham
Willesden and Feltham Yard via Kew East Junction
Exeter Central and Sidmouth
Plymouth Friary and Turnchapel
Eastleigh or Southampton and Fawley
Bournemouth Central and Brockenhurst via Wimborne
Torrington and Halwill

NO. 7

Victoria or Battersea Yard and Portsmouth via Quarry Line and Horsham
Via Maidstone East Line to Victoria or Holborn
Waterloo or Nine Elms and Southampton Docks via Brentford, Chertsey and Woking

NO. 8

London Bridge or Bricklayers' Arms and Eastbourne or Hastings via Quarry Line
Victoria or West London Line and Ramsgate via Herne Hill or Catford Loop
London Bridge or Bricklayers' Arms and Hastings via Chislehurst and Tunbridge Wells Central

94

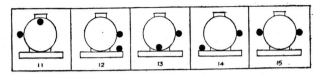

| 11 | 12 | 13 | 14 | 15 |

West London Line to East Croydon via Crystal Palace (L.L.)
Special boat trains Waterloo and Southampton Docks via Northam
Special boat trains from Southampton Docks to Waterloo via Millbrook
Southampton and Andover via Redbridge

NO. 9

Victoria or Battersea Yard and Eastbourne or Hastings via Quarry Line
London and Hither Green Sidings
Victoria and Folkestone Harbour or Dover Marine via Swanley, Otford and
Tonbridge
Waterloo or Nine Elms and Plymouth
Bournemouth Central and Dorchester goods trains
Battersea Yard and Brent via New Kew Junction
Southampton Terminus and Portsmouth Harbour via Netley

NO. 10

London Bridge or Bricklayers' Arms and Portsmouth via Redhill and Horsham
Victoria or Battersea Yard and Norwood Yard via Crystal Palace (L.L.)
London Bridge and New Cross Gate to Eardley Sidings via Peckham Rye
Deptford Wharf and New Cross Gate
London Bridge or Bricklayers' Arms and Folkestone or Dover via Chislehurst
Tonbridge and Ashford
Dover and Margate via Deal and Minster Loop
Special boat trains Waterloo to Southampton Docks via Millbrook
Feltham to Durnsford Road via Chertsey

NO. 11

Victoria or Battersea Yard and Portsmouth via Redhill and Horsham
Via Dartford Loop Line
Victoria or Holborn and Hastings Line via Orpington Loop and Tunbridge
Wells Central
Bricklayers' Arms and Guildford via Leatherhead and Effingham Junction
Waterloo or Nine Elms and Southampton Terminus via Alton
Salisbury and Bournemouth West via Wimborne
Fareham and Gosport
Ballast trains to Meldon Quarry from Exeter Central and stations west thereof

NO. 12

Victoria or Battersea Yard and Portsmouth via Mitcham Junction
London Bridge or Bricklayers' Arms and Eastbourne or Hastings via Redhill
Victoria, Stewarts Lane or Holborn to North Kent Line via Nunhead Line
Nine Elms and Feltham via Mortlake
Exeter Central to Nine Elms (market goods and fish)
Down main line goods terminating at Woking
Southampton Docks and Salisbury via Eastleigh

NO. 13

London Bridge or Bricklayers' Arms and Brighton via Redhill
Three Bridges and Tunbridge Wells West
West London Line to Norwood Yard via Thornton Heath
Victoria or Holborn to Dover via Nunhead Line and Maidstone East
Parcels and empty trains Waterloo to Clapham Junction (Kensington sidings)

Feltham Yard and Neasden via Kew East Junction
Portsmouth Harbour or Portsmouth and Southsea to Fratton Loco. Depot
Exeter Central and Exmouth Junction
Bournemouth West to Dorchester
Southampton and Salisbury via Redbridge

NO. 14

London Bridge and Portsmouth via Mitcham Junction
London Bridge, Oxted and Tunbridge Wells West via Hever
Oxted and Lewes or Seaford or Eastbourne via Haywards Heath and Keymer
    Junction (change to No. 5 or No. 21 code at Lewes)
London Bridge or Bricklayers' Arms and Dover via Chislehurst Loop and
    Maidstone East
Waterloo or Nine Elms and Brockenhurst and Bournemouth West via Sway

NO. 15

Via Bexleyheath Line
Victoria, Stewarts Lane or Holborn via Nunhead Line and Bexleyheath
Oxted and Brighton via Haywards Heath
Waterloo or Nine Elms and Reading via Loop Line
All trains terminating at Portsmouth and Southsea (trains from Salisbury to
    carry No. 17 to Eastleigh)
Exeter Central and Padstow
Light engines, Bournemouth Central or Bournemouth West to Bournemouth
    Central via triangle to turn
Light engines Eastleigh Loco. to Portsmouth and Southsea
Light engines to Guildford Loco. via Woking (except via Staines)

NO. 16

London Bridge or Bricklayers' Arms and Portsmouth via West Croydon
Victoria or Battersea Yard and Eastbourne or Hastings via Redhill
Oxted and Brighton via Eridge
London Bridge or Bricklayers' Arms and Ramsgate via Tonbridge and
    Canterbury West
Waterloo or Nine Elms and Woking via Richmond and Chertsey
Milk and empty trains to Clapham Junction via Byfleet curve and Richmond

NO. 17

London Bridge or Bricklayers' Arms and Tonbridge or Reading via East Croydon
    and Redhill (also Tonbridge and Reading)
Brighton and Hove via Preston Park Spur
Three Bridges and Eridge
Victoria or Holborn and Folkestone or Dover via Orpington Loop, Tonbridge
    and Ashford
London Bridge or Bricklayers' Arms and Gillingham, Faversham, Ramsgate or
    Dover via Chislehurst Loop and Chatham
Waterloo or Nine Elms and Clapham Junction (empty trains and light engines)
Passenger trains Bournemouth Central and Weymouth

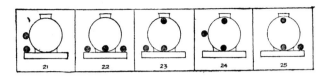

| 21 | 22 | 23 | 24 | 25 |

NO. 18

London Bridge or Bricklayers' Arms and Dover, Ramsgate or Hastings via Chislehurst, Swanley, Otford and Sevenoaks
Victoria, Oxted and Tunbridge Wells West via Hever
Holborn and Ramsgate via Herne Hill or Catford Loop
Light engines and trains requiring to run to up main loop, Clapham Junction, from stations westward
Southampton and Andover via Eastleigh
Light engines or engines with vehicles attached running round the triangle at Bournemouth West to turn

NO. 19

Victoria or Battersea Yard and Brighton via Quarry Line
London Bridge or New Cross Gate and Norwood Yard
Tunbridge Wells West and Eastbourne
Victoria or Holborn and Ramsgate, Dover or Hastings via Nunhead Line and Tonbridge
Horsham and Guildford
Waterloo or Nine Elms and Southampton Docks via East Putney
Salisbury and Portsmouth Harbour via Eastleigh
Portsmouth and Southsea to Salisbury via Eastleigh

NO. 20

Victoria, Stewarts Lane or Holborn to Ramsgate via Nunhead Line, Chislehurst and Chatham
London Bridge or Bricklayers' Arms and North Kent Line via Greenwich
Via Streatham Spur
Feltham Yard and Brent via Kew East Junction
Clapham Junction and Kensington
Portsmouth and Southsea to Salisbury via Redbridge
Salisbury and Portsmouth Harbour via Redbridge

NO. 21

Victoria and Newhaven Harbour
Victoria or Holborn to Ramsgate via Nunhead Line and Maidstone East
Waterloo or Nine Elms and Portsmouth via Woking and Guildford
Light engines from all stations to Feltham Loco.
Light engines from all stations west of Basingstoke to Eastleigh Loco.

NO. 22

Waterloo and Portsmouth Harbour via Eastleigh
Feltham and Brent via Richmond
S.R. and W.R. trains Hither Green Sidings, Stewarts Lane or South Lambeth to Old Oak Common
L.M. (Western Division) trains between Willesden and Redhill via Clapham Junction
L.M. (Midland Division) and E.R. (G.N.) trains to or from Hither Green Sidings
W.R. trains Norwood Yard to Old Oak Common
W.R. trains Cattewater Junction and Plymstock

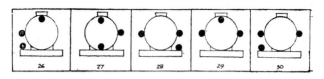

| 26 | 27 | 28 | 29 | 30 |

NO. 23

Nine Elms and Willesden via New Kew Junction
Brighton and Salisbury via Southampton Central
Eastleigh and Micheldever or Basingstoke (light engines for testing)
Windsor and Hastings Excursion trains
Windsor and Margate or Dover Excursion trains or between Windsor and Redhill
W.R. trains to South Lambeth
E.R. trains to or from Lower Sydenham

NO. 24

Waterloo and Guildford via Leatherhead (except light engines Nine Elms to Raynes Park)
Southampton and Willesden via Richmond and Gunnersbury
Southampton or Salisbury and Willesden via Chertsey and Kew East Junction (or from Basingstoke)
Reading to Willesden via Feltham

NO. 25

Nine Elms and Brent via New Kew Junction
Kingston and Shepperton
Brighton and Salisbury through trains via Eastleigh
Windsor and Bognor Regis Excursion trains
To L.M.R. via West London Line

NO. 26

Brighton and Bournemouth
Waterloo and Wimbledon Park Sidings via East Putney (empty trains and light engines)
Merstham and Staines Moor via Guildford, Byfleet Junction and Staines
Victoria (E. or C.), Stewarts Lane, Clapham Junction or Holborn and Eardley Sidings via Herne Hill

NO. 27

Hither Green Sidings and Feltham via Brentford
Feltham to Wimbledon West Yard
London Bridge or Bricklayers' Arms and Brighton via Oxted, Eridge and Lewes

NO. 28

Hither Green Sidings and Feltham via Richmond
London Bridge or Bricklayers' Arms and Brighton via Oxted, East Grinstead and Lewes

NO. 29

Plumstead and Feltham via Brentford
Victoria or Battersea Yard and Brighton via Oxted, Eridge and Lewes

NO. 30

Plumstead and Feltham via Richmond
Victoria or Battersea Yard and Brighton via Oxted, East Grinstead and Lewes

Class H16 4-6-2T No. 30516   [P. B. Whitehouse

Class Z 0-8-0T No. 30955   [E. Gamblin

Class W 2-6-4T No. 31921   [T. C. Lawrence

Class E1 0-6-0T No. 32139   [*D. Marriott*

Class E1/R 0-6-0T Nos. 32124 and 32135   [*N. Fields*

Class E2 0-6-0T No. 32106   [*T. C. Lawrence*

Right: Class E4X
0-6-2T No. 32466
[J. N. Faulkner

Below: Class E4
0-6-2T No. 32559
[G. Wheeler

Right: Class E6
0-6-2T No. 32410
[P. Hutchinson

Class O2 0-4-4T No. 30212   [P. Ransome-Wallis

Class M7 0-4-4T No. 30318   [C. P. Boocock

Class M7 0-4-4T No. 30049 (fitted for push-and-pull working)   [J. A. Young

Class G6 0-6-0T No. 30277   [F. J. Saunders

Class P 0-6-0T No. 31558   [B. C. Bending

Class R1 0-6-0T No. 31174   [D. Penney

Left: Class B4
0-4-0T No. 30102
[P. J. Sharpe

Centre: Class 0298
2-4-0T No. 30586
[P. J. Sharpe

Bottom: Class 0415
4-4-2T No. 30583
[G. Wheeler

Class 3 (Fowler) 2-6-2T No. 40042

Class 3 (Stanier) 2-6-2T No. 40167 (with large boiler)

[R. Sabatini

Class 3 (Stanier) 2-6-2T No. 40168

[B. E. Morrison

Class 4P 4-4-0 No. 41196   [R. J. Buckley

Class 2P (ex-Midland) 4-4-0 No. 40493   [P. H. Groom

Class 2P (ex-L.M.S.) 4-4-0 No. 40688   [G. W. Morrison

Class 6P5F (Hughes-Fowler) 2-6-0 No. 42825 (with Reidinger rotary poppet valve gear)
[C. P. Boocock

Class 6P5F (Hughes-Fowler) 2-6-0 No. 42744
[E. M. Patterson

Class 6P5F (Stanier) 2-6-0 No. 42961
[R. J. Buckley

Class 4 (Fowler) 2-6-4T No. 42415 (with side-window cab)　　　　　[B. K. B. Green

Class 4 (Stanier 3-cylinder) 2-6-4T No. 42529　　　　　[R. J. Buckley

Class 4 (Stanier 2-cylinder) 2-6-4T No. 42655　　　　　[R. A. Panting

BRITISH RAILWAYS LOCOMOTIVES
Nos. 40000-59999

The Code given in bold type to the right of each Class heading,
e.g. "2P" denotes its British Railways power classification.

The numbers of locomotives in service have been checked to **January 25th, 1958.**

2-6-2T   3

Introduced 1930. Fowler L.M.S. design with parallel boiler.
*Introduced 1930. Condensing locos. for working to Moorgate, London.
Weight: { 70 tons 10 cwt.
{ 71 tons 16 cwt.*
Pressure: 200 lb. Su.
Cyls.: (O) 17½″ × 26″.
Driving Wheels: 5′ 3″.
T.E.: 21,485 lb.
Walschaerts valve gear. **P.V.**

40001	40019	40037*	40054
40002	40020	40038*	40055
40003	40021	40039*	40056
40004	40022*	40040*	40057
40005	40023*	40041	40058
40006	40024*	40042	40059
40007	40025*	40043	40060
40008	40026*	40044	40061
40009	40027*	40045	40062
40010	40028*	40046	40063
40011	40029*	40047	40064
40012	40030*	40048	40065
40013	40031*	40049	40066
40014	40032*	40050	40067
40015	40033*	40051	40068
40016	40034*	40052	40069
40017	40035*	40053	40070
40018	40036*		

Total 70

2-6-2T   3

Introduced 1935. Stanier L.M.S. taper boiler, development of Fowler design (*above*).
*Introduced 1941. Rebuilt with larger boiler.
Weight: { 71 tons 5 cwt.
{ 72 tons 10 cwt.*
Pressure: 200 lb. Su.
Cyls.: (O) 17½″ × 26″.
Driving Wheels: 5′ 3″.

T.E.: 21,485 lb.
Walschaerts valve gear. **P.V.**

40071	40106	40141	40176
40072	40107	40142	40177
40073	40108	40143	40178
40074	40109	40144	40179
40075	40110	40145	40180
40076	40111	40146	40181
40077	40112	40147	40182
40078	40113	40148*	40183
40079	40114	40149	40184
40080	40115	40150	40185
40081	40116	40151	40186
40082	40117	40152	40187
40083	40118	40153	40188
40084	40119	40154	40189
40085	40120	40155	40190
40086	40121	40156	40191
40087	40122	40157	40192
40088	40123	40158	40193
40089	40124	40159	40194
40090	40125	40160	40195
40091	40126	40161	40196
40092	40127	40162	40197
40093	40128	40163*	40198
40094	40129	40164	40199
40095	40130	40165	40200
40096	40131	40166	40201
40097	40132	40167*	40202
40098	40133	40168	40203*
40099	40134	40169*	40204
40100	40135	40170	40205
40101	40136	40171	40206
40102	40137	40172	40207
40103	40138	40173	40208
40104	40139	40174	40209
40105	40140	40175	

Total 139

4-4-0   2P

Introduced 1912. Fowler rebuild of Johnson locos. with superheater and piston valves.
Weight: Loco. 53 tons 7 cwt.
Pressure: 160 lb. Su.
Cyls.: $20\frac{1}{2}'' \times 26''$.
Driving Wheels: $7'\ 0\frac{1}{2}''$.
T.E.: 17,585 lb.
P.V.

40332	40439	40493	40541
40337	40443	40501	40542
40396	40447	40502	40543
40402	40452	40504	40548
40407	40453	40511	40550
40411	40454	40513	40552
40412	40461	40534	40553
40413	40464	40536	40557
40416	40487	40537	
40420	40489	40538	
40421	40491	40540	

Total 41

4-4-0   2P

Introduced 1928. Post-grouping development of Midland design, with modified dimensions and reduced boiler mountings.
*Introduced 1928. Locos. built for S. & D.J.R. (taken into L.M.S. stock, 1930).
†Fitted experimentally in 1933 with Dabeg feed-water heater.
Weight: Loco. 54 tons 1 cwt.
Pressure: 180 lb. Su.
Cyls.: $19'' \times 26''$.
Driving Wheels: $6'\ 9''$.
T.E.: 17,730 lb.
P.V.

40563	40575	40587	40600
40564	40576	40588	40601
40565	40577	40589	40602
40566	40578	40590	40603
40567	40579	40592	40604
40568	40580	40593	40605
40569	40581	40594	40606
40570	40582	40595	40607
40571	40583	40596	40608
40572	40584	40597	40609
40573	40585	40598	40610
40574	40586	40599	40611

40612	40634*	40657	40681
40613	40635*	40658	40682
40614	40636	40659	40683
40615	40637	40660	40684
40616	40638	40661	40685
40617	40640	40663	40686
40618	40641	40664	40687
40619	40642	40665	40688
40620	40643	40666	40689
40621	40644	40667	40690
40622	40645	40668	40691
40623	40646	40669	40692
40624	40647	40670	40693
40625	40648	40671	40694
40626	40649	40672	40695
40627	40650	40673	40696
40628	40651	40674	40697
40629	40652	40675	40698
40630	40653†	40677	40699
40631	40654	40678	40700
40632	40655	40679	
40633*†	40656	40680	

Total 134

4-4-0 (3-Cyl. Compd.) 4P

Introduced 1924. Post-grouping development of Johnson Midland compound with modified dimensions and (with some exceptions) reduced boiler mountings.
Weight: Loco. 61 tons 14 cwt.
Pressure: 200 lb. Su.
Cyls.: $\begin{cases} \text{L.P. (2) } 21'' \times 26''. \\ \text{H.P. (1) } 19'' \times 26''. \end{cases}$
Driving Wheels: $6'\ 9''$.
T.E.: (of L.P. cyls. at 80% boiler pressure): 22,650 lb.
P.V. (H.P. cyl. only).

40907	41060	41093	41119
40920	41062	41094	41120
40925	41063	41095	41121
40928	41066	41100	41122
40931	41068	41101	41123
40933	41071	41102	41143
40935	41078	41106	41144
40936	41083	41111	41152
40937	41086	41113	41156
41049	41090	41114	41157

41158	41163	41167	41189	41320*	41323*	41326*	41329*
41159	41164	41168	41193	41321*	41324*	41327*	
41162	41165	41173	41196	41322*	41325*	41328*	

Total 52   Total 130

2-6-2T   2

Introduced 1946. Ivatt L.M.S. taper
  boiler design.
Weight: 63 tons 5 cwt.
Pressure: 200 lb. Su.
Cyls.: $\begin{cases} \text{(O) } 16'' \times 24''. \\ \text{(O) } 16\frac{1}{2}'' \times 24''.* \end{cases}$
Driving Wheels: 5' 0".
T.E.: $\begin{cases} 17,410 \text{ lb.} \\ 18,510 \text{ lb.}* \end{cases}$
Walschaerts valve gear. P.V.

41200	41230	41260	41290*
41201	41231	41261	41291*
41202	41232	41262	41292*
41203	41233	41263	41293*
41204	41234	41264	41294*
41205	41235	41265	41295*
41206	41236	41266	41296*
41207	41237	41267	41297*
41208	41238	41268	41298*
41209	41239	41269	41299*
41210	41240	41270	41300*
41211	41241	41271	41301*
41212	41242	41272	41302*
41213	41243	41273	41303*
41214	41244	41274	41304*
41215	41245	41275	41305*
41216	41246	41276	41306*
41217	41247	41277	41307*
41218	41248	41278	41308*
41219	41249	41279	41309*
41220	41250	41280	41310*
41221	41251	41281	41311*
41222	41252	41282	41312*
41223	41253	41283	41313*
41224	41254	41284	41314*
41225	41255	41285	41315*
41226	41256	41286	41316*
41227	41257	41287	41317*
41228	41258	41288	41318*
41229	41259	41289	41319*

0-4-0ST   0F

Introduced 1897. Johnson Midland
  design.
Weight: 32 tons 3 cwt.
Pressure: 140 lb.
Cyls.: 15" × 20".
Driving Wheels: 3' 10".
T.E.: 11,640 lb.

41518   Total 1

0-4-0T   0F

Introduced 1907. Deeley Midland
  design.
Weight: 32 tons 16 cwt.
Pressure: 160 lb.
Cyls.: (O) 15" × 22".
Driving Wheels: 3' 9¾".
T.E.: 14,635 lb.
Walschaerts valve gear.

41528	41531	41533	41536
41529	41532	41535	41537

Total 8

0-6-0T   1F

Introduced 1878. Johnson Midland
  design.
*Rebuilt with Belpaire firebox.
Weight: 39 tons 11 cwt.
Pressure: $\begin{cases} 150 \text{ lb.} \\ 140 \text{ lb.}* \end{cases}$
Cyls.: 17" × 24".
Driving Wheels: 4' 7".
T.E.: $\begin{cases} 16,080 \text{ lb.} \\ 15,005 \text{ lb.}* \end{cases}$

41661*	41734*	41795*	41855*
41702*	41739*	41797*	41857*
41708*	41754*	41804*	41875*
41712*	41763*	41835	41878*
41724*	41769*	41844*	41879*
41726*	41773*	41847*	

Total 23

111

0-4-4T 2P

Introduced 1932. Stanier L.M.S. design.
Push-and-pull fitted.
Weight: 58 tons 1 cwt.
Pressure: 160 lb.
Cyls.: 18″ × 26″.
Driving Wheels: 5′ 7″.
T.E.: 17,100 lb.

41900	41903	41906	41908
41901	41904	41907	41909
41902	41905		

Total 10

4-4-2T 3P

Introduced 1923. Midland and L.M.S.
development of Whitelegg L.T. & S.
" 79 " Class.
Weight: 71 tons 10 cwt.
Pressure: 170 lb.
Cyls.: (O) 19″ × 26″.
Driving Wheels: 6′ 6″.
T.E.: 17,390 lb.

41928	41945	41949	41975
41936	41946	41950	41977
41939	41947	41969	41978
41941	41948		

Total 14

0-6-2T 3F

Introduced 1903. Whitelegg L.T. & S.
" 69 " Class (Nos. 41990-3 built 1912
taken directly into M.R. stock).
Weight: 64 tons 13 cwt.
Pressure: 170 lb.
Cyls.: 18″ × 26″.
Driving Wheels: 5′ 3″.
T.E.: 19,320 lb.

41980	41984	41988	41991
41981	41985	41989	41992
41982	41986	41990	41993
41983	41987		

Total 14

2-6-4T 4

*Introduced 1927. Fowler L.M.S.
parallel boiler design.
†Introduced 1933. As earlier engines,
but with side-window cab and doors.
‡Introduced 1934. Stanier taper-
boiler 3-cylinder design for L.T. & S.

§Introduced 1935. Stanier taper-
boiler 2-cylinder design.
¶Introduced 1945. Fairburn development of Stanier design with shorter
wheelbase and detail alterations.

Weight:
{ 86 tons 5 cwt.*†
{ 92 tons 5 cwt.‡
{ 87 tons 17 cwt.§
{ 85 tons 5 cwt.¶

Pressure (all types): 200 lb. Su.

Cyls.:
{ (O) 19″ × 26″.*†
{ (3) 16″ × 26″.‡
{ (O) 19⅝″ × 26″.§¶

Driving Wheels (all types): 5′ 9″.

T.E.:
{ 23,125 lb.*†
{ 24,600 lb.‡
{ 24,670 lb.§¶

Walschaerts valve gear. P.V.

¶FAIRBURN LOCOS.

42050	42080	42110	42140
42051	42081	42111	42141
42052	42082	42112	42142
42053	42083	42113	42143
42054	42084	42114	42144
42055	42085	42115	42145
42056	42086	42116	42146
42057	42087	42117	42147
42058	42088	42118	42148
42059	42089	42119	42149
42060	42090	42120	42150
42061	42091	42121	42151
42062	42092	42122	42152
42063	42093	42123	42153
42064	42094	42124	42154
42065	42095	42125	42155
42066	42096	42126	42156
42067	42097	42127	42157
42068	42098	42128	42158
42069	42099	42129	42159
42070	42100	42130	42160
42071	42101	42131	42161
42072	42102	42132	42162
42073	42103	42133	42163
42074	42104	42134	42164
42075	42105	42135	42165
42076	42106	42136	42166
42077	42107	42137	42167
42078	42108	42138	42168
42079	42109	42139	42169

42170	42203	42236	42269
42171	42204	42237	42270
42172	42205	42238	42271
42173	42206	42239	42272
42174	42207	42240	42273
42175	42208	42241	42274
42176	42209	42242	42275
42177	42210	42243	42276
42178	42211	42244	42277
42179	42212	42245	42278
42180	42213	42246	42279
42181	42214	42247	42280
42182	42215	42248	42281
42183	42216	42249	42282
42184	42217	42250	42283
42185	42218	42251	42284
42186	42219	42252	42285
42187	42220	42253	42286
42188	42221	42254	42287
42189	42222	42255	42288
42190	42223	42256	42289
42191	42224	42257	42290
42192	42225	42258	42291
42193	42226	42259	42292
42194	42227	42260	42293
42195	42228	42261	42294
42196	42229	42262	42295
42197	42230	42263	42296
42198	42231	42264	42297
42199	42232	42265	42298
42200	42233	42266	42299
42201	42234	42267	
42202	42235	42268	

42344	42357	42370	42383
42345	42358	42371	42384
42346	42359	42372	42385
42347	42360	42373	42386
42348	42361	42374	42387
42349	42362	42375	42388
42350	42363	42376	42389
42351	42364	42377	42390
42352	42365	42378	42391
42353	42366	42379	42392
42354	42367	42380	42393
42355	42368	42381	42394
42356	42369	42382	

†FOWLER LOCOS. WITH SIDE-WINDOW CAB

42395	42403	42411	42418
42396	42404	42412	42419
42397	42405	42413	42420
42398	42406	42414	42421
42399	42407	42415	42422
42400	42408	42416	42423
42401	42409	42417	42424
42402	42410		

*FOWLER LOCOS.

42300	42311	42322	42333
42301	42312	42323	42334
42302	42313	42324	42335
42303	42314	42325	42336
42304	42315	42326	42337
42305	42316	42327	42338
42306	42317	42328	42339
42307	42318	42329	42340
42308	42319	42330	42341
42309	42320	42331	42342
42310	42321	42332	42343

§STANIER 2-CYL. LOCOS.

42425	42443	42461	42479
42426	42444	42462	42480
42427	42445	42463	42481
42428	42446	42464	42482
42429	42447	42465	42483
42430	42448	42466	42484
42431	42449	42467	42485
42432	42450	42468	42486
42433	42451	42469	42487
42434	42452	42470	42488
42435	42453	42471	42489
42436	42454	42472	42490
42437	42455	42473	42491
42438	42456	42474	42492
42439	42457	42475	42493
42440	42458	42476	42494
42441	42459	42477	
42442	42460	42478	

‡STANIER 3-CYL. LOCOS.

42500	42510	42519	42528
42501	42511	42520	42529
42502	42512	42521	42530
42503	42513	42522	42531
42504	42514	42523	42532
42505	42515	42524	42533
42506	42516	42525	42534
42507	42517	42526	42535
42508	42518	42527	42536
42509			

§STANIER 2-CYL. LOCOS.

42537	42571	42605	42639
42538	42572	42606	42640
42539	42573	42607	42641
42540	42574	42608	42642
42541	42575	42609	42643
42542	42576	42610	42644
42543	42577	42611	42645
42544	42578	42612	42646
42545	42579	42613	42647
42546	42580	42614	42648
42547	42581	42615	42649
42548	42582	42616	42650
42549	42583	42617	42651
42550	42584	42618	42652
42551	42585	42619	42653
42552	42586	42620	42654
42553	42587	42621	42655
42554	42588	42622	42656
42555	42589	42623	42657
42556	42590	42624	42658
42557	42591	42625	42659
42558	42592	42626	42660
42559	42593	42627	42661
42560	42594	42628	42662
42561	42595	42629	42663
42562	42596	42630	42664
42563	42597	42631	42665
42564	42598	42632	42666
42565	42599	42633	42667
42566	42600	42634	42668
42567	42601	42635	42669
42568	42602	42636	42670
42569	42603	42637	42671
42570	42604	42638	42672

¶FAIRBURN LOCOS.

42673	42680	42687	42694
42674	42681	42688	42695
42675	42682	42689	42696
42676	42683	42690	42697
42677	42684	42691	42698
42678	42685	42692	42699
42679	42686	42693	

Total 645

2-6-0   6P5F

Introduced 1926. Hughes L.M.S. design built under Fowler's direction. Walschaerts valve gear. P.V.
*Introduced 1953. Locos. rebuilt experimentally with Lentz R.C. poppet valves in 1931; rebuilt with Reidinger rotary poppet valve gear in 1953.
Weight: Loco. 66 tons 0 cwt.
Pressure: 180 lb. Su.
Cyls. :(O) 21″ × 26″.
Driving Wheels: 5′ 6″.
T.E.: 26,580 lb.

42700	42724	42748	42772
42701	42725	42749	42773
42702	42726	42750	42774
42703	42727	42751	42775
42704	42728	42752	42776
42705	42729	42753	42777
42706	42730	42754	42778
42707	42731	42755	42779
42708	42732	42756	42780
42709	42733	42757	42781
42710	42734	42758	42782
42711	42735	42759	42783
42712	42736	42760	42784
42713	42737	42761	42785
42714	42738	42762	42786
42715	42739	42763	42787
42716	42740	42764	42788
42717	42741	42765	42789
42718	42742	42766	42790
42719	42743	42767	42791
42720	42744	42768	42792
42721	42745	42769	42793
42722	42746	42770	42794
42723	42747	42771	42795

42796	42834	42871	42908
42797	42835	42872	42909
42798	42836	42873	42910
42799	42837	42874	42911
42800	42838	42875	42912
42801	42839	42876	42913
42802	42840	42877	42914
42803	42841	42878	42915
42804	42842	42879	42916
42805	42843	42880	42917
42806	42844	42881	42918
42807	42845	42882	42919
42808	42846	42883	42920
42809	42847	42884	42921
42810	42848	42885	42922
42811	42849	42886	42923
42812	42850	42887	42924
42813	42851	42888	42925
42814	42852	42889	42926
42815	42853	42890	42927
42816	42854	42891	42928
42817	42855	42892	42929
42818*	42856	42893	42930
42819	42857	42894	42931
42820	42858	42895	42932
42821	42859	42896	42933
42822*	42860	42897	42934
42823	42861	42898	42935
42824*	42862	42899	42936
42825*	42863	42900	42937
42826	42864	42901	42938
42827	42865	42902	42939
42828	42866	42903	42940
42829*	42867	42904	42941
42830	42868	42905	42942
42831	42869	42906	42943
42832	42870	42907	42944
42833			**Total 245**

2-6-0   6P5F

Introduced 1933. Stanier L.M.S. taper boiler design, some with safety valves mounted on the top feed.
Weight: Loco. 69 tons 2 cwt.
Pressure: 225 lb. Su.
Cyls.: (O) $18'' \times 28''$.
Driving Wheels: 5′ 6″.
T.E.: 26,290 lb.
Walschaerts valve gear. P.V.

42945	42955	42965	42975
42946	42956	42966	42976
42947	42957	42967	42977
42948	42958	42968	42978
42949	42959	42969	42979
42950	42960	42970	42980
42951	42961	42971	42981
42952	42962	42972	42982
42953	42963	42973	42983
42954	42964	42974	42984
			Total 40

2-6-0   4

Introduced 1947. Ivatt L.M.S. taper boiler design with double chimney. Later engines introduced with single chimney, with which earlier engines are being rebuilt.
Weight: Loco. 59 tons 2 cwt.
Pressure: 225 lb. Su.
Cyls.: (O) $17\frac{1}{2}'' \times 26''$.
Driving Wheels: 5′ 3″.
T.E.: 24,170 lb.
Walschaerts valve gear. P.V.

43000	43023	43046	43069
43001	43024	43047	43070
43002	43025	43048	43071
43003	43026	43049	43072
43004	43027	43050	43073
43005	43028	43051	43074
43006	43029	43052	43075
43007	43030	43053	43076
43008	43031	43054	43077
43009	43032	43055	43078
43010	43033	43056	43079
43011	43034	43057	43080
43012	43035	43058	43081
43013	43036	43059	43082
43014	43037	43060	43083
43015	43038	43061	43084
43016	43039	43062	43085
43017	43040	43063	43086
43018	43041	43064	43087
43019	43042	43065	43088
43020	43043	43066	43089
43021	43044	43067	43090
43022	43045	43068	43091

43092	43110	43128	43146	43258	43368	43502	43630
43093	43111	43129	43147	43261	43369	43506	43631
43094	43112	43130	43148	43263	43370	43507	43634
43095	43113	43131	43149	43266	43371	43509	43637
43096	43114	43132	43150	43267	43373	43510	43638
43097	43115	43133	43151	43268	43374	43514	43639
43098	43116	43134	43152	43271	43378	43515	43644
43099	43117	43135	43153	43274	43379	43520	43645
43100	43118	43136	43154	43277	43381	43521	43650
43101	43119	43137	43155	43278	43386	43522	43651
43102	43120	43138	43156	43282	43387	43523	43652
43103	43121	43139	43157	43284	43388	43529	43656
43104	43122	43140	43158	43287	43389	43531	43657
43105	43123	43141	43159	43292	43394	43538	43658
43106	43124	43142	43160	43294	43395	43548	43660
43107	43125	43143	43161	43295	43398	43553	43664
43108	43126	43144		43300	43399	43558	43665
43109	43127	43145		43301	43400	43562	43668
				43305	43405	43565	43669
				43306	43406	43570	43673
			Total 162	43307	43410	43572	43674
				43308	43411	43574	43675

0-6-0   3F

				43309	43419	43575	43678
				43314	43427	43578	43679

Introduced 1885. Johnson Midland
locos., rebuilt from 1916 by Fowler
with Belpaire firebox.
*Introduced 1885. Johnson Midland
locos., rebuilt from 1920 by Fowler
with Belpaire firebox.
†Introduced 1896. Locos. built for S. &
D.J. (taken into L.M.S. stock 1930).
Weight: Loco. 43 tons 17 cwt.
Pressure: 175 lb.
Cyls.: 18″ × 26″.

Driving Wheels: {5′ 3″.
5′ 3″.†
4′ 11″.*

T.E.: {19,890 lb.
19,890 lb.†
21,240 lb.*

				43315	43428	43579	43680
				43318	43429	43580	43681
				43321	43431	43583	43682
				43323	43433	43584	43687
				43324	43435	43585	43693
				43325	43436	43586	43705
				43326	43440	43587	43709
				43327	43441	43593	43710
				43329	43444	43594	43711
				43330	43446	43599	43712
				43332	43449	43605	43714
43174*	43200	43219	43243	43333	43453	43608	43715
43178*	43203	43222	43244	43335	43456	43612	43721
43180*	43205	43223	43245	43337	43457	43615	43727
43183*	43207	43225	43247	43339	43459	43618	43728
43185*	43208	43231	43248†	43340	43464	43619	43729
43186*	43210	43233	43249	43342	43468	43620	43731
43187*	43211†	43234	43250	43344	43474	43621	43734
43188*	43212	43235	43251	43355	43482	43622	43735
43189*	43213	43237	43253	43356	43484	43623	43737
43192	43214	43240	43254	43357	43490	43624	43742
43193	43216†	43241	43256	43359	43496	43627	43745
43194†	43218†	43242	43257	43361	43499	43629	43749

43750*	43756	43760	43766
43751	43757	43762	43771
43753	43759	43763	43773
43754			

Total 249

0-6-0   3F

Introduced 1906. Deeley Midland design. Rebuilt by Fowler with Belpaire firebox.
Weight: Loco. 46 tons 3 cwt.
Pressure: 175 lb.
Cyls.: 18½″ × 26″.
Driving Wheels: 5′ 3″.
T.E.: 21,010 lb.

43778	43798	43812	43825
43784	43799	43814	43826
43785	43800	43815	43828
43787	43808	43822	43829
43789	43809	43823	43832
43793			

Total 21

0-6-0   4F

Introduced 1911. Fowler superheated Midland design.
Weight: Loco. 48 tons 15 cwt.
Pressure: 175 lb. Su.
Cyls.: 20″ × 26″.
Driving Wheels: 5′ 3″.
T.E.: 24,555 lb.
P.V.

43836	43854	43870	43885
43839	43855	43871	43886
43840	43856	43872	43887
43841	43858	43873	43888
43842	43859	43876	43890
43843	43860	43877	43892
43844	43861	43878	43893
43845	43863	43879	43896
43846	43864	43880	43897
43848	43865	43881	43899
43849	43866	43882	43900
43850	43868	43883	43902
43853	43869	43884	43903

43904	43935	43967	43998
43905	43937	43968	43999
43906	43938	43969	44000
43907	43939	43970	44001
43908	43940	43971	44002
43910	43942	43972	44003
43911	43944	43973	44004
43913	43945	43975	44005
43914	43946	43976	44007
43915	43947	43977	44008
43917	43948	43979	44009
43918	43949	43981	44010
43919	43950	43982	44011
43920	43951	43983	44012
43921	43952	43984	44013
43922	43953	43985	44014
43923	43954	43986	44015
43924	43955	43987	44016
43925	43957	43988	44018
43926	43958	43989	44019
43928	43960	43990	44020
43929	43961	43991	44021
43930	43962	43994	44022
43931	43963	43995	44023
43932	43964	43996	44025
43933	43965	43997	44026
43934	43966		

Total 158

0-6-0   4F

Introduced 1924. Post-grouping development of Midland design with reduced boiler mountings.
*Introduced 1922. Locos. built for S. & D.&R. to M.R. design (taken into L.M.S. stock 1930).
Weight: Loco. 48 tons 15 cwt.
Pressure: 175 lb. Su.
Cyls.: 20″ × 26″.
Driving Wheels: 5′ 3″.
T.E.: 24,555 lb.
P.V.

44027	44032	44037	44042
44028	44033	44038	44043
44029	44034	44039	44044
44030	44035	44040	44045
44031	44036	44041	44046

44047	44094	44141	44188	44235	44282	44329	44376
44048	44095	44142	44189	44236	44283	44330	44377
44049	44096	44143	44190	44237	44284	44331	44378
44050	44097	44144	44191	44238	44285	44332	44379
44051	44098	44145	44192	44239	44286	44333	44380
44052	44099	44146	44193	44240	44287	44334	44381
44053	44100	44147	44194	44241	44288	44335	44382
44054	44101	44148	44195	44242	44289	44336	44383
44055	44102	44149	44196	44243	44290	44337	44384
44056	44103	44150	44197	44244	44291	44338	44385
44057	44104	44151	44198	44245	44292	44339	44386
44058	44105	44152	44199	44246	44293	44340	44387
44059	44106	44153	44200	44247	44294	44341	44388
44060	44107	44154	44201	44248	44295	44342	44389
44061	44108	44155	44202	44249	44296	44343	44390
44062	44109	44156	44203	44250	44297	44344	44391
44063	44110	44157	44204	44251	44298	44345	44392
44064	44111	44158	44205	44252	44299	44346	44393
44065	44112	44159	44206	44253	44300	44347	44394
44066	44113	44160	44207	44254	44301	44348	44395
44067	44114	44161	44208	44255	44302	44349	44396
44068	44115	44162	44209	44256	44303	44350	44397
44069	44116	44163	44210	44257	44304	44351	44398
44070	44117	44164	44211	44258	44305	44352	44399
44071	44118	44165	44212	44259	44306	44353	44400
44072	44119	44166	44213	44260	44307	44354	44401
44073	44120	44167	44214	44261	44308	44355	44402
44074	44121	44168	44215	44262	44309	44356	44403
44075	44122	44169	44216	44263	44310	44357	44404
44076	44123	44170	44217	44264	44311	44358	44405
44077	44124	44171	44218	44265	44312	44359	44406
44078	44125	44172	44219	44266	44313	44360	44407
44079	44126	44173	44220	44267	44314	44361	44408
44080	44127	44174	44221	44268	44315	44362	44409
44081	44128	44175	44222	44269	44316	44363	44410
44082	44129	44176	44223	44270	44317	44364	44411
44083	44130	44177	44224	44271	44318	44365	44412
44084	44131	44178	44225	44272	44319	44366	44413
44085	44132	44179	44226	44273	44320	44367	44414
44086	44133	44180	44227	44274	44321	44368	44415
44087	44134	44181	44228	44275	44322	44369	44416
44088	44135	44182	44229	44276	44323	44370	44417
44089	44136	44183	44230	44277	44324	44371	44418
44090	44137	44184	44231	44278	44325	44372	44419
44091	44138	44185	44232	44279	44326	44373	44420
44092	44139	44186	44233	44280	44327	44374	44421
44093	44140	44187	44234	44281	44328	44375	44422

44423	44469	44515	44561*
44424	44470	44516	44562
44425	44471	44517	44563
44426	44472	44518	44564
44427	44473	44519	44565
44428	44474	44520	44566
44429	44475	44521	44567
44430	44476	44522	44568
44431	44477	44523	44569
44432	44478	44524	44570
44433	44479	44525	44571
44434	44480	44526	44572
44435	44481	44527	44573
44436	44482	44528	44574
44437	44483	44529	44575
44438	44484	44530	44576
44439	44485	44531	44577
44440	44486	44532	44578
44441	44487	44533	44579
44442	44488	44534	44580
44443	44489	44535	44581
44444	44490	44536	44582
44445	44491	44537	44583
44446	44492	44538	44584
44447	44493	44539	44585
44448	44494	44540	44586
44449	44495	44541	44587
44450	44496	44542	44588
44451	44497	44543	44589
44452	44498	44544	44590
44453	44499	44545	44591
44454	44500	44546	44592
44455	44501	44547	44593
44456	44502	44548	44594
44457	44503	44549	44595
44458	44504	44550	44596
44459	44505	44551	44597
44460	44506	44552	44598
44461	44507	44553	44599
44462	44508	44554	44600
44463	44509	44555	44601
44464	44510	44556	44602
44465	44511	44557*	44603
44466	44512	44558*	44604
44467	44513	44559*	44605
44468	44514	44560*	44606

Total 580

Introduced 1934. Stanier L.M.S. taper boiler design.

Experimental locomotives:—

1. Introduced 1947. Stephenson link motion (outside), Timken roller bearings.
2. Introduced 1948. Caprotti valve gear.
3. Introduced 1948. Caprotti valve gear, Timken roller bearings.
4. Introduced 1948. Caprotti valve gear, Timken roller bearings, double chimney.
5. Introduced 1947. Timken roller bearings.
6. Introduced 1947. Timken roller bearings, double chimney.
7. Introduced 1949. Fitted with steel firebox.
8. Introduced 1950. Skefko roller bearings.
9. Introduced 1950. Timken roller bearings on driving coupled axle only.
10. Introduced 1950. Skefko roller bearings on driving coupled axle only.
11. Introduced 1951. Caprotti valve gear, Skefko roller bearings.

Weight: Loco. 72 tons 2 cwt. / 75 tons 6 cwt. (1, 5, 6, 8, 9, 10). / 74 tons 0 cwt. (2, 3, 4, 11). / 72 tons 2 cwt. (7).

Pressure: 225 lb. Su.
Cyls.: (O) 18½″ × 28″.
Driving Wheels: 6′ 0″.
T.E.: 25,455 lb.

Walschaerts valve gear and P.V. except where otherwise shown.

44658	44670[10]	44682[8]	44694[9]
44659	44671[10]	44683[8]	44695[9]
44660	44672[10]	44684[8]	44696[9]
44661	44673[10]	44685[8]	44697[9]
44662	44674[10]	44686[11]	44698
44663	44675[10]	44687[11]	44699
44664	44676[10]	44688[9]	44700
44665	44677[10]	44689[9]	44701
44666	44678[8]	44690[9]	44702
44667	44679[8]	44691[9]	44703
44668[10]	44680[8]	44692[9]	44704
44669[10]	44681[8]	44693[9]	44705

44706	44753[3]	44800	44847	44894	44941	44988	45035
44707	44754[3]	44801	44848	44895	44942	44989	45036
44708	44755[4]	44802	44849	44896	44943	44990	45037
44709	44756[4]	44803	44850	44897	44944	44991	45038
44710	44757[4]	44804	44851	44898	44945	44992	45039
44711	44758[5]	44805	44852	44899	44946	44993	45040
44712	44759[5]	44806	44853	44900	44947	44994	45041
44713	44760[5]	44807	44854	44901	44948	44995	45042
44714	44761[5]	44808	44855	44902	44949	44996	45043
44715	44762[5]	44809	44856	44903	44950	44997	45044
44716	44763[5]	44810	44857	44904	44951	44998	45045
44717	44764[5]	44811	44858	44905	44952	44999	45046
44718[7]	44765[6]	44812	44859	44906	44953	45000	45047
44719[7]	44766[6]	44813	44860	44907	44954	45001	45048
44720[7]	44767[1]	44814	44861	44908	44955	45002	45049
44721[7]	44768	44815	44862	44909	44956	45003	45050
44722[7]	44769	44816	44863	44910	44957	45004	45051
44723[7]	44770	44817	44864	44911	44958	45005	45052
44724[7]	44771	44818	44865	44912	44959	45006	45053
44725[7]	44772	44819	44866	44913	44960	45007	45054
44726[7]	44773	44820	44867	44914	44961	45008	45055
44727[7]	44774	44821	44868	44915	44962	45009	45056
44728	44775	44822	44869	44916	44963	45010	45057
44729	44776	44823	44870	44917	44964	45011	45058
44730	44777	44824	44871	44918	44965	45012	45059
44731	44778	44825	44872	44919	44966	45013	45060
44732	44779	44826	44873	44920	44967	45014	45061
44733	44780	44827	44874	44921	44968	45015	45062
44734	44781	44828	44875	44922	44969	45016	45063
44735	44782	44829	44876	44923	44970	45017	45064
44736	44783	44830	44877	44924	44971	45018	45065
44737	44784	44831	44878	44925	44972	45019	45066
44738[2]	44785	44832	44879	44926	44973	45020	45067
44739[2]	44786	44833	44880	44927	44974	45021	45068
44740[2]	44787	44834	44881	44928	44975	45022	45069
44741[2]	44788	44835	44882	44929	44976	45023	45070
44742[2]	44789	44836	44883	44930	44977	45024	45071
44743[2]	44790	44837	44884	44931	44978	45025	45072
44744[2]	44791	44838	44885	44932	44979	45026	45073
44745[2]	44792	44839	44886	44933	44980	45027	45074
44746[2]	44793	44840	44887	44934	44981	45028	45075
44747[2]	44794	44841	44888	44935	44982	45029	45076
44748[3]	44795	44842	44889	44936	44983	45030	45077
44749[3]	44796	44843	44890	44937	44984	45031	45078
44750[3]	44797	44844	44891	44938	44985	45032	45079
44751[3]	44798	44845	44892	44939	44986	45033	45080
44752[3]	44799	44846	44893	44940	44987	45034	45081

45082	45123	45164	45205	45246	45293	45340	45387
45083	45124	45165	45206	45247	45294	45341	45388
45084	45125	45166	45207	45248	45295	45342	45389
45085	45126	45167	45208	45249	45296	45343	45390
45086	45127	45168	45209	45250	45297	45344	45391
45087	45128	45169	45210	45251	45298	45345	45392
45088	45129	45170	45211	45252	45299	45346	45393
45089	45130	45171	45212	45253	45300	45347	45394
45090	45131	45172	45213	45254	45301	45348	45395
45091	45132	45173	45214	45255	45302	45349	45396
45092	45133	45174	45215	45256	45303	45350	45397
45093	45134	45175	45216	45257	45304	45351	45398
45094	45135	45176	45217	45258	45305	45352	45399
45095	45136	45177	45218	45259	45306	45353	45400
45096	45137	45178	45219	45260	45307	45354	45401
45097	45138	45179	45220	45261	45308	45355	45402
45098	45139	45180	45221	45262	45309	45356	45403
45099	45140	45181	45222	45263	45310	45357	45404
45100	45141	45182	45223	45264	45311	45358	45405
45101	45142	45183	45224	45265	45312	45359	45406
45102	45143	45184	45225	45266	45313	45360	45407
45103	45144	45185	45226	45267	45314	45361	45408
45104	45145	45186	45227	45268	45315	45362	45409
45105	45146	45187	45228	45269	45316	45363	45410
45106	45147	45188	45229	45270	45317	45364	45411
45107	45148	45189	45230	45271	45318	45365	45412
45108	45149	45190	45231	45272	45319	45366	45413
45109	45150	45191	45232	45273	45320	45367	45414
45110	45151	45192	45233	45274	45321	45368	45415
45111	45152	45193	45234	45275	45322	45369	45416
45112	45153	45194	45235	45276	45323	45370	45417
45113	45154*	45195	45236	45277	45324	45371	45418
45114	45155	45196	45237	45278	45325	45372	45419
45115	45156*	45197	45238	45279	45326	45373	45420
45116	45157*	45198	45239	45280	45327	45374	45421
45117	45158*	45199	45240	45281	45328	45375	45422
45118	45159	45200	45241	45282	45329	45376	45423
45119	45160	45201	45242	45283	45330	45377	45424
45120	45161	45202	45243	45284	45331	45378	45425
45121	45162	45203	45244	45285	45332	45379	45426
45122	45163	45204	45245	45286	45333	45380	45427
				45287	45334	45381	45428
				45288	45335	45382	45429
				45289	45336	45383	45430
				45290	45337	45384	45431
				45291	45338	45385	45432
				45292	45339	45386	45433

* NAMES :

45154 Lanarkshire Yeomanry
45156 Ayrshire Yeomanry
45157 The Glasgow Highlander
45158 Glasgow Yeomanry

45434	45451	45468	45484
45435	45452	45469	45485
45436	45453	45470	45486
45437	45454	45471	45487
45438	45455	45472	45488
45439	45456	45473	45489
45440	45457	45474	45490
45441	45458	45475	45491
45442	45459	45476	45492
45443	45460	45477	45493
45444	45461	45478	45494
45445	45462	45479	45495
45446	45463	45480	45496
45447	45464	45481	45497
45448	45465	45482	45498
45449	45466	45483	45499
45450	45467		

Total 842

"Patriot" Class
4-6-0   6P5F & 7P

*6P5F. Introduced 1930. Fowler 3-cyl. rebuild of L.N.W. "Claughton" Class (introduced 1912), retaining original wheels and other details.

Remainder. Introduced 1933. New locos. to Fowler design (45502–41 were officially considered as rebuilds).

†7P. Introduced 1946. Ivatt rebuild of Fowler locos. with larger taper boiler, new cylinders and double chimney.

Weight: Loco. $\begin{cases} 80 \text{ tons } 15 \text{ cwt.} \\ 80 \text{ tons } 15 \text{ cwt.}* \\ 82 \text{ tons } 0 \text{ cwt.}† \end{cases}$

Pressure: $\begin{cases} 200 \text{ lb. Su.} \\ 200 \text{ lb. Su.}* \\ 250 \text{ lb. Su.}† \end{cases}$

Cyls.: $\begin{cases} (3) \ 18'' \times 26''. \\ (3) \ 18'' \times 26''.* \\ (3) \ 17'' \times 26''.† \end{cases}$

Driving Wheels: 6' 9".

T.E.: $\begin{cases} 26,520 \text{ lb.} \\ 26,520 \text{ lb.}* \\ 29,570 \text{ lb.}† \end{cases}$

Walschaerts valve gear.   P.V.

45500* Patriot
45501* St. Dunstan's
45502   Royal Naval Division
45503   The Royal Leicestershire
            Regiment
45504   Royal Signals
45505   The Royal Army
            Ordnance Corps
45506   The Royal Pioneer Corps
45507   Royal Tank Corps
45508
45509   The Derbyshire
            Yeomanry
45510
45511   Isle of Man
45512† Bunsen
45513
45514† Holyhead
45515   Caernarvon
45516   The Bedfordshire and
            Hertfordshire Regiment
45517
45518   Bradshaw
45519   Lady Godiva
45520   Llandudno
45521† Rhyl
45522† Prestatyn
45523† Bangor
45524   Blackpool
45525† Colwyn Bay
45526† Morecambe and
            Heysham
45527† Southport
45528†
45529† Stephenson
45530† Sir Frank Ree
45531† Sir Frederick Harrison
45532† Illustrious
45533   Lord Rathmore
45534† E. Tootal Broadhurst
45535† Sir Herbert Walker
            K.C.B.
45536† Private W. Wood, V.C.
45537   Private E. Sykes, V.C.
45538   Giggleswick
45539   E. C. Trench

45540†	Sir Robert Turnbull
45541	Duke of Sutherland
45542	
45543	Home Guard
45544	
45545†	Planet
45546	Fleetwood
45547	
45548	Lytham St. Annes
45549	
45550	
45551	

Total 52

" Jubilee " Class

4-6-0   6P5F & 7P

6P5F. Introduced 1934. Stanier L.M.S. taper boiler development of the " Patriot " class.

*7P. Introduced 1942. Rebuilt with larger boiler and double chimney.

Weight: Loco. $\begin{cases} 79 \text{ tons } 11 \text{ cwt.} \\ 82 \text{ tons } 0 \text{ cwt.*} \end{cases}$

Pressure: $\begin{cases} 225 \text{ lb. Su.} \\ 250 \text{ lb. Su.*} \end{cases}$

Cyls.: (3) 17″ × 26″.

Driving Wheels: 6′ 9″.

T.E.: $\begin{cases} 26,610 \text{ lb.} \\ 29,570 \text{ lb.*} \end{cases}$

Walschaerts valve gear. P.V.

45552	Silver Jubilee
45553	Canada
45554	Ontario
45555	Quebec
45556	Nova Scotia
45557	New Brunswick
45558	Manitoba
45559	British Columbia

45560	Prince Edward Island
45561	Saskatchewan
45562	Alberta
45563	Australia
45564	New South Wales
45565	Victoria
45566	Queensland
45567	South Australia
45568	Western Australia
45569	Tasmania
45570	New Zealand
45571	South Africa
45572	Eire
45573	Newfoundland
45574	India
45575	Madras
45576	Bombay
45577	Bengal
45578	United Provinces
45579	Punjab
45580	Burma
45581	Bihar and Orissa
45582	Central Provinces
45583	Assam
45584	North West Frontier
45585	Hyderabad
45586	Mysore
45587	Baroda
45588	Kashmir
45589	Gwalior
45590	Travancore
45591	Udaipur
45592	Indore
45593	Kolhapur
45594	Bhopal
45595	Southern Rhodesia
45596	Bahamas
45597	Barbados
45598	Basutoland
45599	Bechuanaland
45600	Bermuda
45601	British Guiana
45602	British Honduras
45603	Solomon Islands
45604	Ceylon
45605	Cyprus
45606	Falkland Islands

45607	Fiji	45655	Keith
45608	Gibraltar	45656	Cochrane
45609	Gilbert and Ellice Islands	45657	Tyrwhitt
45610	Gold Coast	45658	Keyes
45611	Hong Kong	45659	Drake
45612	Jamaica	45660	Rooke
45613	Kenya	45661	Vernon
45614	Leeward Islands	45662	Kempenfelt
45615	Malay States	45663	Jervis
45616	Malta G.C.	45664	Nelson
45617	Mauritius	45665	Lord Rutherford of
45618	New Hebrides		Nelson
45619	Nigeria	45666	Cornwallis
45620	North Borneo	45667	Jellicoe
45621	Northern Rhodesia	45668	Madden
45622	Nyasaland	45669	Fisher
45623	Palestine	45670	Howard of Effingham
45624	St. Helena	45671	Prince Rupert
45625	Sarawak	45672	Anson
45626	Seychelles	45673	Keppel
45627	Sierra Leone	45674	Duncan
45628	Somaliland	45675	Hardy
45629	Straits Settlements	45676	Codrington
45630	Swaziland	45677	Beatty
45631	Tanganyika	45678	De Robeck
45632	Tonga	45679	Armada
45633	Aden	45680	Camperdown
45634	Trinidad	45681	Aboukir
45635	Tobago	45682	Trafalgar
45636	Uganda	45683	Hogue
45638	Zanzibar	45684	Jutland
45639	Raleigh	45685	Barfleur
45640	Frobisher	45686	St. Vincent
45641	Sandwich	45687	Neptune
45642	Boscawen	45688	Polyphemus
45643	Rodney	45689	Ajax
45644	Howe	45690	Leander
45645	Collingwood	45691	Orion
45646	Napier	45692	Cyclops
45647	Sturdee	45693	Agamemnon
45648	Wemyss	45694	Bellerophon
45649	Hawkins	45695	Minotaur
45650	Blake	45696	Arethusa
45651	Shovell	45697	Achilles
45652	Hawke	45698	Mars
45653	Barham	45699	Galatea
45654	Hood	45700	Amethyst

Class 2 (Ivatt) 2-6-2T No. 41300   [R. C. Riley

Class 4 (Ivatt) 2-6-0 No. 43119   [J. Cupit

Class 2 (Ivatt) 2-6-0 No. 46509   [G. Wheeler

Above: Class 2F
0-6-0T No. 47162
[D. McGarry

Left: Class 3F
0-6-0T No. 47478
(push-and-pull fitted)
[K. L. Cook

Below: Class 3F
(ex-Midland) 0-6-0T
No. 47249 (fitted
with condensing
apparatus)
[B. K. B. Green

Class IF 0-6-0T No. 41879   [R. J. Buckley

Class OF 0-4-0T No. 41537   [P. J. Sharpe

Class IP 0-4-4T No. 58065   [P. J. Robinson

Class 2P 0-4-4T No. 41909

[D. McGarry

Class 3F 0-6-2T No. 41980

[B. E. Morrison

Class 3P 4-4-2T No. 41941

[L. King

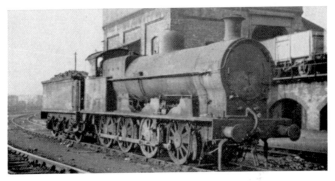

Class 7F 0-8-0 No. 49226

Class 7F 2-8-0 No. 53803

[W. Vaughan-Jenkins

Class 8F 2-8-0 No. 48773

[P. H. Groom

Class 6P5F 4-6-0 No. 45730 *Ocean* [D. A. Anderson

Class 7P 4-6-0 No. 45736 *Phoenix* [B. E. Morrison

Class 7P 4-6-0 No. 46115 *Scots Guardsman* [J. Robertson

Class 6P5F 4-6-0 No. 45508 (with stovepipe chimney) [R. J. Buckley

Class 8P 4-6-2 No. 46203 *Princess Margaret Rose* [D. A. Anderson

Class 8P 4-6-2 No. 46234 *Duchess of Abercorn* G. Wheeler

Class 5 4-6-0 No. 45084 (with combined top feed and dome) [*R. A. Panting*

Class 5 4-6-0 No. 44986 (with self-weighing tender) [*P. J. Sharpe*

Class 5 4-6-0 No. 44746 (with Caprotti valve gear) [*G. Wheeler*

Class 7P6F 4-6-2 No. 70050 *Firth of Clyde* [P. H. Groom

Class 8P 4-6-2 No. 71000 *Duke of Gloucester* [G. Wheeler

Class 6P5F 4-6-2 No. 72003 *Clan Fraser* [D. A. Anderson

Class 9F 2-10-0 No. 92124   [P. J. Sharpe

Class 9F 2-10-0 No. 92061 (fitted with air pumps for working Tyne Dock–Consett
ore traffic)
                                                          [W. H. Whitworth

Class 9F 2-10-0 No. 92022 fitted with Crosti boiler)   P. J. Sharpe

Class 3 2-6-0 No. 77008   [A. W. Martin

Class 4 2-6-4T No. 80122   [R. E. Vincent

Class 2 2-6-2T No. 84002   [J. Davenport

Class 7F 0-8-0 (Fowler) No. 49627   [R. A. Panting

Class 4F 0-6-0 No. 44445 (fitted with tender cab)   [T. K. Widd

Class 3F 0-6-0 No. 43832   [P. H. Groom

Class 2F 0-6-0 No. 58197 (5' 3" driving wheels)   [B. K. B. Green

Class 2F 0-6-0 No. 58246 (4' 11" driving wheels; with round-top firebox)
                                                                   [B. K. B. Green

Class 3P 4-4-0 No. 54488   [W. S. Sellar

Class 2F (Drummond) 0-6-0 No. 57386

[J. R. Paterson

Class 3F (McIntosh) 0-6-0 No. 57595

[J. R. Paterson

Class 3F (Pickersgill 0-6-0 No. 57691

[D. A. Anderson

Class 2P 0-4-4T No. 55224 [P. H. Groom

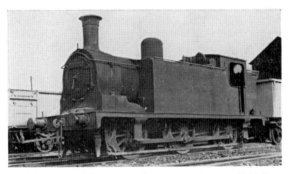

Class 3F 0-6-0T No. 56334 [P. H. Groom

Class 2F 0-6-0T No. 56172 [P. H. Groom

Left: Class 2P
2-4-2T No. 50644
[B. E. Morrison

Centre: Class 3F
(Aspinall) 0-6-0 No.
52179 [P. H. Wells

Left: Class 2F
(Barton Wright)
0-6-0 No. 52044
[B. K. B. Green

45701	Conqueror
45702	Colossus
45703	Thunderer
45704	Leviathan
45705	Seahorse
45706	Express
45707	Valiant
45708	Resolution
45709	Implacable
45710	Irresistible
45711	Courageous
45712	Victory
45713	Renown
45714	Revenge
45715	Invincible
45716	Swiftsure
45717	Dauntless
45718	Dreadnought
45719	Glorious
45720	Indomitable
45721	Impregnable
45722	Defence
45723	Fearless
45724	Warspite
45725	Repulse
45726	Vindictive
45727	Inflexible
45728	Defiance
45729	Furious
45730	Ocean
45731	Perseverance
45732	Sanspareil
45733	Novelty
45734	Meteor
45735*	Comet
45736*	Phoenix
45737	Atlas
45738	Samson
45739	Ulster
45740	Munster
45741	Leinster
45742	Connaught

Total 190

"Royal Scot" Class

4-6-0   7P

Introduced 1943. Stanier rebuild of Fowler locos. (introduced 1927) with taper boiler, new cylinders and double chimney.

*Introduced 1935. Stanier taper boiler rebuild with simple cylinders of experimental high pressure compound loco. No. 6399 Fury. (Introduced 1929.)

Weight: Loco. {83 tons. / 84 tons 1 cwt.*

Pressure: 250 lb. Su.

Cyls.: (3) 18" × 26".

Driving Wheels: 6' 9".

T.E.: 33,150 lb.

Walschaerts valve gear. P.V.

46100	Royal Scot
46101	Royal Scots Grey
46102	Black Watch
46103	Royal Scots Fusilier
46104	Scottish Borderer
46105	Cameron Highlander
46106	Gordon Highlander
46107	Argyll and Sutherland Highlander
46108	Seaforth Highlander
46109	Royal Engineer
46110	Grenadier Guardsman
46111	Royal Fusilier
46112	Sherwood Forester
46113	Cameronian
46114	Coldstream Guardsman
46115	Scots Guardsman
46116	Irish Guardsman
46117	Welsh Guardsman
46118	Royal Welch Fusilier
46119	Lancashire Fusilier
46120	Royal Inniskilling Fusilier
46121	Highland Light Infantry, City of Glasgow Regiment
46122	Royal Ulster Rifleman
46123	Royal Irish Fusilier

46124	London Scottish
46125	3rd Carabinier
46126	Royal Army Service Corps
46127	Old Contemptibles
46128	The Lovat Scouts
46129	The Scottish Horse
46130	The West Yorkshire Regiment
46131	The Royal Warwickshire Regiment
46132	The King's Regiment Liverpool
46133	The Green Howards
46134	The Cheshire Regiment
46135	The East Lancashire Regiment
46136	The Border Regiment
46137	The Prince of Wales's Volunteers (South Lancashire)
46138	The London Irish Rifleman
46139	The Welch Regiment
46140	The King's Royal Rifle Corps
46141	The North Staffordshire Regiment
46142	The York & Lancaster Regiment
46143	The South Staffordshire Regiment
46144	Honourable Artillery Company
46145	The Duke of Wellington's Regt. (West Riding)
46146	The Rifle Brigade
46147	The Northamptonshire Regiment
46148	The Manchester Regiment
46149	The Middlesex Regiment
46150	The Life Guardsman
46151	The Royal Horse Guardsman
46152	The King's Dragoon Guardsman
46153	The Royal Dragoon
46154	The Hussar
46155	The Lancer
46156	The South Wales Borderer
46157	The Royal Artilleryman
46158	The Loyal Regiment
46159	The Royal Air Force
46160	Queen Victoria's Rifleman
46161	King's Own
46162	Queen's Westminster Rifleman
46163	Civil Service Rifleman
46164	The Artists' Rifleman
46165	The Ranger (12th London Regt.)
46166	London Rifle Brigade
46167	The Hertfordshire Regiment
46168	The Girl Guide
46169	The Boy Scout
46170*	British Legion

Total 71

" Princess " Class

4-6-2   **8P**

*Introduced 1933. Stanier L.M.S. taper boiler design.

Remainder. Introduced 1935. Development of original design with alterations to valve gear, boiler and other details.

Weight: Loco. 104 tons 10 cwt.

Pressure: 250 lb. Su.

Cyls.: (4) $16\frac{1}{4}'' \times 28''$.

Driving Wheels: 6' 6".

T.E.: 40,285 lb.

Walschaerts valve gear (inside valves operated by rocking shafts on No. 46205; remainder have four sets of valve gear). P.V.

46200*	The Princess Royal
46201*	Princess Elizabeth
46203	Princess Margaret Rose
46204	Princess Louise
46205	Princess Victoria
46206	Princess Marie Louise
46207	Princess Arthur of Connaught
46208	Princess Helena Victoria
46209	Princess Beatrice
46210	Lady Patricia
46211	Queen Maud
46212	Duchess of Kent

Total 12

" Coronation " Class

4-6-2   8P

Introduced 1937. Stanier L.M.S. enlargement of " Princess Royal " class. All except Nos. 46230–4/49–55 originally streamlined. (Streamlining removed from 1946.)

*Introduced 1947. Ivatt development with roller bearings and detail alterations.

Weight: Loco. $\begin{cases} 105 \text{ tons 5 cwt.} \\ 106 \text{ tons 8 cwt.}* \end{cases}$

Pressure: 250 lb. Su.

Cyls.: (4) $16\frac{1}{2}'' \times 28''$.

Driving Wheels: 6' 9".

T.E.: 40,000 lb.

Walschaerts valve gear and rocking shafts. P.V.

46220	Coronation
46221	Queen Elizabeth
46222	Queen Mary
46223	Princess Alice
46224	Princess Alexandra
46225	Duchess of Gloucester
46226	Duchess of Norfolk
46227	Duchess of Devonshire
46228	Duchess of Rutland
46229	Duchess of Hamilton
46230	Duchess of Buccleuch

46231	Duchess of Atholl
46232	Duchess of Montrose
46233	Duchess of Sutherland
46234	Duchess of Abercorn
46235	City of Birmingham
46236	City of Bradford
46237	City of Bristol
46238	City of Carlisle
46239	City of Chester
46240	City of Coventry
46241	City of Edinburgh
46242	City of Glasgow
46243	City of Lancaster
46244	King George VI
46245	City of London
46246	City of Manchester
46247	City of Liverpool
46248	City of Leeds
46249	City of Sheffield
46250	City of Lichfield
46251	City of Nottingham
46252	City of Leicester
46253	City of St. Albans
46254	City of Stoke-on Trent
46255	City of Hereford
46256*	Sir William A. Stanier, F.R.S.
46257*	City of Salford

Total 38

2-6-0   2

Introduced 1946. Ivatt L.M.S. taper boiler design.

Weight: Loco. 47 tons 2 cwt.

Pressure: 200 lb. Su.

Cyls.: $\begin{cases} (O) \ 16'' \ \times 24''. \\ (O) \ 16\frac{1}{2}'' \times 24''.* \end{cases}$

Driving Wheels: 5' 0".

T.E.: $\begin{cases} 17,410 \text{ lb.} \\ 18,510 \text{ lb.}* \end{cases}$

Walschaerts valve gear. P.V.

46400	46407	46414	46421
46401	46408	46415	46422
46402	46409	46416	46423
46403	46410	46417	46424
46404	46411	46418	46425
46405	46412	46419	46426
46406	46413	46420	46427

46428	46453	46478*	46503*
46429	46454	46479*	46504*
46430	46455	46480*	46505*
46431	46456	46481*	46506*
46432	46457	46482*	46507*
46433	46458	46483*	46508*
46434	46459	46484*	46509*
46435	46460	46485*	46510*
46436	46461	46486*	46511*
46437	46462	46487*	46512*
46438	46463	46488*	46513*
46439	46464	46489*	46514*
46440	46465*	46490*	46515*
46441	46466*	46491*	46516*
46442	46467*	46492*	46517*
46443	46468*	46493*	46518*
46444	46469*	46494*	46519*
46445	46470*	46495*	46520*
46446	46471*	46496*	46521*
46447	46472*	46497*	46522*
46448	46473*	46498*	46523*
46449	46474*	46499*	46524*
46450	46475*	46500*	46525*
46451	46476*	46501*	46526*
46452	46477*	46502*	46527*

Total 128

0-4-0ST   0F

Introduced 1932. Kitson design prepared to Stanier's requirements for L.M.S.

*Introduced 1953. Extended side tanks and coal space.

Weight: $\begin{cases} 33 \text{ tons } 0 \text{ cwt.} \\ 34 \text{ tons } 0 \text{ cwt.*} \end{cases}$

Pressure: 160 lb.
Cyls.: (O) $15\frac{1}{2}'' \times 30''$.
Driving Wheels: 3' 10''.
T.E.: 14,205 lb.

47000	47003	47006*	47008*
47001	47004	47007*	47009*
47002	47005*		

Total 10

0-6-0T   2F

Introduced 1928. Fowler L.M.S. short-wheelbase dock tanks.
Weight: 43 tons 12 cwt.
Pressure: 160 lb.
Cyls.: (O) $17'' \times 22''$.
Driving Wheels: 3' 11''.
T.E.: 18,400 lb.
Walschaerts valve gear.

47160	47163	47166	47168
47161	47164	47167	47169
47162	47165		

Total 10

0-4-0T   Sentinel

Geared Sentinel locos.

Introduced 1929. Single-speed locos. for S. & D.J. (taken into L.M.S. stock 1930).

Weight: 27 tons 15 cwt.
Pressure: 275 lb. Su.
Cyls.: (4) $6\frac{3}{4}'' \times 9''$.
Driving Wheels: 3' 1$\frac{1}{4}$''.
T.E.: 15,500 lb.
Poppet valves.

47190   47191

Total 2

0-6-0T   3F

Introduced 1899. Johnson large Midland design, rebuilt with Belpaire firebox from 1919; fitted with condensing apparatus for London area.

*Introduced 1899. Non-condensing locos.
Weight: 48 tons 15 cwt.
Pressure: 160 lb.
Cyls.: $18'' \times 26''$.
Driving Wheels: 4' 7''.
T.E.: 20,835 lb.

47200	47204	47209	47213
47201*	47205	47210	47214
47202	47207	47211	47216
47203	47208	47212	47217

47218	47228	47238*	47250*
47219	47229	47239*	47251
47221	47230*	47241	47254*
47223	47231*	47246*	47255*
47224	47234*	47247	47257*
47225	47235*	47248*	47259*
47226	47236*	47249	

Total 43

0-6-0T   3F

Introduced 1924. Post-grouping development of Midland design with detail alterations.

*Introduced 1929. Locos. built for S. & D.J. (taken into L.M.S. stock 1930).

†Push-and-pull fitted.

Weight: 49 tons 10 cwt.
Pressure: 160 lb.
Cyls.: 18″ × 26″.
Driving Wheels: 4′ 7″.
T.E.: 20,835 lb.

47260	47284	47308	47332
47261	47285	47309	47333
47262	47286	47310*	47334
47263	47287	47311*	47335
47264	47288	47312*	47336
47265	47289	47313*	47337
47266	47290	47314*	47338
47267	47291	47315*	47339
47268	47292	47316*	47340
47269	47293	47317	47341
47270	47294	47318	47342
47271	47295	47319	47343
47272	47296	47320	47344
47273	47297	47321	47345
47274	47298	47322	47346
47275	47299	47323	47347
47276	47300	47324	47348
47277	47301	47325	47349
47278	47302	47326	47350
47279	47303	47327	47351
47280	47304	47328	47352
47281	47305	47329	47353
47282	47306	47330	47354
47283	47307	47331	47355

47356	47403	47450	47498
47357	47404	47451	47499
47358	47405	47452	47500
47359	47406	47453	47501
47360	47407	47454	47502
47361	47408	47455	47503
47362	47409	47457	47504
47363	47410	47458	47505
47364	47411	47459	47506
47365	47412	47460	47507
47366	47413	47461	47508
47367	47414	47462	47509
47368	47415	47463	47510
47369	47416	47464	47511
47370	47417	47465	47512
47371	47418	47466	47513
47372	47419	47467	47514
47373	47420	47468	47515
47374	47421	47469	47516
47375	47422	47470	47517
47376	47423	47471	47518
47377	47424	47472	47519
47378	47425	47473	47520
47379	47426	47474	47521
47380	47427	47475	47522
47381	47428	47476	47523
47382	47429	47477†	47524
47383	47430	47478†	47525
47384	47431	47479†	47526
47385	47432	47480†	47527
47386	47433	47481†	47528
47387	47434	47482	47529
47388	47435	47483	47530
47389	47436	47484	47531
47390	47437	47485	47532
47391	47438	47486	47533
47392	47439	47487	47534
47393	47440	47488	47535
47394	47441	47489	47536
47395	47442	47490	47537
47396	47443	47491	47538
47397	47444	47492	47539
47398	47445	47493	47540
47399	47446	47494	47541
47400	47447	47495	47542
47401	47448	47496	47543
47402	47449	47497	47544

47545	47580	47614	47648
47546	47581	47615	47649
47547	47582	47616	47650
47548	47583	47618	47651
47549	47584	47619	47652
47550	47585	47620	47653
47551	47586	47621	47654
47552	47587	47622	47655†
47554	47588	47623	47656
47555	47589	47624	47657
47556	47590	47625	47658
47557	47591	47626	47659
47558	47592S	47627	47660
47559	47593	47628	47661
47560	47594	47629	47662
47561	47595	47630	47664
47562	47596	47631	47665
47563	47597	47632	47666
47564	47598	47633	47667
47565	47599	47634	47668
47566	47600	47635	47669
47567	47601	47636	47670
47568	47602	47637	47671
47569	47603	47638	47672
47570	47604	47639	47673
47571	47605	47640	47674
47572	47606	47641	47675
47573	47607	47642	47676
47574	47608	47643	47677
47575	47609	47644	47678
47576	47610	47645	47679
47577	47611	47646	47680
47578	47612	47647	47681†
47579			

Total 417

2-6-6-2T Beyer-Garratt

Introduced 1930. Development of Fowler and Beyer-Peacock, L.M.S., 1927 design, with detail alterations, later fitted with revolving coal bunkers.
Weight: 155 tons 10 cwt.
Pressure: 190 lb. Su.
Cyls. (4) 18½″ × 26″.
Driving Wheels: 5′ 3″.
T.E.: 45,620 lb.
Walschaerts valve gear. P.V.

47994 — **Total 1**

2-8-0   8F

Introduced 1935. Stanier L.M.S. taper boiler design.
Weight: Loco. 72 tons 2 cwt.
Pressure: 225 lb. Su.
Cyls.: (O) 18½″ × 28″.
Driving Wheels: 4′ 8½″.
T.E.: 32,440 lb.
Walschaerts valve gear. P.V.

48000	48063	48107	48144
48001	48064	48108	48145
48002	48065	48109	48146
48003	48067	48110	48147
48004	48069	48111	48148
48005	48070	48112	48149
48006	48073	48113	48150
48007	48074	48114	48151
48008	48075	48115	48152
48009	48076	48116	48153
48010	48077	48117	48154
48011	48078	48118	48155
48012	48079	48119	48156
48016	48080	48120	48157
48017	48081	48121	48158
48018	48082	48122	48159
48020	48083	48123	48160
48024	48084	48124	48161
48026	48085	48125	48162
48027	48088	48126	48163
48029	48089	48127	48164
48033	48090	48128	48165
48035	48092	48129	48166
48036	48093	48130	48167
48037	48094	48131	48168
48039	48095	48132	48169
48045	48096	48133	48170
48046	48097	48134	48171
48050	48098	48135	48172
48053	48099	48136	48173
48054	48100	48137	48174
48055	48101	48138	48175
48056	48102	48139	48176
48057	48103	48140	48177
48060	48104	48141	48178
48061	48105	48142	48179
48062	48106	48143	48180

48181	48248	48295	48345	48392	48439	48500	48547
48182	48249	48296	48346	48393	48440	48501	48548
48183	48250	48297	48347	48394	48441	48502	48549
48184	48251	48301	48348	48395	48442	48503	48550
48185	48252	48302	48349	48396	48443	48504	48551
48186	48253	48303	48350	48397	48444	48505	48552
48187	48254	48304	48351	48398	48445	48506	48553
48188	48255	48305	48352	48399	48446	48507	48554
48189	48256	48306	48353	48400	48447	48508	48555
48190	48257	48307	48354	48401	48448	48509	48556
48191	48258	48308	48355	48402	48449	48510	48557
48192	48259	48309	48356	48403	48450	48511	48558
48193	48260	48310	48357	48404	48451	48512	48559
48194	48261	48311	48358	48405	48452	48513	48600
48195	48262	48312	48359	48406	48453	48514	48601
48196	48263	48313	48360	48407	48454	48515	48602
48197	48264	48314	48361	48408	48455	48516	48603
48198	48265	48315	48362	48409	48456	48517	48604
48199	48266	48316	48363	48410	48457	48518	48605
48200	48267	48317	48364	48411	48458	48519	48606
48201	48268	48318	48365	48412	48459	48520	48607
48202	48269	48319	48366	48413	48460	48521	48608
48203	48270	48320	48367	48414	48461	48522	48609
48204	48271	48321	48368	48415	48462	48523	48610
48205	48272	48322	48369	48416	48463	48524	48611
48206	48273	48323	48370	48417	48464	48525	48612
48207	48274	48324	48371	48418	48465	48526	48613
48208	48275	48325	48372	48419	48466	48527	48614
48209	48276	48326	48373	48420	48467	48528	48615
48210	48277	48327	48374	48421	48468	48529	48616
48211	48278	48328	48375	48422	48469	48530	48617
48212	48279	48329	48376	48423	48470	48531	48618
48213	48280	48330	48377	48424	48471	48532	48619
48214	48281	48331	48378	48425	48472	48533	48620
48215	48282	48332	48379	48426	48473	48534	48621
48216	48283	48333	48380	48427	48474	48535	48622
48217	48284	48334	48381	48428	48475	48536	48623
48218	48285	48335	48382	48429	48476	48537	48624
48219	48286	48336	48383	48430	48477	48538	48625
48220	48287	48337	48384	48431	48478	48539	48626
48221	48288	48338	48385	48432	48479	48540	48627
48222	48289	48339	48386	48433	48490	48541	48628
48223	48290	48340	48387	48434	48491	48542	48629
48224	48291	48341	48388	48435	48492	48543	48630
48225	48292	48342	48389	48436	48493	48544	48631
48246	48293	48343	48390	48437	48494	48545	48632
48247	48294	48344	48391	48438	48495	48546	48633

147

48634	48670	48706	48742	48895	49081	49160	49301
48635	48671	48707	48743	48898	49082	49164	49304
48636	48672	48708	48744	48905	49087	49173	49306
48637	48673	48709	48745	48915	49093	49177	49308
48638	48674	48710	48746	48921	49094	49180	49310
48639	48675	48711	48747	48922	49099	49181	49311
48640	48676	48712	48748	48926	49104	49191	49313
48641	48677	48713	48749	48927	49105	49196	49314
48642	48678	48714	48750	48930	49106	49198	49315
48643	48679	48715	48751	48932	49109	49199	49321
48644	48680	48716	48752	48942	49112	49200	49323
48645	48681	48717	48753	48943	49113	49203	49327
48646	48682	48718	48754	48945	49114	49209	49328
48647	48683	48719	48755	48950	49115	49210	49330
48648	48684	48720	48756	48951	49116	49216	49335
48649	48685	48721	48757	48953	49117	49224	49340
48650	48686	48722	48758	48964	49119	49226	49342
48651	48687	48723	48759	49002	49120	49228	49343
48652	48688	48724	48760	49007	49121	49229	49344
48653	48689	48725	48761	49008	49122	49234	49348
48654	48690	48726	48762	49009	49125	49240	49350
48655	48691	48727	48763	49010	49126	49243	49352
48656	48692	48728	48764	49018	49129	49245	49355
48657	48693	48729	48765	49020	49130	49246	49357
48658	48694	48730	48766	49021	49132	49249	49358
48659	48695	48731	48767	49023	49134	49252	49361
48660	48696	48732	48768	49025	49137	49260	49366
48661	48697	48733	48769	49027	49139	49262	49368
48662	48698	48734	48770	49034	49141	49266	49373
48663	48699	48735	48771	49037	49142	49267	49375
48664	48700	48736	48772	49044	49143	49268	49376
48665	48701	48737	48773	49045	49144	49270	49377
48666	48702	48738	48774	49048	49146	49275	49378
48667	48703	48739	48775	49049	49147	49276	49381
48668	48704	48740		49061	49149	49277	49382
48669	48705	48741		49063	49150	49278	49386
				49064	49153	49281	49387
			Total 666	49070	49154	49287	49391
				49077	49155	49288	49392
				49078	49157	49289	49394
				49079	49158	49293	

0-8-0   **7F**

Introduced 1936. L.N.W. G2a Class.
Bowen-Cooke G1 superheated design
of 1912, rebuilt with G2 boiler and
Belpaire firebox.
Weight: Loco. 62 tons 0 cwt.
Pressure: 175 lb. Su.
Cyls.: $20\frac{1}{2}'' \times 24''$.
Driving Wheels: 4' $5\frac{1}{2}''$.
T.E.: 28,045 lb.
Joy valve gear.   P.V.

Total 163

0-8-0   **7F**

Introduced 1921. Development of
L.N.W. G2 Class. Bowen-Cooke G1
superheated design of 1912 with

higher pressure boiler. Many later rebuilt with Belpaire firebox.
Weight: Loco. 62 tons 0 cwt.
Pressure: 175 lb. Su.
Cyls.: $20\frac{1}{2}'' \times 24''$.
Driving Wheels: 4' 5½".
T.E.: 28,045 lb.
Joy valve gear.   P.V.

49395	49410	49425	49440
49396	49411	49426	49441
49397	49412	49427	49442
49398	49413	49428	49443
49399	49414	49429	49444
49400	49415	49430	49445
49401	49416	49431	49446
49402	49417	49432	49447
49403	49418	49433	49448
49404	49419	49434	49449
49405	49420	49435	49450
49406	49421	49436	49451
49407	49422	49437	49452
49408	49423	49438	49453
49409	49424	49439	49454

Total 60

0-8-0   7F

Introduced 1929. Fowler L.M.S. design, developed from L.N.W. G2.
Weight: Loco. 60 tons 15 cwt.
Pressure: 200 lb. Su.
Cyls.: $19\frac{1}{2}'' \times 26''$.
Driving Wheels: 4' 8½".
T.E.: 29,745 lb.
Walschaerts valve gear.   P.V.

49505	49544	49598	49640
49508	49578	49618	49662
49509	49582	49624	49667
49511	49586	49627	49668
49515	49592	49637	49674

Total 20

2-4-2T   2P

Introduced 1889. Aspinall L. & Y. Class 5 with 2 tons coal capacity.
*Introduced 1890. Locos. built or rebuilt with smaller cylinders.
†Introduced 1898. Locos. with longer tanks and 4 tons coal capacity.

¶Introduced 1910. Locos. rebuilt with Belpaire firebox and extended smoke-box.
Weight: $\begin{cases} 55 \text{ tons } 19 \text{ cwt.} \\ 55 \text{ tons } 19 \text{ cwt.*} \\ 59 \text{ tons } 3 \text{ cwt.†¶} \end{cases}$
Pressure: 180 lb.
Cyls.: $\begin{cases} 17\frac{1}{2}'' \times 26''.* \\ 18'' \times 26''. \text{ (Remainder)} \end{cases}$
Driving Wheels: 5' 8".
T.E.: $\begin{cases} 18,360 \text{ lb.*} \\ 18,955 \text{ lb. (Remainder)} \end{cases}$
Joy valve gear.

50643*	50705	50757	50829†¶
50644	50712	50777¶	50831†
50646	50721	50781	50850†¶
50647	50725	50795*	50855*†
50660	50746	50818	50865*†

Total 20

0-4-0ST   0F

Introduced 1891. Aspinall L. & Y. Class 21.
Weight: 21 tons 5 cwt.
Pressure: 160 lb.
Cyls.: (O) $13'' \times 18''$.
Driving Wheels: 3' 0⅜".
T.E.: 11,335 lb.

51204	51221	51231	51244
51206	51222	51232	51246
51207	51227	51235	51253
51217	51229	51237	
51218	51230	51241	

Total 18

0-6-0ST   2F

Introduced 1891. Aspinall rebuild of L. & Y. Barton Wright Class 23 0-6-0. Originally introduced 1877.
Weight: 43 tons 17 cwt.
Pressure: 140 lb.
Cyls.: $17\frac{1}{2}'' \times 26''$.
Driving Wheels: 4' 6".
T.E.: 17,545 lb.

51304S	51319	51336	51368S
51305S	51321	51343	51371
51316	51324S	51358	51394S

51397	51419	51445	51486
51404	51423	51446S	51496
51408	51424	51453	51497
51412S	51429S	51457	51498
51413	51441	51458	51512
51415	51444S	51484	51524

Total 36

0-6-0T 1F

Introduced 1897. Aspinall L. & Y. Class 24 dock tanks.
Weight: 50 tons 0 cwt.
Pressure: 140 lb.
Cyls.: (O) 17″ × 24″.
Driving Wheels: 4′ 0″.
T.E.: 15,285 lb.
Allan straight link valve gear.

51537   51544   51546

Total 3

0-6-0 2F

Introduced 1887. Barton Wright L. & Y. Class 25.
Weight: Loco. 39 tons 1 cwt.
Pressure: 140 lb.
Cyls.: 17½″ × 26″.
Driving Wheels: 4′ 6″.
T.E.: 17,545 lb.

52044   **Total 1**

0-6-0 3F

Introduced 1889. Aspinall L. & Y. Class 27. Nos. 52515–27 built superheated with roundtop firebox and extended smokebox, later rebuilt with saturated boiler and short smokebox.
*Introduced 1911. Rebuilt with Belpaire firebox and extended smokebox.

Weight: Loco. $\begin{cases} 42 \text{ tons } 3 \text{ cwt.} \\ 43 \text{ tons } 11 \text{ cwt.}^* \end{cases}$

Pressure: 180 lb.
Cyls.: 18″ × 26″.

Driving Wheels: $\begin{cases} 5' \ 1''. \\ 5' \ 1''.^* \end{cases}$

T.E.: $\begin{cases} 21,130 \text{ lb.} \\ 21,130 \text{ lb.}^* \end{cases}$

Joy valve gear.

52089	52095	52119	52121
52093S	52108	52120	52129

52133	52237	52348	52432
52135*	52240	52350	52438*
52139	52244	52351	52441S
52140*	52248	52355	52443
52141	52252	52356	52445*
52154*	52260	52360*	52452
52159	52268	52366	52455
52161*	52269	52378	52456
52162*S	52270	52387	52458
52171	52271	52388	52459S
52179	52275	52389	52461
52182	52278	52393	52464S
52183	52289	52399	52466
52201*	52290	52400*	52515
52207S	52305	52410	52517S
52212S	52311	52411	52523
52216	52312*S	52413*	52526
52218S	52319*	52415	52527
52225	52322	52427	
52230	52341	52429	
52232	52345S	52431*	

Total 89

2-8-0 7F

Introduced 1914. Fowler design for S. & D.J.
(All taken into L.M.S. stock, 1930.)
Weight: Loco. 64 tons 15 cwt.
Pressure: 190 lb. Su.
Cyls.: (O) 21″ × 28″.
Driving Wheels: 4′ 8½″.
T.E.: 35,295 lb.
Walschaerts valve gear.   P.V.

53800	53803	53806	53809
53801	53804	53807	53810
53802	53805	53808	

Total 11

4-4-0 3P

Introduced 1915. Superheated rebuild of McIntosh Caledonian "Dunalastair IV" or "140" class (originally introduced 1904).
Weight: Loco. 61 tons 5 cwt.
Pressure: 180 lb. Su.
Cyls.: 20½″ × 26″.
Driving Wheels: 6′ 6″.
T.E.: 20,915 lb.   P.V.

54439   **Total 1**

4-4-0   3P

Introduced 1916. Pickersgill Caledonian
" 113 " and " 928 " classes.
Weight: Loco. 61 tons 5 cwt.
Pressure: 180 lb. Su.
Cyls.: 20″ × 26″.
Driving Wheels: 6′ 6″.
T.E.: 20,400 lb.
P.V.

54461	54465	54469	54473
54462	54466	54470	54474
54463	54467	54471	54475
54464	54468	54472	54476

Total 16

4-4-0   3P

Introduced 1920. Pickersgill Caledonian
" 72 " class.
Weight: Loco. 61 tons 5 cwt.
Pressure: 180 lb. Su.
Cyls.: 20½″ × 26″.
Driving Wheels: 6′ 6″.
T.E.: 21,435 lb.
P.V.

54477	54486	54494	54502
54478	54487	54495	54503
54479	54488	54496	54504
54480	54489	54497	54505
54482	54490	54498	54506
54483	54491	54499	54507
54484	54492	54500	54508
54485	54493	54501	

Total 31

0-4-4T   2P

*Introduced 1895. McIntosh Cale-
donian " 19 " class, with railed coal
bunker.
Remainder. Introduced 1897. McIntosh
" 92 " class, developed from " 29 "
class with larger tanks and highsided
coal bunker (both classes originally
fitted for condensing on Glasgow
Central Low Level lines).
Weight: $\begin{cases} 53 \text{ tons } 16 \text{ cwt.*} \\ 53 \text{ tons } 19 \text{ cwt.} \end{cases}$

Pressure: 180 lb.
Cyls.: 18″ × 26″.
Driving Wheels: 5′ 9″.
T.E.: 18,680 lb.

55124*   55126   55141

Total 3

0-4-4T   2P

Introduced 1900. McIntosh Caledonian
" 439 " or " Standard Passenger "
class.
*Introduced 1915. Pickersgill locos.
with detail alterations.
Weight: $\begin{cases} 53 \text{ tons } 19 \text{ cwt.} \\ 57 \text{ tons } 12 \text{ cwt.*} \end{cases}$

Pressure: 180 lb.
Cyls.: 18″ × 26″.
Driving Wheels: 5′ 9″.
T.E.: 18,680 lb.

55160	55199	55213	55225
55164	55200	55214	55226
55165	55201	55215	55227*
55167	55202	55216	55228*
55169	55203	55217	55229*
55173	55204	55218	55230*
55176	55206	55219	55231*
55178	55207	55220	55232*
55182	55208	55221	55233*
55185	55209	55222	55234*
55189	55210	55223	55235*
55195	55211	55224	55236*
55198	55212		

Total 50

0-4-4T   2P

Introduced 1922. Pickersgill Caledonian
" 431 " class (developed from " 439 "
class) with cast-iron front buffer
beam for banking.
Weight: 57 tons 17 cwt.
Pressure: 180 lb.
Cyls.: 18¼″ × 26″.
Driving Wheels: 5′ 9″.
T.E.: 19,200 lb.

55237   55238   55239   55240

Total 4

0-4-4T   2P

Introduced 1925. Post-Grouping development of Caledonian " 439 " class.
Weight: 59 tons 12 cwt.
Pressure: 180 lb.
Cyls.: 18¼" × 26".
Driving Wheels: 5' 9".
T.E.: 19,200 lb.

55260	55263	55266	55268
55261	55264	55267	55269
55262	55265		

Total 10

0-4-0ST   0F

Introduced 1885. Drummond and McIntosh Caledonian " Pugs."
Weight: 27 tons 7 cwt.
Pressure: 160 lb.
Cyls.: (O) 14" × 20".
Driving Wheels: 3' 8".
T.E.: 12,115 lb.

56011	56029	56032**S**	56038
56025**S**	56030	56035	56039
56027**S**	56031		

Total 10

0-6-0T   2F

Introduced 1911. McIntosh Caledonian dock shunters, " 498 " class.
Weight: 47 tons 15 cwt.
Pressure: 160 lb.
Cyls.: (O) 17" × 20".
Driving Wheels: 4' 0".
T.E.: 18,015 lb.

56151	56157	56163	56169
56152	56158	56164	56170
56153	56159	56165	56171
56154	56160	56166	56172
56155	56161	56167	56173
56156	56162	56168	

Total 23

0-6-0T   3F

Introduced 1895. McIntosh Caledonian " 29 " and " 782 " classes (56232–9 originally condensing).
Weight: 47 tons 15 cwt.
Pressure: 160 lb.
Cyls.: 18" × 26".
Driving Wheels: 4' 6".
T.E.: 21,215 lb.

56232	56274	56308	56341
56235	56275	56309	56343
56236	56277	56310	56344
56238	56278	56311	56345
56239	56279	56312	56347
56240	56281	56313	56348
56241	56282	56314	56349
56242	56283	56315	56352
56244	56284	56316	56353
56245	56285	56318	56354
56246	56286	56321	56356
56247	56287	56322	56359
56251	56288	56323	56360
56252	56289	56324	56361
56253	56290	56325	56362
56254	56291	56326	56363
56255	56292	56327	56364
56256	56293	56328	56365
56259	56295	56330	56367
56260	56296	56331	56368
56262	56298	56332	56370
56264	56300	56333	56371
56265	56301	56335	56372
56266	56302	56336	56373
56267	56304	56337	56374
56269	56305	56338	56375
56272	56306	56340	56376

Total 108

0-6-0   2F

Introduced 1883. Drummond Caledonian " Standard Goods "; later additions by Lambie and McIntosh.
*Some rebuilt with L.M.S. boiler.
Weight: Loco. { 41 tons 6 cwt.
               42 tons 4 cwt.*
Pressure: 180 lb.
Cyls.: 18" × 26".
Driving Wheels: 5' 0".
T.E.: 21,480 lb.

57232	57243	57253	57264
57233	57244	57254	57265
57236	57245	57256	57266
57237	57246	57257	57267
57238	57247	57258	57268
57239	57249	57259	57269
57240	57250	57261	57270
57241	57251	57262	
57242	57252	57263	

57271	57325	57365	57419
57273	57326	57366	57424
57274	57328	57367	57426
57275	57329	57368	57429
57276	57331	57369	57431
57278	57335	57370	57432
57279	57336	57373	57434
57284	57338	57375	57435
57285	57339	57377	57436
57287	57340	57378	57437
57288	57341	57383	57441
57291	57345	57384	57443
57292	57347	57385	57444
57295	57348	57386	57445
57296	57349	57389	57446
57299	57350	57392	57447
57300	57353	57396	57448
57302	57354	57398	57451
57303	57355	57404	57461
57307	57356	57405	57462
57309	57357	57407	57463
57311	57359	57411	57465
57314	57360	57413	57470
57317	57361	57414	57472
57319	57362	57416	57473
57321	57363	57417	
57324	57364	57418	

Total 140

57596	57609	57622	57635
57597	57611	57623	57637
57599	57612	57625	57638
57600	57613	57626	57640
57601	57614	57627	57642
57602	57615	57628	57643
57603	57617	57630	57644
57604	57618	57631	57645
57605	57619	57632	
57607	57620	57633	
57608	57621	57634	

Total 77

0-6-0   3F

Introduced 1918. Pickersgill Caledonian "294" class (superheated) and "670" classes.
Weight: Loco. 50 tons 13 cwt.
Pressure: 180 lb. Su.
Cyls.: $18\frac{1}{2}'' \times 26''$.
Driving Wheels: 5' 0".
T.E.: 22,690 lb.
P.V.

57650	57661	57670	57682
57651	57663	57671	57684
57652	57665	57672	57686
57653	57666	57673	57688
57654	57667	57674	57689
57655	57668	57679	57690
57658	57669	57681	57691
57659			

Total 29

0-6-0   3F

Introduced 1899. McIntosh Caledonian "812" (Nos. 57550-57623) and "652" (remainder) classes.
Weight: Loco. 45 tons 14 cwt.
Pressure: 180 lb.
Cyls.: $18\frac{1}{2}'' \times 26''$.
Driving Wheels: 5' 0".
T.E.: 22,690 lb.

57550	57560	57571	57585
57552	57562	57572	57586
57553	57563	57575	57587
57554	57564	57576	57590
57555	57565	57577	57591
57556	57566	57579	57592
57557	57568	57580	57593
57558	57569	57581	57594
57559	57570	57583	57595

0-4-4T   1P

*Introduced 1889. Johnson Midland design of 1881 with larger cylinders and higher boiler pressure. All rebuilt with Belpaire firebox.
†Introduced 1895. Final Johnson 0-4-4T design, with higher-pitched boiler and larger tanks, later rebuilt with Belpaire firebox.
Push-and-pull fitted.
Weight: 53 tons 4 cwt.
Pressure: 150 lb.
Cyls.: $\begin{cases} 18'' \times 24''.* \\ 17'' \times 24''.† \end{cases}$
Driving Wheels: 5' 4".
T.E.: $\begin{cases} 18,225 \text{ lb.}* \\ 16,255 \text{ lb.}† \end{cases}$

58065* 58066* 58085† 58086†

Total 4

0-6-0   2F

*Introduced 1875. Johnson Midland 4' 11" design with round top firebox.
†Introduced 1917. Johnson 4' 11" design rebuilt with Belpaire firebox.
§Introduced 1917. Johnson Midland 5' 3" design rebuilt with Belpaire firebox.
Weight: Loco. Various—
    37 tons 12 cwt. to 40 tons 3 cwt.
Pressure: 160 lb.
Cyls.: 18" × 26".

Driving Wheels: $\begin{cases} 4' \ 11".* \\ 4' \ 11".† \\ 5' \ 3".§ \end{cases}$

T.E.: $\begin{cases} 19,420 \text{ lb.*} \\ 19,420 \text{ lb.†} \\ 18,185 \text{ lb.§} \end{cases}$

58115†	58153†	58183†	58221§
58116†	58157†	58185†	58225§
58118†	58158†	58186†	58228§
58119†	58160†	58190§	58246*
58120†	58163†	58191§	58260§
58122†	58165†	58192§	58261§
58123†	58166†	58196§	58271§
58124†	58167†	58197§	58279§
58128†	58168†	58198§	58281§
58130†	58169†	58199§	58283§
58131†	58170†	58204§	58287§
58132†	58171†	58209§	58291§
58135†	58173†	58213§	58293§
58137†	58174†	58214§	58295§
58138†	58175†	58215§	58298§
58143†	58177†	58217§	58305§
58144†	58178†	58218§	58308§
58146†	58181†	58219§	
58148†	58182†	58220§	

Total 74

0-6-0T   2F

Introduced 1879. Park North London design.
Weight: 45 tons 10 cwt.
Pressure: 160 lb.
Cyls.: (O) 17" × 24".
Driving Wheels: 4' 4".
T.E.: 18,140 lb.

    58850   58857

Total 2

0-6-2T   2F

Introduced 1882. Webb L.N.W. " Coal Tanks."
Weight: 43 tons 15 cwt.
Pressure: 150 lb.
Cyls.: 17" × 24".
Driving Wheels: 4' 5½".
T.E.: 16,530 lb.

58926   **Total 1**

4-2-2

Introduced 1886. Neilson & Co. design for the Caledonian Railway incorporating Drummond details.
Weight: Engine and Tender: 75 tons.
Pressure: 150 lb.
Cyls.: 18" × 26".
Driving Wheels: 7' 0".
T.E.: 12,785 lb.

123   **Total 1**

(Withdrawn as L.M.S. No. 14010 in 1935. Returned to service 1958 for hauling enthusiasts' specials.

SERVICE LOCOS.

0-4-0   Diesel

Introduced 1936. Messrs. Fowler diesel.
Weight: 2 tons.

E.D.1	E.D.4	E.D.6
E.D.2	E.D.5	E.D.7
E.D.3		

0-6-0ST   2F

Introduced 1870. Webb version of Ramsbottom " Special Tank."
Weight: 34 tons 10 cwt.
Pressure: 140 lb.
Cyls.: 17" × 24".
Driving Wheels: 4' 5½".
T.E.: 17,005 lb.

C.D.3 Wolverton Carriage Works
C.D.6   "   "   "
C.D.7   "   "   "
C.D.8 *Earlestown*, Wolverton C.W.

CHIEF MECHANICAL ENGINEERS

BRITISH RAILWAYS (L.M. Region)

H. G. Ivatt   ...   1948–1951

L.M.S.

George Hughes	...	...	1923–1925	Sir William Stanier	... 1932–1944
Sir Henry Fowler	...		1925–1931	Charles E. Fairburn	... 1944–1945
E. H. J. Lemon				H. G. Ivatt ...	 1945–1947
(Sir Ernest Lemon)		1931–1932			

LOCOMOTIVE SUPERINTENDENTS AND C.M.E.'S—L.M.S. CONSTITUENT COMPANIES

CALEDONIAN RAILWAY

Robert Sinclair	
(First loco. engineer)*	1847–1856
Benjamin Connor ...	... 1856–1876
George Brittain	... 1876–1882
Dugald Drummond	... 1882–1890
Hugh Smellie	... 1890
J. Lambie ...	 1890–1895
J. F. McIntosh ...	... 1895–1914
William Pickersgill	... 1914–1923

FURNESS RAILWAY

R. Mason ...	... 1890–1897
W. F. Pettigrew ...	... 1897–1918
D. J. Rutherford ...	... 1918–1923

GLASGOW AND SOUTH WESTERN RAILWAY

Patrick Stirling	... 1853–1866
James Stirling	... 1866–1878
Hugh Smellie	... 1878–1890
James Manson	... 1890–1912
Peter Drummond	... 1912–1918
R. H. Whitelegg ...	... 1918–1923

HIGHLAND RAILWAY

William Stroudley	
(First loco. engineer) ...	1866–1869
David Jones ...	... 1869–1896
Peter Drummond ...	... 1896–1911
F. G. Smith...	 1912–1915
C. Cumming ...	... 1915–1923

L. & Y.R.

Sir John Hawkshaw (Consultant),*	
Hurst and Jenkins successively to 1868	
W. Hurst ...	... 1868–1876
W. Barton Wright	... 1876–1886
John A. F. Aspinall	... 1886–1899
H. A. Hoy ...	... 1899–1904
George Hughes ...	... 1904–1921
The L. & Y. amalgamated with L.N.W.R. as from January 1st, 1922.	

L.N.W.R.

Francis Trevithick and J. E. McConnell, first loco. engineers, 1846, with Alexander Allan largely responsible for design at Crewe.*	
John Ramsbottom...	... 1857–1871
Francis William Webb	... 1871–1903
George Whale	... 1903–1909
Charles John Bowen-Cooke	... 1909–1920
Capt. Hewitt Pearson Montague Beames	... 1920–1921
George Hughes ...	... 1922

L.T. & S.R.

Thomas Whitelegg	... 1880–1910
Robert Harben Whitelegg	1910–1912
(L.T. & S.R. absorbed by M.R., control of locos. transferred to Derby as from August, 1912.)	

* Exclusive of previous service with constituent company.

LOCOMOTIVE SUPERINTENDENTS
AND C.M.E.'S (continued)

MARYPORT & CARLISLE

Hugh Smellie	... ...	1870–1878
J. Campbell	... ...	1878–
William Coulthard	... *	–1904
J. B. Adamson	... ...	1904–1923

MIDLAND RAILWAY

Matthew Kirtley (First loco. engineer) ...	1844–1873
Samuel Waite Johnson	...	1873–1903
Richard Mountford Deeley	1903–1909
Henry Fowler	... ...	1909–1923

SOMERSET AND DORSET
JOINT RAILWAY

Until leased by Mid. and L. & S. W. (as from 1st November, 1875) locomotives were bought from outside builders, principally George England of Hatcham Iron Works, S.E. After the above date, Derby and its various Loco. Supts. and C.M.E.'s have acted for S. & D.J. aided by a resident Loco. Supt. stationed at Highbridge Works.

NORTH STAFFORDSHIRE
RAILWAY

L. Clare	... ...	1876–1882
L. Longbottom	... ...	1882–1902
J. H. Adams	... ...	1902–1915
J. A. Hookham	... ...	1915–1923

W. Angus was Loco. Supt. at Stoke prior to 1876. No earlier records can be traced.

WIRRAL

Eric G. Barker	... ...	1892–1902
T. B. Hunter	... ...	1903–1923

Barker of the Wirral Railway is noteworthy for originating the 4-4-4 tank type in this country (1896).

NORTH LONDON RAILWAY

(Worked by L. & N.W. by agreement dated December, 1908.)

William Adams	... ...	1853–1873
J. C. Park	... ...	1873–1893
Henry J. Pryce	... ...	1893–1908

* Date of actual entry into office not known.

HISTORIC LOCOMOTIVES PRESERVED IN STORE

Type	Originating Company	Pre-Grouping No.	L.M.S. No.	Name	Place of Preservation
4-2-2	M.R.	118	(673)	—	Derby
2-4-0	M.R.	158A	—	—	Derby
*4-4-0	M.R.	(1000)	(1000)	—	Crewe
4-4-2T	L.T. & S.	80	(2148)	Thundersley	Derby
2-2-2	L.N.W.	(49)	—	Columbine	York Museum
2-2-2	L.N.W.	3020	—	Cornwall	Crewe
2-4-0	L.N.W.	790	(5031)	Hardwicke	Crewe
0-4-0ST	L.N.W.	1439	—	—	Crewe
†0-4-0T	L.N.W.	—	—	Pet	Crewe
0-4-0	F.R.	3	—	Coppernob	Horwich
0-4-2	Liverpool & Manchester	—	—	Lion	Crewe
4-6-0	H.R.	103	(17916)	—	St. Rollox
‡4-4-0	H.R.	(2)	(14398)	Ben Alder	Boat of Garten

The unbracketed numbers are the ones at present carried by the locos.
* Present number 41000.
† 18 in. gauge works shunter.
‡ Present number 54398.

Class 2F 0-6-2T No. 58926 [J. D. Mills

Class 2F 0-6-0ST No. C.D.8 *Earlestown* [B. K. B. Green

Class 2F 0-6-0T No. 58857 [B. E. Morrison

Class 0F 0-4-0ST No. 47001 [B. E. Morrison

Class 2F 0-6-0ST No. 51445 [C. P. Boocock

Class 0F 0-4-0ST No. 51221   [T. K. Widd

Class 0F 0-4-0ST No. 56035   [P. H. Groom

Class WD 2-10-0 No. 90773   [P. H. Groom

Former Caledonian 4-2-2 No. 123 now restored for use on enthusiasts' specials.

[W. S. Sellar

Class A3 4-6-2 No. 60082 *Neil Gow* [*P. Ransome-Wallis*

Class A4 4-6-2 No. 60005 *Sir Charles Newton* [*J. F. Aylard*

Class V2 2-6-2 No. 60971 [*John Robertson*

Class A2 4-6-2 No. 60527 *Sun Chariot*   [*David A. Anderson*

Class A2/2 4-6-2 No. 60503 *Lord President*   [*P. Ransome-Wallis*

Class A2/3 4-6-2 No. 60522 *Straight Deal*   [*P. H. Wells*

Class A1 4-6-2 No. 60121 *Silurian*

[*P. H. Groom*

Class B16/1 4-6-0 No. 61471

[*P. H. Groom*

Class B16/3 4-6-0 No. 61444

[*B. K. B. Green*

Class B17/6 4-6-0 No. 61654 *Sunderland*   [B. K. B. Green

Class B2 4-6-0 No. 61615 *Culford Hall*   [G. Wheeler

Class D49/2 4-4-0 No. 62743 *The Cleveland*   [P. H. Groom

NUMERICAL LIST OF ENGINES

The Code given in smaller bold type at the head of each class,
e.g. "4MT" denotes its British Railways power classification.

The numbers of locomotives in service have been checked to March 8th, 1958.

4-6-2   8P6F   Class A4

Introduced 1935. Gresley streamlined
design with corridor tender (except
those marked †).
*Inside cylinder reduced to 17".
‡Kylchap blast pipe and double
chimney.

Weight: Loco.   102 tons 19 cwt.
Tender { 64 tons 19 cwt.
{ 60 tons 7 cwt.†

Pressure: 250 lb. Su.

Cyls.: { (3) 18¼" × 26".
{ (2) 18¼" × 26" (1) 17" × 26".*

Driving Wheels: 6' 8".

T.E.: { 35,455 lb.
{ 33,616 lb.*

Walschaerts valve gear and derived
motion. P.V.

60001† Sir Ronald Matthews
60002†‡Sir Murrough Wilson
60003‡ Andrew K. McCosh
60004‡ William Whitelaw
60005†‡Sir Charles Newton
60006†‡Sir Ralph Wedgwood
60007‡ Sir Nigel Gresley
60008† Dwight D. Eisenhower
60009 Union of South Africa
60010‡ Dominion of Canada
60011 Empire of India
60012* Commonwealth of
Australia
60013 Dominion of New
Zealand
60014‡ Silver Link
60015‡ Quicksilver
60016†‡Silver King
60017‡ Silver Fox
60018†‡Sparrow Hawk
60019† Bittern
60020*†‡Guillemot
60021 Wild Swan
60022‡ Mallard
60023† Golden Eagle
60024 Kingfisher
60025 Falcon

60026†‡Miles Beevor
60027 Merlin
60028‡ Walter K. Whigham
60029 Woodcock
60030 Golden Fleece
60031* Golden Plover
60032 Gannet
60033‡ Seagull
60034‡ Lord Faringdon

Total 34

4-6-2   7P6F   Class A3

Introduced 1927. Development of
Gresley G.N. 180 lb. Pacific (introduced 1922, L.N.E.R. A1, later A10)
with 220 lb. pressure (prototype and
others rebuilt from A10). Some have
G.N.-type tender† with coal rails,
remainder L.N.E.R. pattern.
*Kylchap blast pipe and double chimney.

Weight: Loco.   96 tons 5 cwt.
Tender { 56 tons 6 cwt.†
{ 57 tons 18 cwt.

Pressure: 220 lb. Su.

Cyls.: (3) 19" × 26".

Driving Wheels: 6' 8".

T.E.: 32,910 lb.

Walschaerts valve gear and derived
motion. P.V.

60035 Windsor Lad
60036 Colombo
60037 Hyperion
60038 Firdaussi
60039 Sandwich
60040 Cameronian
60041 Salmon Trout
60042 Singapore
60043 Brown Jack
60044 Melton
60045 Lemberg
60046 Diamond Jubilee
60047 Donovan
60048 Doncaster
60049 Galtee More
60050 Persimmon

60051	Blink Bonny
60052	Prince Palatine
60053	Sansovino
60054	Prince of Wales
60055	Woolwinder
60056	Centenary
60057	Ormonde
60058	Blair Athol
60059	Tracery
60060	The Tetrarch
60061	Pretty Polly
60062	Minoru
60063	Isinglass
60064	Tagalie
60065	Knight of Thistle
60066	Merry Hampton
60067	Ladas
60068	Sir Visto
60069	Sceptre
60070	Gladiateur
60071	Tranquil
60072	Sunstar
60073	St. Gatien
60074	Harvester
60075	St. Frusquin
60076	Galopin
60077	The White Knight
60078	Night Hawk
60079	Bayardo
60080	Dick Turpin
60081	Shotover
60082	Neil Gow
60083	Sir Hugo
60084	Trigo
60085	Manna
60086	Gainsborough
60087	Blenheim
60088	Book Law
60089	Felstead
60090	Grand Parade
60091	Captain Cuttle
60092	Fairway
60093	Coronach
60094	Colorado
60095	Flamingo
60096	Papyrus
60097*	Humorist

60098	Spion Kop
60099	Call Boy
60100	Spearmint
60101	Cicero
60102	Sir Frederick Banbury
60103	Flying Scotsman
60104	Solario
60105	Victor Wild
60106	Flying Fox
60107	Royal Lancer
60108	Gay Crusader
60109	Hermit
60110	Robert the Devil
60111	Enterprise
60112	St. Simon

Total 78

4-6-2   8P6F   Class A1

A1/1* Introduced 1945. Thompson rebuild of A10.
A1 Peppercorn development of A1/1 for new construction.
A1† Fitted with roller bearings.
Weight: Loco. $\begin{cases} 101 \text{ tons.*} \\ 104 \text{ tons 2 cwt.} \end{cases}$
         Tender 60 tons 7 cwt.
Pressure: 250 lb. Su.
Cyls.: (3) 19″ × 26″.
Driving Wheels: 6′ 8″.
T.E.: 37,400 lb.
Walschaerts valve gear. P.V.

60113*	Great Northern
60114	W. P. Allen
60115	Meg Merrilies
60116	Hal o' the Wynd
60117	Bois Roussel
60118	Archibald Sturrock
60119	Patrick Stirling
60120	Kittiwake
60121	Silurian
60122	Curlew
60123	H. A. Ivatt
60124	Kenilworth
60125	Scottish Union
60126	Sir Vincent Raven
60127	Wilson Worsdell
60128	Bongrace
60129	Guy Mannering
60130	Kestrel

60131	Osprey
60132	Marmion
60133	Pommern
60134	Foxhunter
60135	Madge Wildfire
60136	Alcazar
60137	Redgauntlet
60138	Boswell
60139	Sea Eagle
60140	Balmoral
60141	Abbotsford
60142	Edward Fletcher
60143	Sir Walter Scott
60144	King's Courier
60145	Saint Mungo
60146	Peregrine
60147	North Eastern
60148	Aboyeur
60149	Amadis
60150	Willbrook
60151	Midlothian
60152	Holyrood
60153†	Flamboyant
60154†	Bon Accord
60155†	Borderer
60156†	Great Central
60157†	Great Eastern
60158	Aberdonian
60159	Bonnie Dundee
60160	Auld Reekie
60161	North British
60162	Saint Johnstoun

Total 50

4-6-2 $\frac{8P7F}{(A2/1: 7P6F)}$ Class A2

A2/2* Introduced 1943. Original Thompson Pacific, rebuilt from Gresley Class P2 2-8-2 (introduced 1934).
Weight: Loco. 101 tons 10 cwt.
Pressure: 225 lb. Su.
Cyls.: (3) 20″ × 26″.
Driving Wheels: 6′ 2″.
T.E.: 40,320 lb.

A2/1† Introduced 1944. Development of Class A2/2, incorporating Class V2 2-6-2 boiler.
Weight: Loco. 98 tons.
Pressure: 225 lb. Su.
Cyls.: (3) 19″ × 26″.
Driving Wheels: 6′ 2″.   T.E.: 36,385 lb.

A2/3‡ Introduced 1946. Development of Class A2/2 for new construction.
Weight: Loco. 101 tons 10 cwt.
Pressure: 250 lb. Su.
Cyls.: (3) 19″ × 26″.
Driving Wheels: 6′ 2″.
T.E.: 40,430 lb.

A2§ Introduced 1947. Peppercorn development of Class A2/2 with shorter wheelbase. (No. 60539 built with double blast pipe.)

A2** Rebuilt with double blast pipe and multiple valve regulator.
Weight: Loco. 101 tons.
Pressure: 250 lb. Su.
Cyls.: (3) 19″ × 26″.
Driving Wheels: 6′ 2″.
T.E.: 40,430 lb.
Tender weight (all parts): 60 tons 7 cwt.
Walschaerts valve gear.   P.V.

60500‡	Edward Thompson
60501*	Cock o' the North
60502*	Earl Marischal
60503*	Lord President
60504*	Mons Meg
60505*	Thane of Fife
60506*	Wolf of Badenoch
60507†	Highland Chieftain
60508†	Duke of Rothesay
60509†	Waverley
60510†	Robert the Bruce
60511‡	Airborne
60512‡	Steady Aim
60513‡	Dante
60514‡	Chamossaire
60515‡	Sun Stream
60516‡	Hycilla
60517‡	Ocean Swell
60518‡	Tehran
60519‡	Honeyway
60520‡	Owen Tudor
60521‡	Watling Street
60522‡	Straight Deal
60523‡	Sun Castle
60524‡	Herringbone
60525§	A. H. Peppercorn
60526**	Sugar Palm
60527§	Sun Chariot
60528§	Tudor Minstrel
60529**	Pearl Diver
60530§	Sayajirao

60531§ Bahram	60810
60532**Blue Peter	60811
60533**Happy Knight	60812
60534§ Irish Elegance	60813
60535§ Hornet's Beauty	60814
60536§ Trimbush	60815
60537§ Bachelor's Button	60816
60538**Velocity	60817
60539§ Bronzino	60818

Total

Class A2	15	Class A2/2	6
Class A2/1	4	Class A2/3	15

4-6-4   8P7F   Class W1

Introduced 1937. Rebuilt from Gresley experimental high-pressure 4-cyl. compound with water-tube boiler, introduced 1929.
Weight: Loco. 107 tons 17 cwt.
       Tender 60 tons 7 cwt.
Pressure: 250 lb. Su.
Cyls.: (3) 19″ × 26″.
Driving Wheels: 6′ 8″.
T.E.: 37,400 lb.
Walschaerts valve gear and derived motion. P.V.

60700   **Total 1**

2-6-2   7P6F   Class V2

Introduced 1936. Gresley design.
Weight: Loco. 93 tons 2 cwt.
       Tender 52 tons.
Pressure: 220 lb. Su.
Cyls.: (3) 18½″ × 26″.
Driving Wheels: 6′ 2″.
T.E.: 33,730 lb.
Walschaerts valve gear and derived motion. P.V.

60800	Green Arrow
60801	
60802	
60803	
60804	
60805	
60806	
60807	
60808	
60809	The Snapper, The East Yorkshire Regiment, The Duke of York's Own

60819	
60820	
60821	
60822	
60823	
60824	
60825	
60826	
60827	
60828	
60829	
60830	
60831	
60832	
60833	
60834	
60835	The Green Howard, Alexandra, Princess of Wales's Own Yorkshire Regiment
60836	
60837	
60838	
60839	
60840	
60841	
60842	
60843	
60844	
60845	
60846	
60847	St. Peter's School York, A.D. 627
60848	
60849	
60850	
60851	
60852	

60853			
60854			
60855			
60856			
60857			
60858			
60859			
60860	Durham School		
60861			
60862			
60863			
60864			
60865			
60866			
60867			
60868			
60869			
60870			
60871			
60872	King's Own Yorkshire Light Infantry		
60873	Coldstreamer		
60874	60899	60924	60949
60875	60900	60925	60950
60876	60901	60926	60951
60877	60902	60927	60952
60878	60903	60928	60953
60879	60904	60929	60954
60880	60905	60930	60955
60881	60906	60931	60956
60882	60907	60932	60957
60883	60908	60933	60958
60884	60909	60934	60959
60885	60910	60935	60960
60886	60911	60936	60961
60887	60912	60937	60962
60888	60913	60938	60963
60889	60914	60939	60964
60890	60915	60940	60965
60891	60916	60941	60966
60892	60917	60942	60967
60893	60918	60943	60968
60894	60919	60944	60969
60895	60920	60945	60970
60896	60921	60946	60971
60897	60922	60947	60972
60898	60923	60948	60973

60974	60977	60980	60983
60975	60978	60981	
60976	60979	60982	

Total 184

4-6-0   5MT   Class B1

Introduced 1942. Thompson design.
Weight: Loco. 71 tons 3 cwt.
         Tender 52 tons.
Pressure: 225 lb. Su.
Cyls.: (O) 20″ × 26″.
Driving Wheels: 6′ 2″.
T.E.: 26,880 lb.
Walschaerts valve gear.   P.V.

61000	Springbok
61001	Eland
61002	Impala
61003	Gazelle
61004	Oryx
61005	Bongo
61006	Blackbuck
61007	Klipspringer
61008	Kudu
61009	Hartebeeste
61010	Wildebeeste
61011	Waterbuck
61012	Puku
61013	Topi
61014	Oribi
61015	Duiker
61016	Inyala
61017	Bushbuck
61018	Gnu
61019	Nilghai
61020	Gemsbok
61021	Reitbok
61022	Sassaby
61023	Hirola
61024	Addax
61025	Pallah
61026	Ourebi
61027	Madoqua
61028	Umseke
61029	Chamois
61030	Nyala
61031	Reedbuck
61032	Stembok
61033	Dibatag

61034	Chiru			61192	
61035	Pronghorn			61193	
61036	Ralph Assheton			61194	
61037	Jairou			61195	
61038	Blacktail			61196	
61039	Steinbok			61197	
61040	Roedeer			61198	
61041	61079	61116	61153	61199	
61042	61080	61117	61154	61200	
61043	61081	61118	61155	61201	
61044	61082	61119	61156	61202	
61045	61083	61120	61157	61203	
61046	61084	61121	61158	61204	
61047	61085	61122	61159	61205	
61048	61086	61123	61160	61206	
61049	61087	61124	61161	61207	
61050	61088	61125	61162	61208	
61051	61089	61126	61163	61209	
61052	61090	61127	61164	61210	
61053	61091	61128	61165	61211	
61054	61092	61129	61166	61212	
61055	61093	61130	61167	61213	
61056	61094	61131	61168	61214	
61058	61095	61132	61169	61215	William Henton Carver
61059	61096	61133	61170	61216	
61060	61097	61134	61171	61217	
61061	61098	61135	61172	61218	
61062	61099	61136	61173	61219	
61063	61100	61137	61174	61220	
61064	61101	61138	61175	61221	Sir Alexander Erskine-Hill
61065	61102	61139	61176		
61066	61103	61140	61177	61222	
61067	61104	61141	61178	61223	
61068	61105	61142	61179	61224	
61069	61106	61143	61180	61225	
61070	61107	61144	61181	61226	
61071	61108	61145	61182	61227	
61072	61109	61146	61183	61228	
61073	61110	61147	61184	61229	
61074	61111	61148	61185	61230	
61075	61112	61149	61186	61231	
61076	61113	61150	61187	61232	
61077	61114	61151	61188	61233	
61078	61115	61152		61234	
61189	Sir William Gray			61235	
61190				61236	
61191				61237	Geoffrey H. Kitson

61238	Leslie Runciman
61239	
61240	Harry Hinchcliffe
61241	Viscount Ridley
61242	Alexander Reith Gray
61243	Sir Harold Mitchell
61244	Strang Steel
61245	Murray of Elibank
61246	Lord Balfour of Burleigh
61247	Lord Burghley
61248	Geoffrey Gibbs
61249	FitzHerbert Wright
61250	A. Harold Bibby
61251	Oliver Bury

61252	61284	61316	61348
61253	61285	61317	61349
61254	61286	61318	61350
61255	61287	61319	61351
61256	61288	61320	61352
61257	61289	61321	61353
61258	61290	61322	61354
61259	61291	61323	61355
61260	61292	61324	61356
61261	61293	61325	61357
61262	61294	61326	61358
61263	61295	61327	61359
61264	61296	61328	61360
61265	61297	61329	61361
61266	61298	61330	61362
61267	61299	61331	61363
61268	61300	61332	61364
61269	61301	61333	61365
61270	61302	61334	61366
61271	61303	61335	61367
61272	61304	61336	61368
61273	61305	61337	61369
61274	61306	61338	61370
61275	61307	61339	61371
61276	61308	61340	61372
61277	61309	61341	61373
61278	61310	61342	61374
61279	61311	61343	61375
61280	61312	61344	61376
61281	61313	61345	61377
61282	61314	61346	61378
61283	61315	61347	

| 61379 | Mayflower |

61380	61388	61396	61404
61381	61389	61397	61405
61382	61390	61398	61406
61383	61391	61399	61407
61384	61392	61400	61408
61385	61393	61401	61409
61386	61394	61402	
61387	61395	61403	

Total 409

4-6-0   5MT   Class B16

B16/1 Introduced 1920. Raven N.E. design with Stephenson valve gear.

B16/2* Introduced 1937. Gresley rebuild of B16/1 with Walschaerts valve gear and derived motion for inside cylinder.

B16/3† Introduced 1944. Thompson rebuild of B16/1 with individual sets of Walschaerts valve gear for each cylinder.

Weight: Loco. { 77 tons 14 cwt.*
79 tons 4 cwt.*
78 tons 19 cwt.†
Tender 46 tons 12 cwt.

Pressure: 180 lb. Su.
Cyls.: (3) 18½″ × 26″.
Driving Wheels: 5′ 8″.
T.E.: 30,030 lb.   P.V.

61410	61427	61444†	61461†
61411	61428	61445	61462
61412	61429	61446	61463†
61413	61430	61447	61464†
61414	61431	61448†	61465
61415	61432	61449†	61466
61416	61433	61450	61467†
61417†	61434†	61451	61468†
61418†	61435*	61452	61469
61419	61436	61453†	61470
61420†	61437*	61454†	61471
61421*	61438*	61455*	61472†
61422	61439†	61456	61473
61423	61440	61457*	61475*
61424	61441	61458	61476†
61425	61442	61459	61477
61426	61443	61460	61478

Total
Class B16/1 44 Class B16/3 17
Class B16/2 7

4-6-0   4P3F   Class B12

B12/3 Introduced 1932. Gresley rebuild of Holden G.E. design of 1911 with large boiler, round-topped firebox and long-travel valves.
(B12/2 was a development of B12/1 with Lentz valves, since rebuilt to B12/3.)

Weight: Loco.   69 tons 10 cwt.
        Tender 39 tons 6 cwt.
Pressure: 180 lb. Su.
Cyls.: 20″ × 28″.
Driving Wheels: 6′ 6″.
T.E.: 21,970 lb.
P.V.

61514	61547	61566	61575
61516	61549	61567	61576
61530	61553	61568	61577
61533	61554	61570	61580
61535	61558	61571	
61542	61561	61572	
61546	61564	61573	

Total 25

4-6-0   4MT (B2 and B17/6: 5P4F)   Classes B2 & B17

B17/1[1] Introduced 1928. Gresley design for G.E. section with G.E.-type tender.

B17/6[2] Introduced 1947. B17/1 fitted with 100A (B1-type) boiler.

B17/4[3] Introduced 1936. Locos. with L.N.E.R. 4,200-gallon tender.

B17/6[4] Introduced 1943. B17/4 fitted with 100A (B1-type) boiler.

B17/6[5] Rebuild of streamlined B17/5 introduced in 1937. Rebuilt with 100A boiler and de-streamlined in 1951.

Weight: Loco.   77 tons 5 cwt.
       Tender $\begin{cases} 39 \text{ tons } 6 \text{ cwt.}^{12} \\ 52 \text{ tons.}^{345} \end{cases}$
Pressure: $\begin{cases} 180 \text{ lb.}^{13} \\ 225 \text{ lb.}^{345} \end{cases}$ Su.
Cyls.: (3) 17½″ × 26″.
Driving Wheels: 6′ 8″.
T.E.: $\begin{cases} 22,485 \text{ lb.}^{13} \\ 28,555 \text{ lb.}^{345} \end{cases}$
Walschaerts valve gear and derived motion. P.V.

B2[6] Introduced 1945. Thompson 2-cyl. rebuild of B17, with 100A boiler and N.E. tender.

B2[7] Introduced 1945, with L.N.E.R. tender.

Weight: Loco.   73 tons 10 cwt.
       Tender $\begin{cases} 46 \text{ tons } 12 \text{ cwt.}^{6} \\ 52 \text{ tons.}^{7} \end{cases}$
Pressure: 225 lb. Su.
Cyls.: (O) 20″ × 26″.
Driving Wheels: 6′ 8″.
T.E.: 24,865 lb.
Walschaerts valve gear. P.V.

61600[2]	Sandringham
61603[6]	Framlingham
61605[2]	Lincolnshire Regiment
61606[2]	Audley End
61607[6]	Blickling
61608[2]	Gunton
61609[2]	Quidenham
61610[2]	Honingham Hall
61611[2]	Raynham Hall
61612[2]	Houghton Hall
61613[2]	Woodbastwick Hall
61614[6]	Castle Hedingham
61615[7]	Culford Hall
61616[6]	Fallodon
61617[6]	Ford Castle
61618[1]	Wynyard Park
61619[2]	Welbeck Abbey
61620[2]	Clumber
61621[1]	Hatfield House
61622[2]	Alnwick Castle
61623[2]	Lambton Castle
61625[2]	Raby Castle
61626[2]	Brancepeth Castle
61627[2]	Aske Hall
61629[1]	Naworth Castle
61630[2]	Tottenham Hotspur
61631[2]	Serlby Hall
61632[7]	Belvoir Castle
61633[2]	Kimbolton Castle
61634[2]	Hinchingbrooke
61635[2]	Milton
61636[2]	Harlaxton Manor
61637[2]	Thorpe Hall
61638[2]	Melton Hall

61639⁶	Norwich City	
61640²	Somerleyton Hall	
61641²	Gayton Hall	
61642²	Kilverstone Hall	
61643²	Champion Lodge	
61644⁶	Earlham Hall	
61645²	The Suffolk Regiment	
61646²	Gilwell Park	
61647¹	Helmingham Hall	
61648⁴	Arsenal	
61649⁴	Sheffield United	
61650⁴	Grimsby Town	
61651⁴	Derby County	
61652³	Darlington	
61653⁴	Huddersfield Town	
61654⁴	Sunderland	
61655⁴	Middlesbrough	
61656⁴	Leeds United	
61657⁴	Doncaster Rovers	
61658⁴	The Essex Regiment	
61659⁵	East Anglian	
61660³	Hull City	
61661⁴	Sheffield Wednesday	
61662⁴	Manchester United	
61663⁴	Everton	
61664⁴	Liverpool	
61665⁴	Leicester City	
61666⁴	Nottingham Forest	
61667³	Bradford	
61668⁴	Bradford City	
61669⁴	Barnsley	
61670⁵	City of London	
61671⁷	Royal Sovereign	
61672⁴	West Ham United	

Total

Class B2	10	Class B17/4	3
Class B17/1	5	Class B17/6	50

IMPORTANT NOTE
A careful reading of the notes on page 2 is essential to understand the use of reference marks in this book.

2-6-0   4MT   Class K2

K2/2 Introduced 1914.   Gresley G.N. design.
K2/1* Introduced 1931.   Rebuilt from small-boilered K1 (introduced 1912).
†K2/2 with side-window cab.
‡K2/1 with side-window cab.
Weight: Loco.   64 tons 8 cwt.
    Tender 43 tons 2 cwt.
Pressure: 180 lb. Su.
Cyls.: (O) 20″ × 26″.
Driving Wheels: 5′ 8″.
T.E.: 23,400 lb.
Walschaerts valve gear. P.V.

61721‡	61741†	61750	61758†
61723*	61742	61751	61759
61728*	61743	61752	61760
61730	61745	61753	61761
61731	61746	61754	61762
61738	61747	61755†	
61739	61748	61756	
61740	61749	61757	

61763	
61764†	Loch Arkaig
61765	
61766	
61767	
61768	
61769†	
61770†	
61771	
61772†	Loch Lochy
61773	
61774†	Loch Garry
61775†	Loch Treig
61776†	
61777	
61778	
61779†	
61780	
61781†	Loch Morar
61782†	Loch Eil
61783†	Loch Shiel
61784†	
61785†	
61786†	
61787†	Loch Quoich
61788†	Loch Rannoch
61789†	Loch Laidon

61790† Loch Lomond
61791† Loch Laggan
61792†
61793†
61794† Loch Oich

Total

Class K2/1 3   Class K2/2 58

Classes
2-6-0   5P6F   K3 & K5

K3/2 Introduced 1924. Development of Gresley G.N. design, built to L.N.E.R. loading gauge.

K3/3* Introduced 1929. Differ in details only, such as springs, from K3/2.

‡K3/2 fitted with G.N. tender.

(K3/1 were G.N. locos. (introduced 1920), with G.N. cabs, and K3/4, K3/5 and K3/6 were variations of K3/2 differing in weight and details. These locos. have now been modified to K3/2.)

Weight: Loco.   72 tons 12 cwt.
Tender { 52 tons.
43 tons 2 cwt.‡
Pressure: 180 lb. Su.
Cyls.: (3) 18½″ × 26″.
Driving Wheels: 5′ 8″.
T.E.: 30,030 lb.
Walschaerts valve gear and derived motion. P.V.

K5† Introduced 1945. Thompson 2-cyl. rebuild of K3.
Weight: Loco. 71 tons 5 cwt.
Tender 52 tons.
Pressure: 225 lb. Su.
Cyls.: (O) 20″ × 26″.
Driving Wheels: 5′ 8″.
T.E.: 29,250 lb.
Walschaerts valve gear. P.V.

61800	61813	61826	61839
61801	61814	61827	61840
61802	61815	61828	61841‡
61803	61816	61829	61842
61804	61817	61830	61843
61805	61818	61831	61844
61806	61819	61832	61845
61807	61820	61833	61846
61808	61821	61834	61847
61809	61822	61835	61848
61810	61823	61836	61849
61811\	61824	61837	61850
61812‡	61825	61838	61851

61852	61888*	61924	61960
61853	61889*	61925	61961
61854‡	61890	61926	61962
61855‡	61891	61927	61963
61856‡	61892	61928	61964
61857‡	61893	61929	61965
61858‡	61894	61930	61966
61859‡	61895	61931	61967
61860	61896	61932	61968
61861	61897	61933	61969
61862	61898	61934	61970
61863†	61899	61935	61971
61864	61900	61936	61972
61865	61901	61937	61973
61866	61902	61938	61974
61867	61903	61939	61975
61868	61904	61940	61976
61869	61905	61941	61977
61870*	61906	61942	61978
61871*	61907	61943	61979
61872*	61908	61944	61980
61873*	61909	61945	61981
61874*	61910	61946	61982
61875*	61911	61947	61983
61876*	61912	61948	61984
61877*	61913	61949	61985
61878*	61914	61950	61986
61879*	61915	61951	61987
61880*	61916	61952	61988
61881*	61917	61953	61989
61882*	61918	61954	61990
61883*	61919	61955	61991
61884*	61920	61956	61992
61885*	61921	61957	
61886*	61922	61958	
61887*	61923	61959	

Total

Class K3/2 172   Class K5 1
Class K3/3 20

Classes
2-6-0   5P6F   K1 & K4

K4* Introduced 1937. Gresley locos. for West Highland line.
Weight: Loco. 68 tons 8 cwt.
Tender 44 tons 4 cwt.
Pressure: 200 lb. Su.

Cyls.: (3) 18½″ × 26″.
Driving Wheels: 5′ 2″.
T.E.: 36,600 lb.
Walschaerts valve gear and derived
motion. P.V.

K1/1† Introduced 1945. Thompson
2-cyl. loco. Rebuilt from K4.

K1 Introduced 1949. Peppercorn
development of Thompson K1/1 (No.
61997) for new construction, with
increased length.
Weight: Loco. 66 tons 17 cwt.
Tender 44 tons 4 cwt.
Pressure: 225 lb. Su.
Cyls.: (O) 20″ × 26″.
Driving Wheels: 5′ 2″.
T.E.: 32,080 lb.
Walschaerts valve gear. P.V.

61993* Loch Long
61994* The Great Marquess
61995* Cameron of Lochiel
61996* Lord of the Isles
61997† MacCailin Mor
61998* Macleod of Macleod

62001	62019	62037	62055
62002	62020	62038	62056
62003	62021	62039	62057
62004	62022	62040	62058
62005	62023	62041	62059
62006	62024	62042	62060
62007	62025	62043	62061
62008	62026	62044	62062
62009	62027	62045	62063
62010	62028	62046	62064
62011	62029	62047	62065
62012	62030	62048	62066
62013	62031	62049	62067
62014	62032	62050	62068
62015	62033	62051	62069
62016	62034	62052	62070
62017	62035	62053	
62018	62036	62054	

Total

Class K1 70 Class K4 5
Class K1/1 1

4-4-0 1P **Class D40**

Introduced 1920. Heywood superheated development of Pickersgill
G.N. of S. 1899 design.

Weight: Loco. 48 tons 13 cwt.
Tender 37 tons 8 cwt.
Pressure: 165 lb. Su.
Cyls.: 18″ × 26″.
Driving Wheels: 6′ 1″.
T.E.: 16,185 lb.

62277 Gordon Highlander

Total 1

4-4-0 3P **Class D30**

D30/2 Introduced 1914. Development
of D30/1, introduced 1912 (Reid N.B.
"Scott" class) with detail differences.
Weight: Loco. 57 tons 16 cwt.
Tender 46 tons 13 cwt.
Pressure: 165 lb. Su.
Cyls.: 20″ × 26″.
Driving Wheels: 6′ 6″.
T.E.: 18,700 lb.
P.V.

62418 The Pirate
62421 Laird o' Monkbarns
62422 Caleb Balderstone
62425 Ellangowan
62426 Cuddie Headrigg
62427 Dumbiedykes
62428 The Talisman
62431 Kenilworth
62432 Quentin Durward
62434 Kettledrummle
62436 Lord Glenvarloch
62437 Adam Woodcock
62439 Father Ambrose
62440 Wandering Willie
62441 Black Duncan
62442 Simon Glover

Total 16

4-4-0 3P **Class D34**

Introduced 1913. Reid N.B. " Glen "
class.
Weight: Loco. 57 tons 4 cwt.
Tender 46 tons 13 cwt.
Pressure: 165 lb. Su.
Cyls.: 20″ × 26″.
Driving Wheels: 6′ 0″.
T.E.: 20,260 lb.
P.V.

62467 Glenfinnan
62468 Glen Orchy

62469	Glen Douglas		
62470	Glen Roy		
62471	Glen Falloch		
62472	Glen Nevis		
62474	Glen Croe		
62475	Glen Beasdale		
62477	Glen Dochart		
62478	Glen Quoich		
62479	Glen Sheil		
62480	Glen Fruin		
62482	Glen Mamie		
62483	Glen Garry		
62484	Glen Lyon		
62485	Glen Murran		
62487	Glen Arklet		
62488	Glen Aladale		
62489	Glen Dessary		
62490	Glen Fintaig		
62492	Glen Garvin		
62493	Glen Gloy		
62494	Glen Gour		
62495	Glen Luss		
62496	Glen Loy		
62497	Glen Mallie		
62498	Glen Moidart		

Total 27

4-4-0   3P1F   Class D16

D16/3¹ Introduced 1933. Gresley rebuild of D15 with larger boiler, round-topped firebox and modified footplating. D15 was Belpaire firebox development of original J. Holden (G.E.) " Claud Hamilton " class.

D16/3³ Introduced 1933. Rebuild of D15 with larger boiler, round-topped firebox, modified footplate and 8″ piston valves.

D16/3³ Introduced 1936. Rebuild of D15 with larger boiler, round-topped firebox, modified footplating and 9½″ piston valves.

D16/3⁴ Introduced 1938. Rebuild of D16/2 with round-topped firebox, but retaining original footplating and slide valves.

D16/3⁵ Introduced 1939. Rebuild of D16/2 with round-topped firebox and modified footplating, retaining slide valves.

Weight: Loco.   55 tons 18 cwt.
          Tender 39 tons 5 cwt.
Pressure: 180 lb. Su.
Cyls.: 19″ × 26″.
Driving Wheels: 7′ 0″.
T.E.: 17,095 lb.

62511¹	62540¹	62572¹	62610¹
62513¹	62543⁴	62580⁴	62612⁴
62515¹	62544⁴	62582¹	62613⁴
62517¹	62545¹	62588²	62614⁵
62518¹	62555¹	62589⁴	62615⁴
62522¹	62564⁴	62592⁴	62618⁴
62524¹	62566¹	62597¹	
62529¹	62568²	62599³	
62530¹	62570⁴	62604¹	
62534¹	62571¹	62606⁴	

Total 36

4-4-0   3P2F   Class D11

D11/1* Introduced 1920. Robinson G.C. " Large Director "development of D10 (introduced 1913).

D11/2 Introduced 1924. Post-grouping locos. built to Scottish loading gauge. From 1938 the class has been rebuilt with long-travel valves.

Weight: Loco.   61 tons 3 cwt.
          Tender 48 tons 6 cwt.
Pressure: 180 lb. Su.
Cyls.: 20″ × 26″.
Driving Wheels: 6′ 9″.
T.E.: 19,645 lb.
P.V.

62660*	Butler-Henderson
62661*	Gerard Powys Dewhurst
62662*	Prince of Wales
62663*	Prince Albert
62664*	Princess Mary
62665*	Mons
62666*	Zeebrugge
62667*	Somme
62668*	Jutland
62669*	Ypres
62670*	Marne
62671	Bailie MacWheeble
62672	Baron of Bradwardine
62673	Evan Dhu
62674	Flora MacIvor
62675	Colonel Gardiner
62676	Jonathan Oldbuck

62677	Edie Ochiltree
62678	Luckie Mucklebackit
62679	Lord Glenallan
62680	Lucy Ashton
62681	Captain Craigengelt
62682	Haystoun of Bucklaw
62683	Hobbie Elliott
62684	Wizard of the Moor
62685	Malcolm Graeme
62686	The Fiery Cross
62687	Lord James of Douglas
62688	Ellen Douglas
62689	Maid of Lorn
62690	The Lady of the Lake
62691	Laird of Balmawhapple
62692	Allan-Bane
62693	Roderick Dhu
62694	James Fitzjames

Total
Class D11/1 11 Class D11/2 24

4-4-0   4P   **Class D49**

D49/1* Introduced 1927. Gresley design with piston valves. Walschaerts valve gear and derived motion.

D49/2† Introduced 1928. Development of D49/1 with Lentz Rotary Cam poppet valves.

D49/2‡ Introduced 1949. Fitted with Reidinger R.R. Rotary valve gear.

(D49/3 comprised locos. 62720-5 as built with Lentz Oscillating Cam poppet valves. From 1938 these locos. were converted to D49/1. 62751-75 have larger valves than the earlier D49/2, and were at first classified D49/4).

[1]Fitted with G.C. tender.
[2]Fitted with N.E. tender.
[3]The remainder have L.N.E.R. tenders.

Weight: Loco. $\begin{cases} 66 \text{ tons.*†} \\ 64 \text{ tons 10 cwt.‡} \\ 48 \text{ tons 6 cwt.}^1 \end{cases}$
Tender $\begin{cases} 44 \text{ tons 2 cwt.}^2 \\ 52 \text{ tons.}^3 \end{cases}$

Pressure: 180 lb. Su.
Cyls.: (3) 17″ × 26″.
Driving Wheels: 6′ 8″.
T.E.: 21,555 lb.

62700*[1]	Yorkshire
62701*[1]	Derbyshire
62702*[1]	Oxfordshire
62703*[2]	Hertfordshire
62704*[1]	Stirlingshire
62705*[1]	Lanarkshire
62706*[1]	Forfarshire
62707*[1]	Lancashire
62708*[1]	Argyllshire
62709*[1]	Berwickshire
62710*[1]	Lincolnshire
62711*[1]	Dumbartonshire
62712*[1]	Morayshire
62713*[1]	Aberdeenshire
62714*[1]	Perthshire
62715*[1]	Roxburghshire
62716*[1]	Kincardineshire
62717*[1]	Banffshire
62718*[1]	Kinross-shire
62719*[1]	Peebles-shire
62720*[1]	Cambridgeshire
62721*[1]	Warwickshire
62722*[1]	Huntingdonshire
62723*[2]	Nottinghamshire
62725*[1]	Inverness-shire
62727†[2]	The Quorn
62728*[1]	Cheshire
62729*[1]	Rutlandshire
62730*[1]	Berkshire
62731*[1]	Selkirkshire
62732*[1]	Dumfries-shire
62733*[1]	Northumberland
62734*[2]	Cumberland
62735*[2]	Westmorland
62736†[3]	The Bramham Moor
62738†[3]	The Zetland
62739†[3]	The Badsworth
62740†[3]	The Bedale
62741†[3]	The Blankney
62742†[3]	The Braes of Derwent
62743†[3]	The Cleveland
62744†[3]	The Holderness
62745†[3]	The Hurworth
62746†[3]	The Middleton
62747†[3]	The Percy
62749†[3]	The Cottesmore
62750†[3]	The Pytchley
62751†[3]	The Albrighton
62752†[2]	The Atherstone

62753†³ The Belvoir			
62754†³ The Berkeley			
62755†³ The Bilsdale			
62756†² The Brocklesby			
62759†³ The Craven			
62760†³ The Cotswold			
62762†³ The Fernie			
62763‡³ The Fitzwilliam			
62764‡³ The Garth			
62765†³ The Goathland			
62766†³ The Grafton			
62767†³ The Grove			
62769†³ The Oakley			
62770†³ The Puckeridge			
62771†³ The Rufford			
62772†³ The Sinnington			
62773†³ The South Durham			
62774†³ The Staintondale			
62775†³ The Tynedale			

Total

Class D49/1 33 Class D49/2 35

2-4-0   1MT   Class E4

Introduced 1891. J. Holden G.E. design.
*Fitted with side-window cab.
Weight: Loco.   40 tons 6 cwt.
          Tender 30 tons 13 cwt.
Pressure: 160 lb.
Cyls.: 17½″ × 24″.
Driving Wheels: 5′ 8″.
T.E.: 14,700 lb.

62785   62797*

Total 2

0-8-0   6F   Class Q6

Introduced 1913. Raven N.E. design.
*Some locos. are fitted with tender from withdrawn B15 locos.
Weight: Loco.   65 tons 18 cwt.
          Tender { 44 tons 2 cwt.
                  { 44 tons.*
Pressure: 180 lb. Su.
Cyls.: (O) 20″ × 26″.
Driving Wheels: 4′ 7½″.
T.E.: 28,800 lb.
P.V.

63340	63370	63400	63430
63341	63371	63401	63431
63342	63372	63402	63432
63343	63373	63403	63433
63344	63374	63404	63434
63345	63375	63405	63435
63346	63376	63406	63436
63347	63377	63407	63437
63348	63378	63408	63438
63349	63379	63409	63439
63350	63380	63410	63440
63351	63381	63411	63441
63352	63382	63412	63442
63353	63383	63413	63443
63354	63384	63414	63444
63355	63385	63415	63445
63356	63386	63416	63446
63357	63387	63417	63447
63358	63388	63418	63448
63359	63389	63419	63449
63360	63390	63420	63450
63361	63391	63421	63451
63362	63392	63422	63452
63363	63393	63423	63453
63364	63394	63424	63454
63365	63395	63425	63455
63366	63396	63426	63456
63367	63397	63427	63457
63368	63398	63428	63458
63369	63399	63429	63459

Total 120

0-8-0   8F   Class Q7

Introduced 1919. Raven N.E. design.
Weight: Loco.   71 tons 12 cwt.
          Tender 44 tons 2 cwt.
Pressure: 180 lb. Su.
Cyls.: (3) 18½″ × 26″.
Driving Wheels: 4′ 7¼″
T.E.: 36,965 lb.
P.V.

63460	63464	63468	63472
63461	63465	63469	63473
63462	63466	63470	63474
63463	63467	63471	

Total 15

Classes
2-8-0   8F (O1)   O1 & O4
7F (O4)

O4/1[1] Introduced 1911. Robinson G.C. design with small boiler, Belpaire firebox, steam and vacuum brakes and water scoop.

O4/3[2] Introduced 1917. R.O.D. locos. with steam brake only and no scoop.

O4/2[3] Introduced 1925. O4/3 with cabs and boiler mountings reduced.

O4/5[4] Introduced 1932. Rebuilt with shortened O2-type boiler and separate smokebox saddle.

O4/6[5] Introduced 1924. Rebuilt from O5 retaining higher cab (63914–20 with side windows).

O4/7[6] Introduced 1939. Rebuilt with shortened O2-type boiler, retaining G.C. smokebox.

O4/8[7] Introduced 1944. Rebuilt with 100A (B1) boiler, retaining original cylinders.

(O4/4 were rebuilds with O2 boilers, since rebuilt again; O5 was a G.C. development of O4 with larger boiler and Belpaire firebox.)

Weight: Loco.
- 73 tons 4 cwt.[1]
- 73 tons 4 cwt.[2]
- 73 tons 4 cwt.[3]
- 74 tons 13 cwt.[4]
- 73 tons 4 cwt.[5]
- 73 tons 17 cwt.[6]
- 72 tons 10 cwt.[7]

Tender
- 48 tons 6 cwt. (with scoop)
- 47 tons 6 cwt. (without scoop)

Pressure: 180 lb. Su.
Cyls.: (O) 21″ × 26″.
Driving Wheels: 4′ 8″.
T.E.: 31,325 lb.
P.V.

O1[8] Introduced 1944. Thompson rebuild with 100A boiler, Walschaerts valve gear and new cylinders.
Weight: Loco. 73 tons 6 cwt.
Tender as O4.
Pressure: 225 lb. Su.
Cyls.: (O) 20″ × 26″.
Driving Wheels: 4′ 8″.
T.E.: 35,520 lb.
Walschaerts valve gear.   P.V.

63570[6]	63575[7]	63581[1]	63586[1]
63571[8]	63576[1]	63582[6]	63587[1]
63572[1]	63577[1]	63583[1]	63588[6]
63573[7]	63578[8]	63584[1]	63589[8]
63574[1]	63579[8]	63585[1]	63590[8]

63591[8]	63639[7]	63686[2]	63733[2]
63592[8]	63640[1]	63687[8]	63734[7]
63593[1]	63641[7]	63688[7]	63735[2]
63594[8]	63642[2]	63689[8]	63736[1]
63595[6]	63643[6]	63690[3]	63737[2]
63596[8]	63644[7]	63691[7]	63738[7]
63597[1]	63645[7]	63692[1]	63739[2]
63598[1]	63646[8]	63693[1]	63740[8]
63599[1]	63647[3]	63694[2]	63741[2]
63600[6]	63648[3]	63695[2]	63742[7]
63601[1]	63649[2]	63696[2]	63743[1]
63602[1]	63650[8]	63697[2]	63744[2]
63603[6]	63651[7]	63698[1]	63745[4]
63604[7]	63652[8]	63699[6]	63746[8]
63605[1]	63653[7]	63700[1]	63747[6]
63606[7]	63654[1]	63701[2]	63748[8]
63607[7]	63655[7]	63702[8]	63749[6]
63608[1]	63656[2]	63703[7]	63750[7]
63609[1]	63657[2]	63704[7]	63751[2]
63610[8]	63658[1]	63705[6]	63752[8]
63611[1]	63659[2]	63706[7]	63753[2]
63612[7]	63660[1]	63707[1]	63754[7]
63613[7]	63661[6]	63708[6]	63755[8]
63614[1]	63662[6]	63709[3]	63756[2]
63615[6]	63663[8]	63710[1]	63757[1]
63616[6]	63664[1]	63711[8]	63758[6]
63617[1]	63665[8]	63712[8]	63759[2]
63618[1]	63666[2]	63713[2]	63760[8]
63619[8]	63667[2]	63714[2]	63761[6]
63620[1]	63668[2]	63715[7]	63762[1]
63621[1]	63669[6]	63716[2]	63763[7]
63622[1]	63670[8]	63717[2]	63764[2]
63623[1]	63671[1]	63718[7]	63765[7]
63624[7]	63672[7]	63719[1]	63766[2]
63625[1]	63673[6]	63720[7]	63767[2]
63626[1]	63674[7]	63721[7]	63768[8]
63628[7]	63675[7]	63722[1]	63769[2]
63629[2]	63676[8]	63723[1]	63770[6]
63630[8]	63677[1]	63724[2]	63771[2]
63631[7]	63678[8]	63725[8]	63772[6]
63632[1]	63679[2]	63726[7]	63773[8]
63633[7]	63680[3]	63727[1]	63774[2]
63634[6]	63681[2]	63728[7]	63775[5]
63635[1]	63682[3]	63729[2]	63776[7]
63636[7]	63683[7]	63730[3]	63777[8]
63637[2]	63684[1]	63731[7]	63779[2]
63638[2]	63685[2]	63732[7]	63780[8]

179

63781²	63813²	63852⁷	63884⁷
63782²	63816⁷	63853⁷	63885⁷
63783²	63817⁸	63854⁸	63886⁶
63784⁸	63818⁷	63855²	63887⁸
63785⁷	63819⁷	63856⁸	63888⁷
63786⁸	63821²	63857⁷	63889⁷
63787²	63822²	63858⁷	63890⁸
63788⁷	63823⁷	63859²	63891⁶
63789⁸	63824⁶	63860⁶	63893⁷
63790²	63827⁷	63861²	63894⁶
63791⁷	63828⁷	63862⁷	63895⁷
63792⁸	63829²	63863⁸	63897⁷
63793²	63832⁷	63864⁷	63898⁷
63794⁷	63833²	63865⁸	63899⁷
63795⁸	63835²	63867⁸	63900²
63796⁸	63836⁷	63868⁸	63901⁸
63797¹	63837⁷	63869⁸	63902⁵
63798²	63838⁸	63870²	63904⁵
63799¹	63839⁶	63872⁸	63905⁵
63800⁷	63840⁷	63873⁷	63906⁵
63801⁷	63841⁷	63874⁸	63907⁵
63802⁷	63842²	63876⁶	63908⁵
63803⁸	63843⁶	63877⁷	63911⁵
63804²	63845²	63878⁷	63912⁵
63805⁷	63846²	63879⁸	63913⁵
63806⁸	63847³	63880⁶	63914⁷
63807⁷	63848⁶	63881²	63915⁷
63808⁸	63850⁷	63882⁷	63917⁵
63812²	63851⁴	63883²	63920⁵

Total

Class O1   58   Class O4/5   2
Class O4/1 46   Class O4/6 11
Class O4/2   8   Class O4/7 34
Class O4/3 81   Class O4/8 84

2-8-0   8F   Class O2

O2/1* Introduced 1921. Development of experimental Gresley G.N. 3-cyl. loco. (L.N.E.R. 3921). Subsequently rebuilt with side-window cab, and reduced boiler mountings.

O2/2† Introduced 1924. Development of O2/1 with detail differences.

O2/3 Introduced 1932. Development of O2/2 with side-window cab and reduced boiler mountings.

O2/4‡ Introduced 1943. Rebuilt with 100A (B1 type) boiler and smokebox extended backwards (63924 retaining G.N. tender).

Weight: Loco. { 75 tons 16 cwt.*†
                78 tons 13 cwt.
                74 tons 2 cwt.‡
        Tender { 43 tons 2 cwt.
                (63922–46)
                52 tons (63947–87).

Pressure: 180 lb. Su.
Cyls.: (3) 18½″ × 26″.
Driving Wheels: 4′ 8″.
T.E.: 36,740 lb.
Walschaerts valve gear and derived motion. P.V.

63922*	63939†	63956	63973
63923*	63940†	63957	63974
63924‡	63941†	63958	63975
63925*	63942†	63959	63976
63926*	63943†	63960	63977
63927*	63944†	63961	63978
63928*	63945‡	63962‡	63979
63929*	63946†	63963	63980
63930*	63947	63964	63981
63931*	63948	63965	63982‡
63932‡	63949‡	63966	63983‡
63933†	63950†	63967	63984
63934†	63951	63968	63985
63935†	63952	63969	63986
63936†	63953	63970	63987
63937†	63954	63971	
63938†	63955	63972	

Total

Class O2/1   9   Class O2/3 36
Class O2/2 13   Class O2/4   8

0-6-0   2P3F   Class J6

Introduced 1911. Gresley G.N. design.
Weight: Loco. 50 tons 10 cwt.
        Tender 43 tons 2 cwt.
Pressure: 170 lb. Su.
Cyls.: 19″ × 26″.
Driving Wheels: 5′ 2″.
T.E.: 21,875 lb.
P.V.

64170	64174	64178	64182
64171	64175	64179	64183
64172	64176	64180	64184
64173	64177	64181	64185

64188	64215	64238	64260
64189	64216	64239	64261
64190	64217	64240	64262
64191	64218	64241	64263
64192	64219	64243	64265
64196	64220	64244	64266
64197	64222	64245	64267
64198	64223	64246	64268
64199	64224	64247	64269
64201	64225	64248	64270
64202	64226	64249	64271
64203	64227	64250	64272
64205	64228	64251	64273
64206	64229	64252	64274
64207	64231	64253	64275
64208	64232	64254	64276
64209	64233	64255	64277
64210	64234	64256	64278
64211	64235	64257	64279
64213	64236	64258	
64214	64237	64259	

Total 98

64298	64340	64382	64421
64302	64341	64383	64422
64304*	64343	64384	64423
64305	64344	64385	64425
64306	64345	64386*	64427*
64308	64346*	64387	64428
64310	64348	64388	64429
64311	64351	64389	64430
64313	64352*	64392	64433
64314*	64354*	64393*	64434
64315	64355	64394*	64435
64316*	64357	64395*	64437
64317*	64359*	64396	64438
64318*	64361	64397	64439*
64319	64362*	64402*	64440
64321	64363	64403	64441*
64324*	64364*	64404	64442*
64325	64365	64405	64443
64328	64368	64406*	64444
64329	64371	64407	64445
64331	64373*	64409	64446
64332*	64375*	64416	64447
64333*	64376	64417*	64450*
64336	64377	64418*	64451
64337	64379*	64419	64452
64338	64381	64420*	

Total
Class J11/3   33
Class J11 (other parts) 82

0-6-0   2P3F   Class J11

Introduced 1901. Robinson G.C. design.
Parts 1 and 4 have 3,250-gallon
tenders; Parts 2 and 5, 4,000-gallon.
Parts 1 and 2 have high boiler
mountings; Parts 4 and 5 low. All
of Parts 4 and 5 are superheated, and
some of Parts 1 and 2. There are
frequent changes between parts.

J11/3* Introduced 1942. Rebuilt with
long-travel piston valves and boiler
higher pitched.

Weight: Loco.$\begin{cases} 51 \text{ tons } 19 \text{ cwt. (Sat.)} \\ 52 \text{ tons } 2 \text{ cwt. (Su.)} \\ 53 \text{ tons } 6 \text{ cwt.*} \end{cases}$

Tender$\begin{cases} 44 \text{ tons } 3 \text{ cwt. (3,250 gall.)} \\ 48 \text{ tons } 6 \text{ cwt. (4,000 gall.)} \end{cases}$

Pressure: 180 lb. SS.
Cyls.: 18½″ × 26″.
Driving Wheels: 5′ 2″.
T.E.: 21,960 lb.

64280	64284*	64288	64294
64281	64285	64290	64296
64283*	64287	64292	64297

0-6-0   3F   Class J35

J35/5* Introduced 1906. Reid N.B.
design with piston valves.

J35/4 Introduced 1908. Slide valves.
(Parts 1, 2 and 3 were variations of
Parts 4 and 5 before superheating.)

Weight: Loco.$\begin{cases} 51 \text{ tons.*} \\ 50 \text{ tons } 15 \text{ cwt.} \end{cases}$

Tender$\begin{cases} 38 \text{ tons } 1 \text{ cwt.*} \\ 37 \text{ tons } 15 \text{ cwt.} \end{cases}$

Pressure: 180 lb. Su.
Cyls.: 18½″ × 26″.
Driving Wheels: 5′ 0″.
T.E.: 22,080 lb.

64460*	64482	64500	64520
64461*	64483	64501	64521
64462*	64484	64502	64522
64463*	64485	64504	64523
64464*	64486	64505	64524
64466*	64487	64506	64525
64468*	64488	64507	64526
64470*	64489	64509	64527
64471*	64490	64510	64528
64472*	64491	64511	64529
64473*	64492	64512	64530
64474*	64493	64513	64531
64475*	64494	64514	64532
64476*	64495	64515	64533
64477*	64496	64516	64534
64478	64497	64517	64535
64479	64498	64518	
64480	64499	64519	

Total
Class J35/4 55   Class J35/5 15

0-6-0   5F   Class J37

Introduced 1914. Reid N.B. design.
Superheated development of J35.
Weight: Loco.   54 tons 14 cwt.
        Tender 40 tons 19 cwt.
Pressure: 180 lb. Su.
Cyls.: 19¼″ × 26″.
Driving Wheels: 5′ 0″.
T.E.: 25,210 lb.
P.V.

64536	64552	64568	64584
64537	64553	64569	64585
64538	64554	64570	64586
64539	64555	64571	64587
64540	64556	64572	64588
64541	64557	64573	64589
64542	64558	64574	64590
64543	64559	64575	64591
64544	64560	64576	64592
64545	64561	64577	64593
64546	64562	64578	64594
64547	64563	64579	64595
64548	64564	64580	64596
64549	64565	64581	64597
64550	64566	64582	64598
64551	64567	64583	64599

64600	64610	64620	64630
64601	64611	64621	64631
64602	64612	64622	64632
64603	64613	64623	64633
64604	64614	64624	64634
64605	64615	64625	64635
64606	64616	64626	64636
64607	64617	64627	64637
64608	64618	64628	64638
64609	64619	64629	64639

Total 104

0-6-0   3P5F   Class J19

Introduced 1912. S. Holden G.E.
design rebuilt with round-topped
firebox from 1934.
*Rebuilt with 19″ cyls. and 180 lb.
pressure.
†Rebuilt with 19″ cyls. and 160 lb.
pressure.
Weight: Loco.   50 tons 7 cwt.
        Tender 38 tons 5 cwt.
Pressure: { 170 lb. Su.
           { 180 lb. Su.*
           { 160 lb. Su.†
Cyls.: { 20″ × 26″.
       { 19″ × 26″.*†
Driving Wheels: 4′ 11″.
T.E.: { 27,430 lb.
      { 26,215 lb.*
      { 23,300 lb.†

64640	64649	64658	64667
64641	64650	64659	64668
64642	64651	64660	64669
64643	64652	64661	64670
64644	64653	64662	64671*
64645	64654	64663	64672†
64646	64655	64664*	64673
64647	64656	64665	64674
64648	64657	64666	

Total 35

0-6-0   5F   Class J20

J20/1 Introduced 1943. Hill G.E.
design with Belpaire firebox (introduced 1920) rebuilt with B12/1-type
boiler with round-topped firebox.
Weight: Loco.   54 tons 15 cwt.
        Tender 38 tons 5 cwt.

182

Class K2/2 2-6-0 No. 61787 *Loch Quoich* (with side-window cab) [P. H. Groom

Class K3/2 2-6-0 No. 61897 [John Robertson

Class K1 2-6-0 No. 62055 [K. R. Pirt

Class K4 2-6-0 No. 61996 *Lord of the Isles* [David A. Anderson

Class O2/2 2-8-0 No. 63934 [A. Robey

Class O2/3 2-8-0 No. 63971 [C. G. Pearson

Class D34 4-4-0 No. 62493 *Glen Gloy* [L. King

Class D16/3 4-4-0 No. 62618 (retaining original footplating) [B. K. B. Green

Class D11/2 4-4-0 No. 62687 *Lord James of Douglas* [P. H. Groom

Class O4/1 2-8-0 No. 63640　　　　　　　　　　　　　　　　[A. R. Carpenter

Class O4/6 2-8-0 No. 63905　　　　　　　　　　　　　　　　[A. W. Martin

Class O4/7 2-8-0 No. 63634　　　　　　　　　　　　　　　　[K. R. Pirt

Class O4/8 2-8-0 No. 63805 [Brian E. Morrison

Class O1 2-8-0 No. 63856 [Brian E. Morrison

Class Q6 0-8-0 No. 63418 [Peter J. Robinson

Class J38 0-6-0 No. 65917
[David A. Anderson

Class J39/2 0-6-0 No. 64950
[David A. Anderson

Class J26 0-6-0 No. 65762
[R. A. Panting

Class J6 0-6-0 No. 64173 (with extended smokebox)   [B. K. B. Green

Class J6 0-6-0 No. 64277   [B. K. B. Green

Class J27 0-6-0 No. 65876   [J. Davenport

Class J10/4 0-6-0 No. 65158   [Brian E. Morrison

Class J11 0-6-0 No. 64377   [P. J. Sharpe

Class J15 0-6-0 No. 65466   Brian E. Morrison

Class J17 0-6-0 No. 65527

[B. K. B. Green

Class J19 0-6-0 No. 64650

Class J20 0-6-0 No. 64682

[B. K. B. Green

Class J36 0-6-0 No. 65222 *Somme*   [*R. E. Vincent*

Class J35/4 0-6-0 No. 64498   [*R. E. Vincent*

Class J37 0-6-0 No. 64572   [*R. E. Vincent*

Above : Class C12
4-4-2T No. 67366
[K. L. Cook

Right : Class G5
0-4-4T No. 67340
(with extended
tanks)
[Peter J. Robinson

Below : Class C16
4-4-2T No. 67484
[David A. Anderson

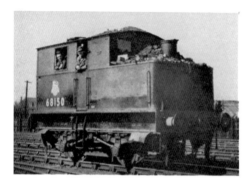

Above : Class F5
2-4-2T No. 67192
[Brian E. Morrison

Left : Class Y1 2
0-4-0T No. 68150
[L. Marshall

Below : Class F6
2-4-2T No. 67227
[Brian E. Morrison

Class Z5 0-4-2T No. 68192 and (right) Class Z4 0-4-2T No. 68190   [Peter J. Robinson

Class J68 0-6-0T No. 68650

Class J69/1 0-6-0T No. 68491   [A. R. Carpenter

Left: Class Y9
0-4-0ST No. 68113
[R. K. Evans

Centre: Class J72
0-6-0T No. 68726
[R. J. Buckley

Bottom: Class J77
0-6-0T No. 68406
[D. Penney

Pressure: 180 lb. Su.
Cyls.: 20″ × 28″.
Driving Wheels: 4′ 11″.
T.E.: 29,045 lb.
P.V.

64675	64682	64689	64696
64676	64683	64690	64697
64677	64684	64691	64698
64678	64685	64692	64699
64679	64686	64693	
64680	64687	64694	
64681	64688	64695	

Total 25

0-6-0   4P5F   Class J39

Introduced 1926. Gresley design.
J39/1   Standard 3,500-gallon tender.
J39/2*   Standard 4,200-gallon tender.
J39/3†   Various N.E. tenders (3,940-gallon on 64843-5, 4,125-gallon on 64855-9).
Weight: Loco.   57 tons 17 cwt.
Tender $\begin{cases} 44 \text{ tons } 4 \text{ cwt.} \\ 52 \text{ tons } 13 \text{ cwt.*} \\ \text{and others.} \end{cases}$

Pressure: 180 lb. Su.
Cyls.: 20″ × 26″.
Driving Wheels: 5′ 2″.
T.E.: 25,665 lb.
P.V.

64700†	64719	64738	64757
64701	64720	64739	64758
64702	64721	64740	64759
64703	64722	64741	64760
64704	64723	64742	64761
64705	64724	64743	64762
64706	64725	64744	64763
64707	64726	64745	64764
64708	64727	64746	64765
64709	64728	64747	64766
64710	64729	64748	64767
64711	64730	64749	64768
64712	64731	64750	64769
64713	64732	64751	64770
64714	64733	64752	64771
64715	64734	64753	64772
64716	64735	64754	64773
64717	64736	64755	64774
64718	64737	64756	64775

64776	64823	64870	64917*
64777	64824	64871	64918*
64778	64825	64872*	64919*
64779	64826	64873*	64920*
64780	64827	64874*	64921*
64781	64828	64875*	64922*
64782	64829	64876*	64923*
64783	64830	64877*	64924*
64784*	64831	64878*	64925*
64785*	64832	64879*	64926†
64786*	64833	64880*	64927*
64787*	64834	64881*	64928*
64788*	64835	64882*	64929*
64789*	64836	64883*	64930*
64790*	64837	64884*	64931*
64791*	64838*	64885*	64932*
64792*	64839*	64886*	64933
64793*	64840*	64887*	64934
64794*	64841*	64888*	64935
64795*	64842*	64889*	64936
64796	64843†	64890*	64937
64797	64844†	64891*	64938
64798	64845†	64892*	64939
64799	64846	64893*	64940
64800	64847	64894*	64941
64801	64848	64895*	64942
64802	64849	64896*	64943
64803	64850	64897*	64944
64804	64851	64898*	64945*
64805	64852	64899*	64946*
64806	64853	64900*	64947*
64807	64854	64901*	64948*
64808	64855†	64902*	64949*
64809	64856†	64903*	64950*
64810	64857†	64904*	64951*
64811	64858†	64905*	64952*
64812	64859†	64906*	64953*
64813	64860	64907*	64954*
64814	64861	64908*	64955*
64815	64862	64909*	64956*
64816	64863	64910*	64957*
64817	64864	64911*	64958*
64818	64865	64912*	64959*
64819	64866	64913*	64960*
64820*	64867	64914*	64961*
64821*	64868	64915*	64962*
64822*	64869	64916*	64963*

64964*	64971†	64978†	64985†	65156*	65169*	65187	65200
64965*	64972†	64979†	64986†	65157*	65170*	65192	65202
64966*	64973†	64980†	64987†	65158*	65175	65194	65208
64967*	64974†	64981†	64988†	65160*	65177	65196	65209
64968*	64975†	64982†		65166*	65178*	65198	
64969*	64976†	64983†		65167*	65184	65199	
64970*	64977†	64984†					

Total

Class J39/1 155 Class J39/3 28
Class J39/2 106

Total

Class J10/4 20 Class J10/6 14

0-6-0   2F   Class J21

Introduced 1886. T. W. Worsdell N.E. design. Majority built as 2-cyl. compounds and later rebuilt as simple locos.
*Rebuilt with superheater, Stephenson valve gear and piston valves.
†Rebuilt with superheater and piston valves, superheater subsequently removed.
Weight: Loco. $\begin{cases} 43 \text{ tons } 15 \text{ cwt.*} \\ 42 \text{ tons } 9 \text{ cwt.†} \end{cases}$
        Tender 36 tons 19 cwt.
Pressure: 160 lb. SS.
Cyls.: 19″ × 24″.
Driving Wheels: 5′ 1¼″.
T.E.: 19,240 lb.

65033†	65064*	65099†	65110†
65039†	65070†	65103*	65117†
65061*			

Total 9

0-6-0   2F   Class J10

J10/4* Introduced 1896. Pollitt development of J10/2 with larger bearings and larger tender.
J10/6 Introduced 1901. Robinson locos. with larger bearings and small tender.
Weight: Loco. 41 tons 6 cwt.
        Tender $\begin{cases} 37 \text{ tons } 6 \text{ cwt.} \\ 43 \text{ tons.*} \end{cases}$
Pressure: 160 lb.
Cyls.: 18″ × 26″.
Driving Wheels: 5′ 1″.
T.E.: 18,780 lb.

65131	65134*	65140*	65145*
65132*	65135*	65142*	65146*
65133*	65138*	65144*	65147*

0-6-0   2F   Class J36

Introduced 1888. Holmes N.B. design.
Weight: Loco. 41 tons 19 cwt.
        Tender 33 tons 9 cwt.
Pressure: 165 lb.
Cyls.: 18¼″ × 26″.
Driving Wheels: 5′ 0″.
T.E.: 19,690 lb.

65210	65211	65214
65216	Byng	
65217	French	
65218		
65221		
65222	Somme	
65224	Mons	
65227		
65228		
65229		
65230		
65232		
65233	Plumer	
65234		
65235	Gough	
65237		
65239		
65241		
65243	Maude	
65246		
65247		
65249		
65251		
65252		
65253	Joffre	
65257		
65258		
65259		
65260		

65261			
65265			
65266			
65267			
65268	Allenby		
65270	65281	65293	65304
65273	65282	65295	65305
65275	65285	65296	65306
65276	65287	65297	65307
65277	65288	65300	65309
65280	65290	65303	65310
65311	Haig		
65312	65320	65331	65342
65313	65321	65333	65343
65315	65323	65334	65344
65316	65325	65335	65345
65317	65327	65338	65346
65318	65329	65339	
65319	65330	65341	

Total 87

0-6-0   1P2F   Class J15

Introduced 1883. Worsdell G.E. design, modified by J. Holden.
*Fitted with side-window cab for Colne Valley line.
Weight: Loco.   37 tons 2 cwt.
Tender 30 tons 13 cwt.
Pressure: 160 lb.
Cyls:. 17½″ × 24″.
Driving Wheels: 4′ 11″.
T.E.: 16,940 lb.

65361	65442	65455	65468
65388	65443	65456	65469
65389	65444	65457	65470
65390	65445	65458	65471
65391*	65446	65459	65472
65405*	65447	65460	65473
65420	65448	65461	65474
65424*	65449	65462	65475
65432*	65450	65463	65476
65434	65451	65464	65477
65438*	65452	65465	65478
65440	65453	65466	65479
65441	65454	65467	

Total 51

0-6-0   2P4F   Class J17

Introduced 1901. J. Holden G.E. design. Many rebuilt from round-top firebox J16, introduced 1900.
*Fitted with small tender.
Weight: Loco.   45 tons 8 cwt.
Tender { 38 tons 5 cwt.
30 tons 12 cwt.*
Pressure: 180 lb. Su.
Cyls.: 19″ × 26″.
Driving Wheels: 4′ 11″.
T.E.: 24,340 lb.

65502*	65526	65546	65567
65503*	65527	65548	65568
65504*	65528*	65549	65570
65505	65529	65551	65573
65506*	65530	65553	65576
65507*	65531	65554	65577
65508*	65532	65555	65578
65511*	65533	65556	65580
65512*	65534	65557	65581
65513*	65535	65558	65582
65514*	65536	65559	65583
65515*	65538	65560	65584
65518*	65539	65561	65586
65519*	65540	65562	65587
65520	65541	65563	65588
65521	65542	65564	65589
65522	65543	65565	
65525	65545	65566	

Total 70

0-6-0   3F   Class J25

Introduced 1898. W. Worsdell N.E. design.
*Original design, saturated, with slide valves.
†Rebuilt with superheater and piston valves.
‡Rebuilt with piston valves, superheater removed.
Weight: Loco. { 39 tons 11 cwt.*
41 tons 14 cwt.†
40 tons 17 cwt.‡
Tender 36 tons 19 cwt.
Pressure: 160 lb. SS.
Cyls.: 18½″ × 26″.
Driving Wheels: 4′ 7¼″.
T.E.: 21,905 lb.

65645†	65654‡	65656*	65662†
65648*	65655*	65657*	65663*

65666*	65687*	65700*	65720*	65780	65809	65838	65867†
65670*	65691*	65702‡	65726*	65781	65810	65839	65868†
65673‡	65693*	65706†	65727*	65782	65811	65840	65869†
65675*	65695*	65712*	65728*	65783	65812	65841	65870†
65677‡	65696*	65713*		65784	65813	65842	65871*
65683‡	65697*	65714*		65785	65814	65843	65872†
65685*	65698*	65717†		65786	65815	65844	65873†

Total 33

0-6-0   5F   Class J26

Introduced 1904. W. Worsdell N.E. design.
Weight: Loco.   46 tons 16 cwt.
           Tender 36 tons 19 cwt.
Pressure: 180 lb.
Cyls.: 18½″ × 26″.
Driving Wheels: 4′ 7¼″.
T.E.: 24,640 lb.

65730	65743	65756	65769	65787	65816	65845	65874*
65731	65744	65757	65770	65788	65817	65846	65875†
65732	65745	65758	65771	65789	65818	65847	65876†
65733	65746	65759	65772	65790	65819	65848	65877†
65734	65747	65760	65773	65791	65820	65849	65878*
65735	65748	65761	65774	65792	65821	65850	65879†
65736	65749	65762	65775	65793	65822	65851	65880*
65737	65750	65763	65776	65794	65823	65852	65881*
65738	65751	65764	65777	65795	65824	65853	65882†
65739	65752	65765	65778	65796	65825	65854	65883*
65740	65753	65766	65779	65797	65826	65855	65884†
65741	65754	65767		65798	65827	65856	65885*
65742	65755	65768		65799	65828	65857	65886*
				65800	65829	65858	65887*
				65801	65830	65859	65888†
				65802	65831	65860†	65889*
				65803	65832	65861†	65890*
				65804	65833	65862†	65891†
				65805	65834	65863*	65892*
				65806	65835	65864†	65893*
				65807	65836	65865†	65894*
				65808	65837	65866*	

Total 50

Total 115

0-6-0   5F   Class J27

Introduced 1906. W. Worsdell N.E. design developed from J26.
*Introduced 1921. Raven locos. Superheated, with piston valves.
†Introduced 1943. Piston valves, superheater removed.
Weight: Loco. $\begin{cases} 47 \text{ tons Sat.} \\ 49 \text{ tons 10 cwt. Su.} \end{cases}$
           Tender 36 tons 19 cwt.
Pressure: 180 lb. SS.
Cyls.: 18½″ × 26″.
Driving Wheels: 4′ 7¼″.
T.E.: 24,640 lb.

0-6-0   6F   Class J38

Introduced 1926. Gresley design.
Predecessor of J39, with 4′ 8″ wheels, boiler 6″ longer than J39 and smokebox 6″ shorter.
*Rebuilt with J39 boiler.
Weight: Loco.   58 tons 19 cwt.
           Tender 44 tons 4 cwt.
Pressure: 180 lb. Su.
Cyls.: 20″ × 26″.
Driving Wheels: 4′ 8″.
T.E.: 28,415 lb.
P.V.

65900	65903*	65906*	65909
65901	65904	65907	65910
65902	65905	65908*	65911

65912	65918*	65924	65930
65913	65919	65925	65931
65914	65920	65926*	65932
65915	65921	65927*	65933
65916	65922	65928	65934
65917*	65923	65929	

Total 35

2-4-2T IMT Class F5

Introduced 1911. S. D. Holden G.E. design. (Rebuilt from Worsdell G.E. F4.)
*Introduced 1949. Push-and-pull fitted.
Weight: 53 tons 19 cwt.
Pressure: 180 lb.
Cyls.: $17\frac{1}{2}'' \times 24''$.
Driving Wheels: 5' 4".
T.E.: 17,570 lb.

| 67192 | 67212 | 67214 | 67218* |
| 67195 | | | |

Total 5

2-4-2T IMT Class F6

Introduced 1911. S. D. Holden G.E. design, development of Worsdell G.E. F4 with higher pressure and larger tanks.
Weight: 56 tons 9 cwt.
Pressure: 180 lb.
Cyls.: $17\frac{1}{2}'' \times 24''$.
Driving Wheels: 5' 4".
T.E.: 17,570 lb.

| 67227 | 67229 | 67230 | 67231 |
| 67228 | | | |

Total 5

0-4-4T IMT Class G5

Introduced 1894. W. Worsdell N.E. design.
*Push-and-pull fitted.
†Push-and-pull fitted and rebuilt with larger tanks.
Weight: 54 tons 4 cwt.
Pressure: 160 lb.
Cyls.: $18'' \times 24''$.
Driving Wheels: 5' $1\frac{1}{4}''$.
T.E.: 17,265 lb.

| 67246 | 67253* | 67262 | 67265 |
| 67248 | 67261* | 67263 | 67274 |

67280*	67311*	67323*	67340†
67281*	67315	67325	67341
67297*	67320	67329	67342
67305*			

Total 21

4-4-2T IMT Class C12

Introduced 1898. Ivatt G.N. design.
*Boiler pressure reduced to 170 lb.
†Push-and-pull fitted.
Weight: 62 tons 6 cwt.
Pressure: $\begin{cases} 175 \text{ lb.} \\ 170 \text{ lb.*†} \end{cases}$
Cyls.: $18'' \times 26''$.
Driving Wheels: 5' 8".
T.E.: $\begin{cases} 18,425 \text{ lb.} \\ 17,900 \text{ lb.*†} \end{cases}$

67352	67366	67379	67397
67357	67367	67380	67398*
67363*†	67374*†	67386†	
67365	67376	67394	

Total 14

4-4-2T 2PIF Class C13

Introduced 1903. Robinson G.C. design, later rebuilt with superheater.
*Push-and-pull fitted.
Weight: 66 tons 13 cwt.
Pressure: 160 lb. Su.
Cyls.: $18'' \times 26''$.
Driving Wheels: 5' 7".
T.E.: 17,100 lb.

| 67416* | 67418* | 67421* | 67439 |
| 67417* | 67420* | 67424 | |

Total 7

4-4-2T 2PIF Class C14

Introduced 1907. Robinson G.C. design, later superheated, development of C13, with detail differences.
Weight: 71 tons.
Pressure: 160 lb. Su.
Cyls.: $18'' \times 26''$.
Driving Wheels: 5' 7".
T.E.: 17,100 lb.

| 67445 | 67447 | 67448 | 67450 |

Total 4

4-4-2T 2P Class C15

Introduced 1911. Reid N.B. design.
  Push-and-pull fitted.
Weight: 68 tons 15 cwt.
Pressure: 175 lb.
Cyls.: 18″ × 26″.
Driving Wheels: 5′ 9″.
T.E.: 18,160 lb.

| 67460 | 67474 | | **Total 2** |

4-4-2T 2P Class C16

Introduced 1915. Reid N.B. design,
  superheated development of C15.
Weight: 72 tons 10 cwt.
Pressure: 165 lb. Su.
Cyls.: 19″ × 26″.
Driving Wheels: 5′ 9″.
T.E.: 19,080 lb.
P.V.

67482	67487	67491	67497
67484	67488	67492	67500
67485	67489	67494	67501
67486	67490	67496	67502

Total 16

Classes
2-6-2T V1 (3MT) V1 & V3
  V3 (4MT)

V1 Introduced 1930. Gresley design.
V3* Introduced 1939. Development of
  V1 with higher pressure (locos. num-
  bered below 67682 rebuilt from V1).
  P.V.
Weight: { 84 tons.
         { 86 tons 16 cwt.*
Pressure: { 180 lb. Su.
          { 200 lb. Su.*
Cyls.: (3) 16″ × 26″.
Driving Wheels: 5′ 8″.
T.E.: { 22,465 lb.
      { 24,960 lb.*
Walschaerts valve gear and derived
  motion. P.V.

67600*	67604*	67608	67612*
67601	67605*	67609*	67613
67602	67606*	67610	67614
67603	67607	67611*	67615*

67616	67635	67654*	67673
67617*	67636*	67655	67674*
67618	67637	67656*	67675*
67619*	67638*	67657*	67676
67620*	67639	67658	67677
67621	67640	67659	67678
67622	67641	67660*	67679*
67623	67642	67661	67680
67624*	67643*	67662*	67681*
67625*	67644	67663*	67682*
67626*	67645	67664	67683*
67627*	67646*	67665	67684*
67628*	67647	67666	67685*
67629	67648	67667	67686*
67630	67649	67668*	67687*
67631	67650	67669*	67688*
67632*	67651*	67670*	67689*
67633	67652*	67671	67690*
67634*	67653*	67672*	67691*

Total
Class V1 43   **Class V3 49**

2-6-4T 4MT Class L1

Introduced 1945. Thompson design.
*Introduced 1954. Boiler pressure
  reduced to 200 lb.
†Introduced 1954. Cylinder diameter
  reduced.
Weight: 89 tons 9 cwt.
Pressure: { 225 lb.
          { 200 lb.*
Cyls.: { (O) 20″ × 26″.
       { (O) 18¾″ × 26″.†
Driving Wheels: 5′ 2″.
T.E.: { 32,080 lb.
      { 28,515 lb.*
      { 28,180 lb.†
Walschaerts valve gear. P.V.

67701	67710	67719	67728
67702	67711	67720	67729
67703	67712	67721	67730
67704	67713	67722	67731
67705	67714	67723	67732
67706	67715	67724	67733
67707	67716	67725	67734
67708	67717	67726	67735
67709	67718	67727	67736

67737	67753	67769	67785
67738	67754	67770†	67786
67739	67755	67771†	67787
67740	67756	67772†	67788
67741	67757	67773	67789
67742	67758	67774	67790
67743	67759	67775	67791
67744	67760	67776†	67792
67745	67761*	67777	67793
67746	67762	67778	67794
67747*	67763	67779†	67795
67748	67764	67780	67796
67749	67765	67781	67797
67750	67766	67782	67798*
67751	67767	67783	67799
67752	67768	67784	67800

Total 100

0-6-0ST   4F   Class J94

Introduced 1943. Riddles M.o.S. design.
(Bought from M.o.S., 1946.)
Weight: 48 tons 5 cwt.
Pressure: 170 lb.
Cyls.: 18″ × 26″.
Driving Wheels: 4′ 3″.
T.E.: 23,870 lb.

68006	68025	68044	68063
68007	68026	68045	68064
68008	68027	68046	68065
68009	68028	68047	68066
68010	68029	68048	68067
68011	68030	68049	68068
68012	68031	68050	68069
68013	68032	68051	68070
68014	68033	68052	68071
68015	68034	68053	68072
68016	68035	68054	68073
68017	68036	68055	68074
68018	68037	68056	68075
68019	68038	68057	68076
68020	68039	68058	68077
68021	68040	68059	68078
68022	68041	68060	68079
68023	68042	68061	68080
68024	68043	68062	

Total 75

0-4-0ST   0F   Class Y9

Introduced 1882. Holmes N.B. design.
*Locos. running permanently attached
to wooden tender.
Weight: Loco.   27 tons 16 cwt.
        Tender   6 tons.*
Pressure: 130 lb.
Cyls.: (O) 14″ × 20″.
Driving Wheels: 3′ 8″.
T.E.: 9,845 lb.

68095	68104	68114*	68118*
68097*	68108*	68115	68119*
68100*	68110	68116*	68123
68101	68113	68117*	68124
68102*			

Total 17

0-4-0T   Unclass.   Class Y1

Sentinel Wagon Works design. Single-
speed Geared Sentinel locomotives.
The parts of this class differ in details,
including size of boiler and fuel
capacity.
Y1/1* Introduced 1925.
Y1/2† Introduced 1927.
§Sprocket gear ratio 9:25 (remainder
11:25).
Weight: { 20 tons 17 cwt.*
          19 tons 16 cwt.†
          19 tons 7 cwt.‡
Pressure: 275 lb. Su.
Cyls.: 6¾″ × 9″.
Driving Wheels: 2′ 6″.
T.E.: { 7,260 lb.*†‡
        8,870 lb.§
Poppet valves.
     (See also E.R. Departmental Locos.)

68138†   68150† §

Total
Class Y1/1   3   Class Y1/2   3

0-4-2T   0F   Class Z4

Introduced 1915. Manning-Wardle
design for G.N. of S.
Weight: 25 tons 17 cwt.
Pressure: 160 lb.
Cyls.: (O) 13″ × 20″.
Driving Wheels: 3′ 6″.
T.E.: 10,945 lb.

68190   68191   **Total 2**

DEPARTMENTAL LOCOMOTIVES

(Former running no. in brackets)

0-6-0ST 3F Class J52/2

1 (68845)   2 (68858)

0-4-0T Un-class. Class Y3

Introduced 1927.
Sentinel Wagon Works design.
  Two-speed Geared Sentinel locos.
Sprocket gear ratio 15 : 19.
Weight: 20 tons 16 cwt.
Pressure: 275 lb. Su.
Cyls.: $6\frac{3}{4}'' \times 9''$.
Driving Wheels: 2' 6".
T.E.: { Low Gear: 15,960 lb.
       { High Gear: 5,960 lb.
Poppet valves.

3 (68181)	38 (68168)
5 (68165)	40 (68173)
7 (68166)	41 (68177)
8 (68183)	42 (68178)
21 (68162)	57 (68160)

Total 10

0-4-0T Un-class. Class Y1/1

4 (68132)	39 (68131)
6 (68133)	53 (68152)

0-6-0T 2F Class J66

Introduced 1886. J. Holden G.E.
  design.
Weight: 40 tons 6 cwt.
Pressure: 160 lb.
Cyls.: $16\frac{1}{2}'' \times 22''$.
Driving Wheels: 4' 0".
T.E.: 16,970 lb.

31 (68382)	36 (68378)
32 (68370)	

Total 3

0-4-0T Dock Tank Class Y4

Introduced 1913. Hill G.E. design.
Weight: 38 tons 1 cwt.
Pressure: 180 lb.
Cyls.: (O) $17'' \times 20''$.
Driving Wheels: 3' 10".
T.E.: 19,225 lb.
Walschaerts valve gear.

33 (68129)   **Total 1**

0-4-0 Diesel Mechanical

Introduced 1950. Hibberd & Co.
for North Eastern Region.
Weight: 11 tons.
Engine: English National Gas type
DA 4, 4-cyls, 52 h.p. at 1,250
r.p.m. Transmission spur type
gear box with roller chains:
three forward and three reverse
gears.

52 (11104)   **Total 1**

0-4-0T Un-class. Class Y1/2

54 (68153)

0-4-0T Dock Tank Class Y8

Introduced 1890. T. W. Worsdell
N.E. design.
Weight: 15 tons 10 cwt.
Pressure: 140 lb.
Cyls.: $11'' \times 15''$.
Driving Wheels: 3' 0".
T.E.: 6,000 lb.

55 (68091)   **Total 1**

0-4-0 Diesel Mechanical

Introduced 1956. Ruston & Hornsby
88-h.p. Shunting locomotive.

56

0-4-2T 0F Class Z5

Introduced 1915. Manning-Wardle design for G.N. of S.
Weight 30 tons 18 cwt.
Pressure: 160 lb.
Cyls.: (O) 14″ × 20″.
Driving Wheels: 4′ 0″.
T.E.: 11,105 lb.

68192   Total 1

68320	68329	68338	68347
68321	68330	68339	68348
68322	68331	68340	68349
68324	68332	68342	68350
68325	68333	68343	68352
68326	68334	68344	68353
68327	68335	68345	68354
68328	68336	68346	

Total 31

0-6-0T Unclass. Class J71

Introduced 1886. T. W. Worsdell N.E. design.
*†Altered cylinder dimensions.
Weight: 37 tons 12 cwt.
Pressure: 140 lb.
Driving Wheels 4′ 7¼″.
Cyls.: $\begin{cases} 16″ \times 22″. \\ 16\frac{3}{4}″ \times 22″.* \\ 18″ \times 22″.† \end{cases}$
T.E.: $\begin{cases} 12,130 \text{ lb.} \\ 13,300 \text{ lb.*} \\ 15,355 \text{ lb.†} \end{cases}$

68230*	68251	68272	68306*
68233	68254	68275	68308*
68235	68260	68278	68309*
68242	68262	68283	68312†
68244	68263	68290	68314
68245	68264	68295	68316*
68246*	68265	68296	
68250*	68269	68305*	

Total 30

0-6-0T 0F Class J88

Introduced 1904. Reid N.B. design with short wheelbase.
Weight: 38 tons 14 cwt.
Pressure: 130 lb.
Cyls.: (O) 15″ × 22″.
Driving Wheels: 3′ 9″.
T.E.: 12,155 lb.

0-6-0T 3F Class J73

Introduced 1891. W. Worsdell N.E. design.
Weight: 46 tons 15 cwt.
Pressure: 160 lb.
Cyls.: 19″ × 24″.
Driving Wheels: 4′ 7¼″.
T.E.: 21,320 lb.

68355	68359	68361	68364
68356	68360	68363	

Total 7

0-6-0T 2F Class J77

Introduced 1899. W. Worsdell N.E. rebuild of Fletcher 0-4-4T originally built 1874-84.
Some engines of this class have square-cornered and some round-cornered cab roofs.
Weight: 43 tons.
Pressure: 160 lb.
Cyls.: 17″ × 22″.
Driving Wheels: 4′ 1¼″.
T.E.: 17,560 lb.

68392	68406	68410	68431
68399	68408	68414	68435
68402	68409	68424	
68405			

Total 12

0-6-0T 2F Class J83

Introduced 1900. Holmes N.B. design.
Weight: 45 tons 5 cwt.
Pressure: 150 lb.
Cyls.: 17″ × 26″.
Driving Wheels: 4′ 6″.
T.E.: 17,745 lb.

68442	68453	68464	68477
68443	68454	68466	68478
68444	68456	68467	68479
68445	68457	68468	68480
68447	68458	68470	68481
68448	68459	68471	
68449	68460	68472	
68451	68461	68474	
68452	68463	68475	

Total 32

Classes

0-6-0T 2F J67 & J69

J67/1* Introduced 1890. J. Holden G.E. design with 160 lb. pressure.

J69/1† Introduced 1902. Development of J67 with 180 lb. pressure, larger tanks and larger firebox (some rebuilt from J67).

J69/2§ Introduced 1950. J67/1 rebuilt with 180 lb. boiler and large firebox.

Weight: {40 tons.*‡ / 40 tons 9 cwt.†§
Pressure: {160 lb.*‡ / 180 lb.†§
Cyls.: 16½″ × 22″.
Driving Wheels: 4′ 0″.
T.E.: {16,970 lb.*‡ / 19,090 lb.†§

68490§	68497†	68501†	68510§
68491†	68498§	68502†	68513§
68494†	68499†	68507†	68519§
68495†	68500†	68508†	68520§

68522§	68554†	68579†	68618†
68524†	68555†	68581†	68619†
68526†	68556†	68583*	68621†
68527†	68557†	68585†	68623†
68528†	68558†	68587†	68625†
68529†	68560†	68588†	68626†
68530†	68561†	68591†	68629†
68532†	68563†	68596†	68630†
68535†	68565†	68599†	68631†
68537†	68566†	68600†	68632†
68538†	68568†	68601†	68633†
68541†	68569†	68602†	68635†
68542†	68570†	68605†	68636†
68543†	68571†	68607†	
68545†	68573†	68608*	
68546†	68574†	68609†	
68549†	68575†	68612†	
68550†	68576†	68613†	
68552†	68577†	68616*	
68553†	68578†	68617†	

Total

Class J67/1 3 Class J69/1 79
Class J69/2 7

0-6-0T 2F Class J68

Introduced 1912. Hill G.E. development of J69 with side-window cab.
Weight: 42 tons 9 cwt.
Pressure: 180 lb.
Cyls.: 16½″ × 22″.
Driving Wheels: 4′ 0″.
T.E.: 19,090 lb.

68638	68646	68654	68662
68639	68647	68655	68663
68640	68648	68656	68664
68641	68649	68657	68665
68642	68650	68658	68666
68643	68651	68659	
68644	68652	68660	
68645	68653	68661	

Total 29

0-6-0T 2F Class J72

Introduced 1898. W. Worsdell N.E. design.
*Altered cylinder dimensions.
Weight: 38 tons 12 cwt.
Pressure: 140 lb.
Cyls.: $\begin{cases} 17'' \times 24'' \\ 18'' \times 24''.* \end{cases}$
Driving Wheels: 4' 1¼".
T.E.: $\begin{cases} 16,760 \text{ lb.} \\ 18,790 \text{ lb.*} \end{cases}$

68670	68692	68714	68736
68671	68693	68715	68737
68672	68694	68716	68738
68673	68695	68717	68739
68674	68696	68718	68740
68675	68697	68719	68741
68676	68698	68720	68742
68677	68699	68721	68743
68678	68700	68722	68744
68679	68701	68723	68745
68680	68702	68724	68746
68681	68703	68725	68747
68682	68704	68726	68748
68683	68705	68727	68749
68684	68706	68728	68750
68685*	68707	68729	68751
68686	68708	68730	68752
68687	68709	68731	68753
68688	68710	68732	68754
68689	68711	68733	
68690	68712	68734	
68691	68713	68735	

(Class continued with No. 69001)

0-6-0ST 3F Class J52

J52/2 Introduced 1897. Ivatt G.N. saddletank with domed boiler.
J52/1* Introduced 1922. Rebuild of Stirling domeless saddletank (introduced 1892)—non-condensing.
Weight: 51 tons 14 cwt.
Pressure: 170 lb.

Cyls.: 18" × 26".
Driving Wheels: 4' 8".
T.E.: 21,735 lb.
(See also E.R. Departmental Locos.)

68800*	68834	68847	68866
68815	68837	68848	68869
68817	68839	68857	68870
68824	68842	68862	68875
68831	68846	68863	68889

Total
Class J52/1 1 Class J52/2 21

0-6-0T 4F Class J50

J50/2* Introduced 1922. Gresley G.N. design (68900–19 rebuilt from smaller J51, built 1915–22.)
J50/3† Introduced 1926. Post-grouping development with detail differences.
J50/1‡ Introduced 1929. Rebuilt from smaller J51, built 1913–14.
J50/4§ Introduced 1937. Development of J50/3 with larger bunker.
Weight: $\begin{cases} 57 \text{ tons.*} \\ 56 \text{ tons 6 cwt.‡} \\ 58 \text{ tons 3 cwt.†§} \end{cases}$
Pressure: 175 lb.
Cyls.: 18½" × 26".
Driving Wheels: 4' 8".
T.E.: 23,635 lb.

68890‡	68903*	68916*	68929*
68891‡	68904*	68917*	68930*
68892‡	68905*	68918*	68931*
68893‡	68906*	68919*	68932*
68894‡	68907*	68920*	68933*
68895‡	68908*	68921*	68934*
68896‡	68909*	68922*	68935*
68897‡	68910*	68923*	68936*
68898‡	68911*	68924*	68937*
68899‡	68912*	68925*	68938*
68900‡	68913*	68926*	68939*
68901*	68914*	68927*	68940†
68902*	68915*	68928*	68941†

68942†	68955†	68968†	68981§
68943†	68956†	68969†	68982§
68944†	68957†	68970†	68983§
68945†	68958†	68971†	68984§
68946†	68959†	68972†	68985§
68947†	68960†	68973†	68986§
68948†	68961†	68974†	68987§
68949†	68962†	68975†	68988§
68950†	68963†	68976†	68989§
68951†	68964†	68977†	68990§
68952†	68965†	68978§	68991§
68953†	68966†	68979§	
68954†	68967†	68980§	

Total

Class J50/1 10   Class J50/3 38
Class J50/2 40   Class J50/4 14

0-6-0T   2F   Class J72

(Continued from 68754)

69001	69008	69015	69022
69002	69009	69016	69023
69003	69010	69017	69024
69004	69011	69018	69025
69005	69012	69019	69026
69006	69013	69020	69027
69007	69014	69021	69028

Total 113

0-6-2T   3F   Class N10

Introduced 1902. W. Worsdell N.E. design.
Weight: 57 tons 14 cwt.
Pressure: 160 lb.
Cyls.: $18\frac{1}{2}'' \times 26''$.
Driving Wheels: $4'\ 7\frac{1}{4}''$.
T.E.: 21,905 lb.

69092	69101	69104	69106
69097	69102	69105	69109
69099			

Total 9

0-6-2T   3MT   Class N15

N15/2* Introduced 1910. Reid N.B. design developed from N14. Cowlairs Incline banking locos.

N15/1 Introduced 1910. Development of N15/2 with smaller bunker for normal duties.

Weight: $\begin{cases} 62 \text{ tons } 1 \text{ cwt.*} \\ 60 \text{ tons } 18 \text{ cwt.} \end{cases}$

Pressure: 175 lb.
Cyls.: $18'' \times 26''$.
Driving Wheels: $4'\ 6''$.
T.E.: 23,205 lb.

69126*	69151	69176	69200
69127*	69152	69177	69202
69128*	69153	69178	69203
69129*	69154	69179	69204
69131*	69155	69180	69205
69132	69156	69181	69206
69133	69157	69182	69207
69134	69158	69183	69208
69135	69159	69184	69209
69136	69160	69185	69211
69137	69161	69186	69212
69138	69162	69187	69213
69139	69163	69188	69214
69140	69164	69189	69215
69141	69165	69190	69216
69142	69166	69191	69217
69143	69168	69192	69218
69144	69169	69193	69219
69145	69170	69194	69220
69146	69171	69195	69221
69147	69172	69196	69222
69148	69173	69197	69223
69149	69174	69198	69224
69150	69175	69199	

Total

Class N15/1 90 Class N15/2 5

0-6-2T   2MT   Class N5

N5/2. Introduced 1891. Parker M.S. & L. design developed from N4.
*Push-and-pull fitted.
Weight: 62 tons 7 cwt.

Pressure: 160 lb.
Cyls.: 18″ × 26″.
Driving Wheels: 5′ 1″.
T.E.: 18,780 lb.

69257*	69276	69299	69342
69258	69281	69307	69343
69259	69283	69308	69344
69262	69286	69309	69349
69263	69290	69314	69354
69265	69292	69315	69355
69266	69293	69319	69360
69267	69294	69320	69361
69268	69295	69322	69362
69269	69296	69327	69370
69271	69297	69332	
69274	69298	69341	

Total 46

0-6-2T   2MT   Class N1

††§Introduced 1907. Standard Ivatt G.N. design.

§Rebuilt with superheater and reduced pressure.

‡Fitted with condensing apparatus.

Weight: 65 tons 17 cwt.
Pressure: $\begin{cases} 175 \text{ lb.} \dagger\ddagger \\ 170 \text{ lb. Su.} \S \end{cases}$
Cyls.: 18″ × 26″.
Driving Wheels: 5′ 8″.
T.E.: $\begin{cases} 18,430 \text{ lb.} \dagger\ddagger \\ 17,900 \text{ lb.} \S \end{cases}$

69434‡	69452§	69462‡	69474†
69443†	69453§	69472§	69477‡
69450†			

Total 9

0-6-2T   3P2F   Class N2

N2/2* Introduced 1925. Post-grouping development of Gresley G.N. N2/1, introduced 1920, which class is now included in N2/2. Built with condensing apparatus and small chimney.

N2/2† Condensing apparatus removed.

N2/3‡ Introduced 1925. Locos. built non-condensing, originally fitted with large chimney. Some now with small chimney.

N2/4§ Introduced 1928. Development of N2/2, slightly heavier. Built with condensing apparatus and small chimney.

(The small chimneys are to suit the Metropolitan loading gauge, for working to Moorgate. Condensing apparatus has been removed from or added to certain locos. transferred from or to the London area.)

Weight: $\begin{cases} 70 \text{ tons 5 cwt.} *† \\ 70 \text{ tons 8 cwt.} ‡ \\ 71 \text{ tons 9 cwt.} \S \end{cases}$
Pressure: 170 lb. Su.
Cyls.: 19″ × 26″.
Driving Wheels: 5′ 8″.
T.E.: 19,945 lb.
P.V.

69490*	69520*	69544*	69573§
69491*	69521*	69545*	69574§
69492*	69522*	69546*	69575§
69493*	69523*	69547*	69576§
69495*	69524*	69548*	69577§
69496*	69525*	69549*	69578§
69497*	69526*	69550†	69579§
69498*	69527*	69551†	69580§
69499*	69528*	69552†	69581§
69502†	69529*	69553†	69582§
69504*	69530*	69554†	69583§
69505*	69531*	69555†	69584§
69506*	69532*	69556§	69585§
69507†	69533*	69560†	69586§
69508†	69534*	69561†	69587§
69509*	69535*	69563‡	69588§
69510†	69536*	69564‡	69589§
69511†	69537*	69565‡	69591§
69512*	69538*	69567‡	69592§
69513*	69539*	69568§	69593§
69515†	69540*	69569§	69594‡
69516†	69541*	69570§	69596‡
69517*	69542*	69571§	
69518†	69543*	69572§	

Total

Class N2/2 62   Class N2/4 26
Class N2/3 6

0-6-2T 3MT Class N7

N7/2[5] Introduced 1926. Post-grouping development of Hill G.E. design (N7) with long-travel valves.

N7/3[1] Introduced 1927. Doncaster-built version of N7/2 but with round-topped firebox.

N7/3[3] Introduced 1943. N7/2 rebuilt with round-topped firebox.

N7/4[3] Introduced 1940. Pre-grouping G.E. design N7, rebuilt with round-topped firebox, retaining short-travel valves.

N7/5[4] Introduced 1943. Post-grouping development of G.E. design N7/1, rebuilt with round-topped firebox, retaining short-travel valves.

Weight: $\begin{cases} 64 \text{ tons.}^{1\,2\,4} \\ 61 \text{ tons 16 cwt.}^3 \\ 64 \text{ tons 17 cwt.}^5 \end{cases}$

Pressure: 180 lb. Su.

Cyls.: $18'' \times 24''$.

Driving Wheels: 4' 10".

T.E.: 20,515 lb.

Walschaerts valve gear. P.V.

69600[3]	69623[4]	69646[4]	69669[4]
69601[3]	69624[4]	69647[4]	69670[4]
69602[3]	69625[4]	69648[4]	69671[4]
69603[3]	69626[4]	69649[4]	69672[4]
69604[3]	69627[4]	69650[4]	69673[2]
69605[3]	69628[4]	69651[4]	69674[2]
69606[3]	69629[4]	69652[4]	69675[2]
69607[3]	69630[4]	69653[4]	69676[2]
69608[3]	69631[4]	69654[4]	69677[2]
69609[3]	69632[4]	69655[4]	69678[2]
69610[3]	69633[4]	69656[4]	69679[2]
69611[3]	69634[4]	69657[4]	69680[2]
69612[3]	69635[4]	69658[4]	69681[2]
69613[3]	69636[4]	69659[4]	69682[2]
69614[3]	69637[4]	69660[4]	69683[2]
69615[3]	69638[4]	69661[4]	69684[2]
69616[3]	69639[4]	69662[4]	69685[2]
69617[3]	69640[4]	69663[4]	69686[2]
69618[3]	69641[4]	69664[4]	69687[2]
69619[3]	69642[4]	69665[4]	69688[2]
69620[3]	69643[4]	69666[4]	69690[2]
69621[3]	69644[4]	69667[4]	69691[2]
69622[4]	69645[4]	69668[4]	69692[2]

69693[2]	69704[1]	69715[1]	69726[1]
69694[2]	69705[1]	69716[1]	69727[1]
69695[5]	69706[1]	69717[1]	69728[1]
69696[2]	69707[1]	69718[1]	69729[1]
69697[2]	69708[1]	69719[1]	69730[1]
69698[2]	69709[1]	69720[1]	69731[1]
69699[2]	69710[1]	69721[1]	69732[1]
69700[2]	69711[1]	69722[1]	69733[1]
69701[2]	69712[1]	69723[1]	
69702[1]	69713[1]	69724[1]	
69703[1]	69714[1]	69725[1]	

Total

Class N7/2 1 Class N7/4 22

Class N7/3 60 Class N7/5 50

4-6-2T 3MT Class A5

A5/1 Introduced 1911. Robinson G.C. design.

A5/2* Introduced 1925. Post-grouping development of A5/1 with reduced boiler mountings and detail differences.

Weight: $\begin{cases} 85 \text{ tons 18 cwt.} \\ 90 \text{ tons 11 cwt.}^* \end{cases}$

Pressure: 180 lb. Su.

Cyls.: $20'' \times 26''$.

Driving Wheels: 5' 7".

T.E.: 23,750 lb.

P.V.

69800	69811	69824	69836*
69801	69812	69825	69837*
69802	69813	69826	69838*
69803	69814	69827	69839*
69804	69816	69828	69840*
69805	69817	69829	69841*
69806	69818	69830*	69842*
69807	69820	69831*	
69808	69821	69832*	
69809	69822	69834*	
69810	69823	69835*	

Total

Class A5/1 28 Class A5/2 12

4-6-2T 3MT Class A8

Introduced 1931. Gresley rebuild of Raven N.E. Class "D" 4-4-4T (introduced 1913).
Weight: 86 tons 18 cwt.
Pressure: 175 lb. Su.
Cyls.: (3) 16½" × 26".
Driving Wheels: 5' 9".
T.E.: 22,940 lb.
P.V.

69850	69861	69873	69885
69851	69862	69874	69886
69852	69863	69875	69887
69853	69864	69877	69888
69854	69865	69878	69889
69855	69866	69879	69891
69856	69867	69880	69892
69857	69869	69881	69893
69858	69870	69882	69894
69859	69871	69883	
69860	69872	69884	

Total 42

4-8-0T 5F Class T1

Introduced 1909. W. Worsdell N.E. design.
Weight: 85 tons 8 cwt.

Pressure: 175 lb.
Cyls.: (3) 18" × 26".
Driving Wheels: 4' 7¼".
T.E.: 34,080 lb.
P.V.

69910	69915	69918	69921
69912	69917	69920	

Total 7

0-8-0T 5F Class Q1

Thompson rebuild of Robinson G.C. Q4 0-8-0, introduced 1902.
Q1/1* Introduced 1942. 1,500 gallon tanks.
Q1/2 Introduced 1943. 2,000 gallon tanks.
Weight: { 69 tons 18 cwt.*
{ 73 tons 13 cwt.
Pressure: 180 lb.
Cyls.: (O) 19" × 26".
Driving Wheels: 4' 8".
T.E.: 25,645 lb.

69928*	69931	69933	69935
69929	69932	69934	69936
69930			

Total 9

BRITISH RAILWAYS
EASTERN & NORTH EASTERN REGIONS

CHIEF MECHANICAL ENGINEER

A. H. Peppercorn ... 1948–1949
(post abolished)

LOCOMOTIVE SUPERINTENDENTS AND CHIEF MECHANICAL ENGINEERS OF THE L.N.E.R.

| Sir Nigel Gresley ... | ... | 1923–1941 | E. Thompson | ... | ... | 1941–1946 |
| | A. H. Peppercorn ... | ... | 1946–1947 | | | |

GREAT NORTHERN RAILWAY

A. Sturrock	...	...	1850–1866
P. Stirling ...	...	...	1866–1895
H. A. Ivatt ...	...	...	1896–1911
H. N. Gresley	...	...	1911–1922

NORTH EASTERN RAILWAY

E. Fletcher	...	...	1854–1883
A. McDonnell*	...	...	1883–1884
T. W. Worsdell	...	...	1885–1890
W. Worsdell	...	...	1890–1910
Sir Vincent Raven	...	1910–1922

GREAT EASTERN RAILWAY

R. Sinclair ...	...	...	1862–1866
S. W. Johnson	...	...	1866–1873
W. Adams ...	...	...	1873–1878
M. Bromley	...	...	1878–1881
T. W. Worsdell	...	...	1881–1885
J. Holden ...	...	...	1885–1907
S. D. Holden	...	...	1908–1912
A. J. Hill ...	...	...	1912–1922

LANCASHIRE, DERBYSHIRE AND EAST COAST RAILWAY

| R. A. Thom | ... | ... | 1902–1907 |

MANCHESTER, SHEFFIELD AND LINCOLNSHIRE RAILWAY

| Richard Peacock | ... | ... | –1854 |
| W. G. Craig | ... | ... | 1854–1859 |

Charles Sacré	...	...	1859–1886
T. Parker ...	...	...	1886–1893
H. Pollitt ...	...	...	1893–1897

GREAT CENTRAL RAILWAY

| H. Pollitt ... | ... | ... | 1897–1900 |
| J. G. Robinson | ... | ... | 1900–1922 |

HULL AND BARNSLEY RAILWAY

| M. Stirling ... | ... | ... | 1885–1922 |

MIDLAND AND GREAT NORTHERN JOINT RAILWAY

| W. Marriott | ... | ... | 1884–1924 |

NORTH BRITISH RAILWAY

T. Wheatley†	...	...	1867–1874
D. Drummond	...	...	1875–1882
M. Holmes ...	...	...	1882–1903
W. P. Reid	...	...	1903–1919
W. Chalmers	...	...	1919–1922

GREAT NORTH OF SCOTLAND RAILWAY

D. K. Clark	...	...	1853–1855
J. F. Ruthven	...	...	1855–1857
W. Cowan ...	...	...	1857–1883
J. Manson ...	...	...	1883–1890
J. Johnson ...	...	...	1890–1894
W. Pickersgill	...	...	1594–1914
T. E. Heywood	...	...	1914–1922

* Between McDonnell and T. W. Worsdell there was an interval during which the office was covered by a Locomotive Committee.

† Previous to whom the records are indeterminate.

Top : Class J83
0-6-0T No. 68468
[P. H. Groom

Centre : Class J88
0-6-0T No. 68322
[P. H. Groom

Right : Class N15/1
0-6-2T No. 69170
[W. S. Sellar

Class N1 0-6-2T No. 69477   [B. K. B. Green

Class N2/3 0-6-2T No. 69565   [David A. Anderson

Class N2/4 0-6-2T No. 69571   [B. K. B. Green

Class N7/3 0-6-2T No. 69716   [A. R. Carpenter

Class N7/5 0-6-2T No. 69624   [Brian E. Morrison

Class N5 0-6-2T No. 69342   [Peter J. Robinson

Class A5/2 4-6-2T No. 69839

[B. K. B. Green

Class A8 4-6-2T No. 69877

[L. King

Class V1 2-6-2T No. 67644

David A. Anderson

BRITISH RAILWAYS STANDARD LOCOMOTIVES
Chief Officer (Mechanical Engineering) :
R. C. BOND

4-6-2　　　　　　　　　**7P6F**

Introduced 1951. Designed at Derby.
Weight: Loco. 94 tons 0 cwt.
Pressure: 250 lb. Su.
Cyls.: (O) 20″ × 28″.
Driving Wheels: 6′ 2″. T.E.: 32,150 lb.
Walschaerts valve gear. P.V.

70000	Britannia
70001	Lord Hurcomb
70002	Geoffrey Chaucer
70003	John Bunyan
70004	William Shakespeare
70005	John Milton
70006	Robert Burns
70007	Coeur-de-Lion
70008	Black Prince
70009	Alfred the Great
70010	Owen Glendower
70011	Hotspur
70012	John of Gaunt
70013	Oliver Cromwell
70014	Iron Duke
70015	Apollo
70016	Ariel
70017	Arrow
70018	Flying Dutchman
70019	Lightning
70020	Mercury
70021	Morning Star
70022	Tornado
70023	Venus
70024	Vulcan
70025	Western Star
70026	Polar Star
70027	Rising Star
70028	Royal Star
70029	Shooting Star
70030	William Wordsworth
70031	Byron
70032	Tennyson
70033	Charles Dickens
70034	Thomas Hardy
70035	Rudyard Kipling
70036	Boadicea
70037	Hereward the Wake
70038	Robin Hood
70039	Sir Christopher Wren
70040	Clive of India
70041	Sir John Moore
70042	Lord Roberts
70043	Lord Kitchener
70044	Earl Haig
70045	Lord Rowallan
70046	
70047	
70048	
70049	
70050	Firth of Clyde
70051	Firth of Forth
70052	Firth of Tay
70053	Moray Firth
70054	Dornoch Firth

Total 55

4-6-2　　　　　　　　　**8P**

Introduced 1954. Designed at Derby.
Weight: Loco. 101 tons 5 cwt.
Pressure: 250 lb. Su.
Cyls.: (3) 18″ × 28″.
Driving Wheels: 6′ 2″. T.E.: 39,080 lb.
Caprotti valve gear.

71000	Duke of Gloucester

Total 1

4-6-2　　　　　　　　　**6P5F**

Introduced 1952. Designed at Derby.
Weight: Loco. 86 tons 19 cwt.
Pressure: 225 lb. Su.
Cyls.: (O) 19½″ × 28″.
Driving Wheels: 6′ 2″. T.E.: 27,520 lb.
Walschaerts valve gear. P.V.

72000	Clan Buchanan
72001	Clan Cameron
72002	Clan Campbell

72003	Clan Fraser	
72004	Clan Macdonald	
72005	Clan Macgregor	
72006	Clan Mackenzie	
72007	Clan Mackintosh	
72008	Clan Macleod	
72009	Clan Stewart	**Total 10**

4-6-0   5

Introduced 1951. Designed at Doncaster.
*Introduced 1956. Fitted with Caprotti valve gear.
Weight: Loco. 76 tons 4 cwt.
Pressure: 225 lb. Su.
Cyls.: (O) 19″ × 28″.
Driving Wheels: 6′ 2″. T.E.: 26,120 lb.
Walschaerts valve gear. P.V.

73000	73028	73056	73084
73001	73029	73057	73085
73002	73030	73058	73086
73003	73031	73059	73087
73004	73032	73060	73088
73005	73033	73061	73089
73006	73034	73062	73090
73007	73035	73063	73091
73008	73036	73064	73092
73009	73037	73065	73093
73010	73038	73066	73094
73011	73039	73067	73095
73012	73040	73068	73096
73013	73041	73069	73097
73014	73042	73070	73098
73015	73043	73071	73099
73016	73044	73072	73100
73017	73045	73073	73101
73018	73046	73074	73102
73019	73047	73075	73103
73020	73048	73076	73104
73021	73049	73077	73105
73022	73050	73078	73106
73023	73051	73079	73107
73024	73052	73080	73108
73025	73053	73081	73109
73026	73054	73082	73110
73027	73055	73083	73111

73112	73127*	73142*	73157
73113	73128*	73143*	73158
73114	73129*	73144*	73159
73115	73130*	73145*	73160
73116	73131*	73146*	73161
73117	73132*	73147*	73162
73118	73133*	73148*	73163
73119	73134*	73149*	73164
73120	73135*	73150*	73165
73121	73136*	73151*	73166
73122	73137*	73152*	73167
73123	73138*	73153*	73168
73124	73139*	73154*	73169
73125*	73140*	73155	73170
73126*	73141*	73156	73171

Total 172

4-6-0   4

Introduced 1951. Designed at Brighton.
*Introduced 1957. Fitted with double chimney.
Weight: Loco. 69 tons 0 cwt.
Pressure: 225 lb. Su.
Cyls.: (O) 18″ × 28″.
Driving Wheels: 5′ 8″. T.E.: 25,100 lb.
Walschaerts valve gear. P.V.

75000	75020	75040	75060
75001	75021	75041	75061
75002	75022	75042	75062
75003	75023	75043	75063
75004	75024	75044	75064
75005	75025	75045	75065
75006	75026	75046	75066
75007	75027	75047	75067
75008	75028	75048	75068
75009	75029*	75049	75069
75010	75030	75050	75070
75011	75031	75051	75071
75012	75032	75052	75072
75013	75033	75053	75073
75014	75034	75054	75074
75015	75035	75055	75075
75016	75036	75056	75076
75017	75037	75057	75077
75018	75038	75058	75078
75019	75039	75059	75079

Total 80

2-6-0   4

Introduced 1953. Designed at Doncaster.
Weight: Loco. 59 tons 2 cwt.
Pressure: 225 lb. Su.
Cyls.: (O) $17\frac{1}{2}'' \times 26''$.
Driving Wheels: 5' 3". T.E.: 24,170 lb.
Walschaerts valve gear. P.V.

76000	76029	76058	76087
76001	76030	76059	76088
76002	76031	76060	76089
76003	76032	76061	76090
76004	76033	76062	76091
76005	76034	76063	76092
76006	76035	76064	76093
76007	76036	76065	76094
76008	76037	76066	76095
76009	76038	76067	76096
76010	76039	76068	76097
76011	76040	76069	76098
76012	76041	76070	76099
76013	76042	76071	76100
76014	76043	76072	76101
76015	76044	76073	76102
76016	76045	76074	76103
76017	76046	76075	76104
76018	76047	76076	76105
76019	76048	76077	76106
76020	76049	76078	76107
76021	76050	76079	76108
76022	76051	76080	76109
76023	76052	76081	76110
76024	76053	76082	76111
76025	76054	76083	76112
76026	76055	76084	76113
76027	76056	76085	76114
76028	76057	76086	

Total 115

2-6-0   3

Introduced 1954. Designed at Swindon.
Weight: Loco. 57 tons 9 cwt.
Pressure: 200 lb. Su.
Cyls.: (O) $17\frac{1}{2}'' \times 26''$.
Driving Wheels: 5' 3". T.E.: 21,490 lb.
Walschaerts valve gear. P.V.

77000	77005	77010	77015
77001	77006	77011	77016
77002	77007	77012	77017
77003	77008	77013	77018
77004	77009	77014	77019

Total 20

2-6-0   2

Introduced 1953. Designed at Derby.
Weight: Loco. 49 tons 5 cwt.
Pressure: 200 lb. Su.
Cyls.: (O) $16\frac{1}{2}'' \times 24''$.
Driving Wheels: 5' 0". T.E.: 18,515 lb.
Walschaerts valve gear. P.V.

78000	78017	78034	78051
78001	78018	78035	78052
78002	78019	78036	78053
78003	78020	78037	78054
78004	78021	78038	78055
78005	78022	78039	78056
78006	78023	78040	78057
78007	78024	78041	78058
78008	78025	78042	78059
78009	78026	78043	78060
78010	78027	78044	78061
78011	78028	78045	78062
78012	78029	78046	78063
78013	78030	78047	78064
78014	78031	78048	
78015	78032	78049	
78016	78033	78050	

Total 65

2-6-4T   4

Introduced 1951. Designed at Brighton.
Weight: 88 tons 10 cwt.
Pressure: 225 lb. Su.
Cyls.: (O) $18'' \times 28''$.
Driving Wheels: 5' 8". T.E.: 25,100 lb.
Walschaerts valve gear. P.V.

80000	80005	80010	80015
80001	80006	80011	80016
80002	80007	80012	80017
80003	80008	80013	80018
80004	80009	80014	80019

80020	80054	80088	80122
80021	80055	80089	80123
80022	80056	80090	80124
80023	80057	80091	80125
80024	80058	80092	80126
80025	80059	80093	80127
80026	80060	80094	80128
80027	80061	80095	80129
80028	80062	80096	80130
80029	80063	80097	80131
80030	80064	80098	80132
80031	80065	80099	80133
80032	80066	80100	80134
80033	80067	80101	80135
80034	80068	80102	80136
80035	80069	80103	80137
80036	80070	80104	80138
80037	80071	80105	80139
80038	80072	80106	80140
80039	80073	80107	80141
80040	80074	80108	80142
80041	80075	80109	80143
80042	80076	80110	80144
80043	80077	80111	80145
80044	80078	80112	80146
80045	80079	80113	80147
80046	80080	80114	80148
80047	80081	80115	80149
80048	80082	80116	80150
80049	80083	80117	80151
80050	80084	80118	80152
80051	80085	80119	80153
80052	80086	80120	80154
80053	80087	80121	

Total 155

2-6-2T 3

Introduced 1952. Designed at Swindon.
Weight: 73 tons 10 cwt.
Pressure: 200 lb. Su.
Cyls.: (O) $17\frac{1}{2}'' \times 26''$.
Driving Wheels: 5' 3". T.E.: 21,490 lb.
Walschaerts valve gear. P.V.

82000	82002	82004	82006
82001	82003	82005	82007

82008	82018	82028	82038
82009	82019	82029	82039
82010	82020	82030	82040
82011	82021	82031	82041
82012	82022	82032	82042
82013	82023	82033	82043
82014	82024	82034	82044
82015	82025	82035	
82016	82026	82036	
82017	82027	82037	

Total 45

2-6-2T 2

Introduced 1953. Designed at Derby.
Weight: 63 tons 5 cwt.
Pressure: 200 lb. Su.
Cyls.: (O) $16\frac{1}{2}'' \times 24''$.
Driving Wheels: 5' 0". T.E.: 18,515 lb.
Walschaerts valve gear. P.V.

84000	84008	84016	84024
84001	84009	84017	84025
84002	84010	84018	84026
84003	84011	84019	84027
84004	84012	84020	84028
84005	84013	84021	84029
84006	84014	84022	
84007	84015	84023	

Total 30

2-8-0 8F WD

Ministry of Supply " Austerity " 2-8-0
locomotives purchased by British
Railways, 1948.
Introduced 1943. Riddles M.o.S. design.
Weight: Loco.   70 tons 5 cwt.
         Tender 55 tons 10 cwt.
Pressure: 225 lb. Su.
Cyls.: (O) $19'' \times 28''$.
Driving Wheels: 4' 8½". T.E.: 34,215 lb.
Walschaerts valve gear. P.V.

90000	90009	90018	90027
90001	90010	90019	90028
90002	90011	90020	90029
90003	90012	90021	90030
90004	90013	90022	90031
90005	90014	90023	90032
90006	90015	90024	90033
90007	90016	90025	90034
90008	90017	90026	90035

90036	90083	90130	90177	90224	90271	90318	90365
90037	90084	90131	90178	90225	90272	90319	90366
90038	90085	90132	90179	90226	90273	90320	90367
90039	90086	90133	90180	90227	90274	90321	90368
90040	90087	90134	90181	90228	90275	90322	90369
90041	90088	90135	90182	90229	90276	90323	90370
90042	90089	90136	90183	90230	90277	90324	90371
90043	90090	90137	90184	90231	90278	90325	90372
90044	90091	90138	90185	90232	90279	90326	90373
90045	90092	90139	90186	90233	90280	90327	90374
90046	90093	90140	90187	90234	90281	90328	90375
90047	90094	90141	90188	90235	90282	90329	90376
90048	90095	90142	90189	90236	90283	90330	90377
90049	90096	90143	90190	90237	90284	90331	90378
90050	90097	90144	90191	90238	90285	90332	90379
90051	90098	90145	90192	90239	90286	90333	90380
90052	90099	90146	90193	90240	90287	90334	90381
90053	90100	90147	90194	90241	90288	90335	90382
90054	90101	90148	90195	90242	90289	90336	90383
90055	90102	90149	90196	90243	90290	90337	90384
90056	90103	90150	90197	90244	90291	90338	90385
90057	90104	90151	90198	90245	90292	90339	90386
90058	90105	90152	90199	90246	90293	90340	90387
90059	90106	90153	90200	90247	90294	90341	90388
90060	90107	90154	90201	90248	90295	90342	90389
90061	90108	90155	90202	90249	90296	90343	90390
90062	90109	90156	90203	90250	90297	90344	90391
90063	90110	90157	90204	90251	90298	90345	90392
90064	90111	90158	90205	90252	90299	90346	90393
90065	90112	90159	90206	90253	90300	90347	90394
90066	90113	90160	90207	90254	90301	90348	90395
90067	90114	90161	90208	90255	90302	90349	90396
90068	90115	90162	90209	90256	90303	90350	90397
90069	90116	90163	90210	90257	90304	90351	90398
90070	90117	90164	90211	90258	90305	90352	90399
90071	90118	90165	90212	90259	90306	90353	90400
90072	90119	90166	90213	90260	90307	90354	90401
90073	90120	90167	90214	90261	90308	90355	90402
90074	90121	90168	90215	90262	90309	90356	90403
90075	90122	90169	90216	90263	90310	90357	90404
90076	90123	90170	90217	90264	90311	90358	90405
90077	90124	90171	90218	90265	90312	90359	90406
90078	90125	90172	90219	90266	90313	90360	90407
90079 -	90126	90173	90220	90267	90314	90361	90408
90080	90127	90174	90221	90268	90315	90362	90409
90081	90128	90175	90222	90269	90316	90363	90410
90082	90129	90176	90223	90270	90317	90364	90411

90412	90459	90506	90553	90600	90634	90668	90702
90413	90460	90507	90554	90601	90635	90669	90703
90414	90461	90508	90555	90602	90636	90670	90704
90415	90462	90509	90556	90603	90637	90671	90705
90416	90463	90510	90557	90604	90638	90672	90706
90417	90464	90511	90558	90605	90639	90673	90707
90418	90465	90512	90559	90606	90640	90674	90708
90419	90466	90513	90560	90607	90641	90675	90709
90420	90467	90514	90561	90608	90642	90676	90710
90421	90468	90515	90562	90609	90643	90677	90711
90422	90469	90516	90563	90610	90644	90678	90712
90423	90470	90517	90564	90611	90645	90679	90713
90424	90471	90518	90565	90612	90646	90680	90714
90425	90472	90519	90566	90613	90647	90681	90715
90426	90473	90520	90567	90614	90648	90682	90716
90427	90474	90521	90568	90615	90649	90683	90717
90428	90475	90522	90569	90616	90650	90684	90718
90429	90476	90523	90570	90617	90651	90685	90719
90430	90477	90524	90571	90618	90652	90686	90720
90431	90478	90525	90572	90619	90653	90687	90721
90432	90479	90526	90573	90620	90654	90688	90722
90433	90480	90527	90574	90621	90655	90689	90723
90434	90481	90528	90575	90622	90656	90690	90724
90435	90482	90529	90576	90623	90657	90691	90725
90436	90483	90530	90577	90624	90658	90692	90726
90437	90484	90531	90578	90625	90659	90693	90727
90438	90485	90532	90579	90626	90660	90694	90728
90439	90486	90533	90580	90627	90661	90695	90729
90440	90487	90534	90581	90628	90662	90696	90730
90441	90488	90535	90582	90629	90663	90697	90731
90442	90489	90536	90583	90630	90664	90698	90732
90443	90490	90537	90584	90631	90665	90699	Vulcan
90444	90491	90538	90585	90632	90666	90700	
90445	90492	90539	90586	90633	90667	90701	
90446	90493	90540	90587				
90447	90494	90541	90588				
90448	90495	90542	90589				
90449	90496	90543	90590				
90450	90497	90544	90591				
90451	90498	90545	90592				
90452	90499	90546	90593				
90453	90500	90547	90594				
90454	90501	90548	90595				
90455	90502	90549	90596				
90456	90503	90550	90597				
90457	90504	90551	90598				
90458	90505	90552	90599				

Total 733

2-10-0   WD

Ministry of Supply " Austerity " 2-10-0 locomotives purchased by British Railways, 1948.
Introduced 1943. Riddles M.o.S. design.
Weight: Loco. 78 tons 6 cwt.
         Tender 55 tons 10 cwt.
Pressure: 225 lb. Su.
Cyls.: (O) 19″ × 28″.
Driving Wheels: 4′ 8½″. T.E.: 34,215 lb.
Walschaerts valve gear. P.V.

90750	90757	90764	90771
90751	90758	90765	90772
90752	90759	90766	90773
90753	90760	90767	90774
90754	90761	90768	
90755	90762	90769	
90756	90763	90770	

Total 25

2-10-0   9F

Introduced 1954. Designed at Brighton.

*Introduced 1955. Fitted with Crosti boiler.

†Introduced 1957. Fitted with double chimney.

Weight: Loco. { 86 tons 14 cwt.
{ 90 tons 4 cwt.*

Pressure: 250 lb. Su.

Cyls.: (O) 20″ × 28″.

Driving Wheels: 5′ 0″. T.E.: 39,670 lb.

Walschaerts valve gear. P.V.

92000	92025*	92050	92075
92001	92026*	92051	92076
92002	92027*	92052	92077
92003	92028*	92053	92078
92004	92029*	92054	92079
92005	92030	92055	92080
92006	92031	92056	92081
92007	92032	92057	92082
92008	92033	92058	92083
92009	92034	92059	92084
92010	92035	92060	92085
92011	92036	92061	92086
92012	92037	92062	92087
92013	92038	92063	92088
92014	92039	92064	92089
92015	92040	92065	92090
92016	92041	92066	92091
92017	92042	92067	92092
92018	92043	92068	92093
92019	92044	92069	92094
92020*	92045	92070	92095
92021*	92046	92071	92096
92022*	92047	92072	92097
92023*	92048	92073	92098
92024*	92049	92074	92099

92100	92126	92152	92178†
92101	92127	92153	92179
92102	92128	92154	92180
92103	92129	92155	92181
92104	92130	92156	92182
92105	92131	92157	92183
92106	92132	92158	92184†
92107	92133	92159	92185†
92108	92134	92160	92186
92109	92135	92161	92187†
92110	92136	92162	92188
92111	92137	92163	92189
92112	92138	92164	92190
92113	92139	92165	92191
92114	92140	92166	92192
92115	92141	92167	92193
92116	92142	92168	92194
92117	92143	92169	92195
92118	92144	92170	92196
92119	92145	92171	92197
92120	92146	92172	92198
92121	92147	92173	92199
92122	92148	92174	92200
92123	92149	92175	92201
92124	92150	92176	92202
92125	92151	92177	

Engines of this class are still being delivered.

BRITISH RAILWAYS STANDARD TENDERS

N.B.—*These pairings are not permanent and are liable to alteration with changed operating conditions.*

Type	Capacity		Weight in full W.O.		Locos. to which Allocated
	Water galls.	Coal tons	tons	cwt.	
BRI ...	4,250	7	49	3	70000–24/30–44 72000–9 73000–49
BRIA ...	5,000	7	52	10	70025–29
BRIB ...	4,725	7	50	5	92020–29/60–6/97–9 73080–89 73100–9/20–34/45–71 75065–79 76053–69
BRIC ...	4,725	9	53	5	92015–19/45–59/77–86 92100–39/50–67 73065–79/90–9 73135–44
BRID ...	4,725	9	54	10	70045–54
BRIE ...	4,725	10	55	10	71000
BRIF ...	5,625	7	55	5	92010–14/30–44/67–76 92087–96 92140–49/68–92202 73110–19
BRIG ...	5,000	7	52	10	92000–9 73050–52
BRIH ...	4,250	7	49	3	73053–64
BR2 ...	3,500	6	42	3	75000–49 76000–44
BR2A ...	3,500	6	42	3	75050–64/80–9 76045–52/70–76114 77000–24
BR3 ...	3,000	4	36	17	78000–64

ELECTRIC TRAIN UNIT NUMBERS
Eastern and North Eastern Regions

LIVERPOOL ST.–SOUTHEND 4-CAR ELECTRIC TRAIN UNITS

01s	05s	09s	13s	17s	21s	25s	29s
02s	06s	10s	14s	18s	22s	26s	30s
03s	07s	11s	15s	19s	23s	27s	31s
04s	08s	12s	16s	20s	24s	28s	32s

LIVERPOOL ST.–SHENFIELD 3-CAR ELECTRIC TRAIN UNITS

01	11	21	31	41	51	61	71	81	91
02	12	22	32	42	52	62	72	82	92
03	13	23	33	43	53	63	73	83	
04	14	24	34	44	54	64	74	84	
05	15	25	35	45	55	65	75	85	
06	16	26	36	46	56	66	76	86	
07	17	27	37	47	57	67	77	87	
08	18	28	38	48	58	68	78	88	
09	19	29	39	49	59	69	79	89	
10	20	30	40	50	60	70	80	90	

GRIMSBY–IMMINGHAM ELECTRIC TRAMS

1	11	15	18	21	24	27	30	33
4	12	16	19	22	25	28	31	
5	14	17	20	23	26	29	32	

SOUTH TYNESIDE ELECTRIC MOTOR COACHES

E65311	E65314	E65317	E65320	E65323
E65312	E65315	E65318	E65321	E65324
E65313	E65316	E65319	E65322	E65325

Motor Parcels Van E68000

NORTH TYNESIDE ELECTRIC TWIN-UNIT MOTOR COACHES

E29101E	E29113E	E29124E	E29135E	E29147E	E29158E
E29102E	E29114E	E29125E	E29136E	E29148E	E29159E
E29103E	E29115E	E29126E	E29137E	E29149E	E29160E
E29104E	E29116E	E29127E	E29138E	E29150E	E29161E
E29105E	E29117E	E29128E	E29139E	E29151E	E29162E
E29106E	E29118E	E29129E	E29140E	E29152E	E29163E
E29107E	E29119E	E29130E	E29141E	E29153E	E29164E
E29108E	E29120E	E29131E	E29142E	E29154E	
E29109E	E29121E	E29132E	E29144E	E29155E	
E29110E	E29122E	E29133E	E29145E	E29156E	
E29111E	E29123E	E29134E	E29146E	E29157E	

Motor Parcels Vans		Motor Coaches	
E29467E	E29468E	E29165E	E29166E

| E59401E | E59403E | E59405E | E59407E |
| E59402E | E59404E | E59406E | E59408E |

London Midland Region
(Motor coach numbers)
LONDON DISTRICT

OPEN STOCK

			M28267M	M28281M	M28292M
M28000M	M28246M	M28258M	M28269M	M28282M	M28294M
M28224M	M28248M	M28259M	M28270M	M28283M	M28295M
M28225M	M28249M	M28260M	M28272M	M28284M	M28296M
M28226M	M28252M	M28261M	M28273M	M28285M	M28297M
M28228M	M28253M	M28262M	M28274M	M28286M	M28298M
M28229M	M28254M	M28263M	M28275M	M28287M	M28299M
M28230M	M28255M	M28264M	M28277M	M28288M	
M28237M	M28256M	M28265M	M28279M	M28289M	
M28242M	M28257M	M28266M	M28280M	M28290M	

COMPARTMENT STOCK

			M28013M	M28018M	M28023M
M28001M	M28005M	M28009M	M28014M	M28019M	M28024M
M28002M	M28006M	M28010M	M28015M	M28020M	M28025M
M28003M	M28007M	M28011M	M28016M	M28021M	
M28004M	M28008M	M28012M	M28017M	M28022M	

1957 STOCK

	M61149	M61158	M61167	M61176	M61185
M61133	M61141	M61150	M61159	M61168	M61177	M61186
M61134	M61142	M61151	M61160	M61169	M61178	M61187
M61135	M61143	M61152	M61161	M61170	M61179	M61188
M61136	M61144	M61153	M61162	M61171	M61180	M61189
M61137	M61145	M61154	M61163	M61172	M61181	
M61138	M61146	M61155	M61164	M61173	M61182	
M61139	M61147	M61156	M61165	M61174	M61183	
M61140	M61148	M61157	M61166	M61175	M61184	

LIVERPOOL–SOUTHPORT

COMPARTMENT STOCK

			M28333M	M28345M	M28358M
M28301M	M28305M	M28308M	M28334M	M28347M	M28359M
M28302M	M28306M	M28309M	M28335M	M28348M	M28360M
M28303M	M28307M	M28310M	M28336M	M28349M	M28361M
M28304M			M28337M	M28350M	M28362M
			M28338M	M28351M	M28363M
			M28339M	M28352M	M28364M

OPEN STOCK

			M28340M	M28353M	M28365M
M28311M	M28318M	M28326M	M28341M	M28354M	M28366M
M28312M	M28319M	M28327M	M28342M	M28355M	M28367M
M28313M	M28321M	M28328M	M28343M	M28356M	M28368M
M28314M	M28322M	M28329M	M28344M	M28357M	M28369M
M28315M	M28323M	M28330M			
M28316M	M28324M	M28331M			

BAGGAGE CARS

M28317M	M28325M	M28332M	M28496M	M23497M

MANCHESTER–BURY

M28500M	M28506M	M28512M	M28518M	M28525M	M28531M
M28501M	M28507M	M28513M	M28519M	M28526M	M28532M
M28502M	M28508M	M28514M	M28521M	M28527M	M28533M
M28503M	M28509M	M28515M	M28522M	M28528M	M28534M
M28504M	M28510M	M28516M	M28523M	M28529M	M28535M
M28505M	M28511M	M28517M	M28524M	M28530M	M28537M

WIRRAL & MERSEY

M28371M	M28379M	M28387M	M28672M	M28680M	M28688M
M28372M	M28380M	M28388M	M28673M	M28681M	M28689M
M28373M	M28381M	M28389M	M28674M	M28682M	M28690M
M28374M	M28382M	M28390M	M28675M	M28683M	
M28375M	M28383M	M28391M	M28676M	M28684M	
M28376M	M28384M	M28392M	M28677M	M28685M	
M28377M	M28385M	M28393M	M28678M	M28686M	
M28378M	M28386M	M28394M	M28679M	M28687M	

LANCASTER–MORECAMBE–HEYSHAM

M28219M	M28221M
M28220M*	M28222M

* Fitted with Germanium Rectifier

MANCHESTER, S. JUNCT & ALTRINCHAM

M28571M	M28579M	M28587M
M28572M	M28580M	M28588M
M28573M	M28581M	M28589M
M28574M	M28582M	M28590M
M28575M	M28583M	M28591M
M28576M	M28584M	M28592M
M28577M	M28585M	M28593M
M28578M	M28586M	M28594M

Southern Region

(Number to be seen on front and rear of each set)

TWO-CAR NON-CORRIDOR MOTOR UNITS

Motor Brake Second, Driving Trailer Composite.

(2-NOL.)

1813	1818	1823	1829	1834	1840	1845	1850
1814	1819	1824	1830	1835	1841	1846	
1815	1820	1825	1831	1836	1842	1847	
1816	1821	1826	1832	1837	1843	1848	
1817	1822	1827	1833	1839	1844	1849	

TWO-CAR MOTOR LAVATORY UNITS

Motor Lavatory Brake Second, Driving Trailer Lavatory Composite.

(2-BIL.)

2001†	2005†	2009†	2013	2018	2022	2026	2030
2002†	2006†	2010†	2015	2019	2023	2027	2031
2003†	2007†	2011	2016	2020	2024	2028	2032
2004†	2008†	2012	2017	2021	2025	2029	2033

2034	2063	2092	2123	2641	2657	2672	2688
2035	2064	2093	2124	2642	2658	2673	2689
2036	2065	2094	2125	2643	2659	2674	2690
2037	2066	2095	2126	2644	2660	2675	2691
2038	2067	2096	2127	2645	2661	2676	2692
2039	2068	2097	2128	2647	2662	2677	2693
2040	2069*	2098	2129	2648	2663	2678	2694
2041	2070	2099	2130	2649	2664	2679	2695
2042	2071	2100*	2132	2650	2665	2681	2696
2043	2072	2101	2133*	2651	2666	2682	2697
2044	2073	2103	2134	2652	2667	2683	2698
2045	2074	2104	2135	2653	2668	2684	2699
2046	2075	2105	2136	2654	2669	2685	2700
2047	2076	2106	2137	2655	2670	2686	
2048	2077	2107	2138	2656	2671	2687	
2049	2078	2108	2139				

FOUR-CAR MOTOR LAVATORY UNITS

Motor Brake Second, Composite, Lavatory Composite, Motor Brake Second.

(4-LAV.)

2921	2930	2939	2948
2922	2931	2940	2949
2923	2932	2941	2950
2924	2933	2942	2951
2925	2934	2943	2952
2926*	2935	2944	2953
2927	2936	2945	2954†
2928	2937	2946	2955†
2929	2938	2947	

*One motor coach with electro-pneumatic control gear.
†With electro-pneumatic control gear.

Left table continued:

2050	2079	2109	2140
2051	2080	2110	2141
2052	2081	2111	2142
2053	2082	2112	2143
2054	2083	2113	2144
2055	2084	2114	2145
2056*	2085	2115	2146
2057	2086	2116	2147
2058	2087	2117	2148
2059	2088*	2118	2149
2060	2089	2120	2150
2061	2090	2121	2151
2062	2091	2122	2152

†88 2nd Class seats instead of 84, and all-electric control gear.
*BIL Motor Coach and HAL trailer.

TWO-CAR MOTOR LAVATORY UNITS

Motor Brake Second, Driving Trailer Lavatory Composite.

(2-HAL.)

2601	2611	2621	2631
2602	2612	2622	2632
2603	2613	2623	2633
2604	2614	2624	2634
2605	2615	2625	2635
2606	2616	2626	2636
2607	2617	2627	2637
2608	2618	2628	2638
2609	2619	2629	2639
2610	2620	2630	2640

SIX-CAR MOTOR CORRIDOR UNITS (*with Pullman Car*)

Gangwayed within set

Motor Brake Second, Second, Composite, Composite Pullman, Composite, Motor Brake Second.

(6-PUL.)

3001	3007	3013	3019
3002	3008	3014	3020
3003	3009	3015	3041*
3004	3010	3016	3042*
3005	3011	3017	3043*
3006	3012	3018	

*Ex- " 6-CIT " Units. Trailers (except Pullman) formerly Firsts.

SIX-CAR MOTOR CORRIDOR UNITS (*with Pantry Car*)

Gangwayed within set

Motor Brake Second, Second, First, Pantry First, Second, Motor Brake Second.

(6-PAN.)

3021	3026	3030	3034
3022	3027	3031	3035
3023	3028	3032	3036
3024	3029	3033	3037
3025			

FIVE-CAR PULLMAN MOTOR UNITS

(*For " Brighton Belle " Service*)

All-Pullman
Gangwayed within set

Motor Second, Second, First, First, Motor Second.

(5-BEL.)

3051	3052	3053

FOUR-CAR KITCHEN CORRIDOR MOTOR UNITS

Gangwayed throughout

Motor Brake Second, First (and First Dining) Kitchen Second Dining, Motor Brake Second.

(4-RES.)

3054	3059	3065	3069
3055	3061	3066	3070
3056	3062	3067	3071
3057	3064	3068	3072

FOUR-CAR BUFFET CORRIDOR MOTOR UNITS

Gangwayed throughout

Motor Brake Second, Composite, Buffet, Motor Brake Second.

(4-BUF.)

3073	3077	3080	3083
3074	3078	3081	3084
3075	3079	3082	3085
3076			

FOUR-CAR CORRIDOR MOTOR UNITS

Gangwayed throughout

Motor Brake Second, Second, Composite, Motor Brake Second.

(4-COR.)

3101	3116	3131	3145
3102	3117	3132	3146
3103	3118	3133	3147
3104	3119	3134	3148
3105	3120	3135	3149
3106	3121	3136	3150
3107	3122	3137	3151
3108	3123	3138	3152
3109	3124	3139	3153
3110	3125	3140	3154
3111	3126	3141	3155
3112	3127	3142	3156
3113	3128	3143	3157
3114	3129	3144	3158
3115	3130		

FOUR-CAR DOUBLE DECK SUBURBAN UNITS

Motor Brake Second, 2 Trailer Seconds, Motor Brake Second.

(4-DD.)

4001	4002

FOUR-CAR NON-CORRIDOR SUBURBAN UNITS

Motor Brake Second, 2 Trailer Seconds, Motor Brake Second (Some Saloon).

(4-SUB.)

4101	4120	4285	4304
4102	4121	4286	4305
4103	4122	4287	4306
4104	4123	4288	4307
4105	4124	4289	4308
4106	4125	4290	4309
4107	4126	4291	4310
4108	4127	4292	4311
4109	4128	4293	4312
4110	4129	4294	4313
4111	4130	4295	4314
4112	4277	4296	4315
4113	4278	4297	4316
4114	4279	4298	4317
4115	4280	4299	4318
4116	4281	4300	4319
4117	4282	4301	4320
4118	4283	4302	4321
4119	4284	4303	4322

4323	4371	4626	4673
4324	4372	4627	4674
4325	4373	4628	4675
4326	4374	4629	4676
4327	4375	4630	4677
4328	4376	4631	4678
4329	4377	4632	4679
4330	4378	4633	4680
4331	4379	4634	4681
4332	4380	4635	4682
4333	4381	4636	4683
4334	4382	4637	4684
4335	4383	4638	4685
4336	4384	4639	4686
4337	4385	4640	4687
4338	4386	4641	4688
4339	4387	4642	4689
4340	4501	4643	4690
4341	4502	4644	4691
4342	4503	4645	4692
4343	4504	4646	4693
4344	4505	4647	4694
4345	4506	4648	4695
4346	4507	4649	4696
4347	4508	4650	4697
4348	4509	4651	4698
4349	4510	4652	4699
4351	4511	4653	4700
4352	4512	4654	4701
4353	4513	4655	4702
4354	4514	4656	4703
4355	4515	4657	4704
4356	4516	4658	4705
4357	4517	4659	4706
4358	4518	4660	4707
4359	4601	4661	4708
4360	4602	4662	4709
4361	4603	4663	4710
4362	4604	4664	4711
4363	4605	4665	4712
4364	4606	4666	4713
4365	4607	4667	4714
4366	4621	4668	4715
4367	4622	4669	4716
4368	4623	4670	4717
4369	4624	4671	4718
4370	4625	4672	4719

4720	4729	4738	4747
4721	4730	4739	4748
4722	4731	4740	4749
4723	4732	4741	4750
4724	4733	4742	4751
4725	4734	4743	4752
4726	4735	4744	4753
4727	4736	4745	4754
4728	4737	4746	

FOUR-CAR NON-CORRIDOR SUBURBAN UNITS

Motor Saloon Brake Second, Trailer Second, Trailer Saloon Second, Motor Saloon Brake Second.

(4-EPB)

5001	5033	5112	5144
5002	5034	5113	5145
5003	5035	5114	5146
5004	5036	5115	5147
5005	5037	5116	5148
5006	5038	5117	5149
5007	5039	5118	5150
5008	5040	5119	5151
5009	5041	5120	5152
5010	5042	5121	5153
5011	5043	5122	5154
5012	5044	5123	5155
5013	5045	5124	5156
5014	5046	5125	5157
5015	5047	5126	5158
5016	5048	5127	5159
5017	5049	5128	5160
5018	5050	5129	5161
5019	5051	5130	5162
5020	5052	5131	5163
5021	5053	5132	5164
5022	5101	5133	5165
5023	5102	5134	5166
5024	5103	5135	5167
5025	5104	5136	5168
5026	5105	5137	5169
5027	5106	5138	5170
5028	5107	5139	5171
5029	5108	5140	5172
5030	5109	5141	5173
5031	5110	5142	5174
5032	5111	5143	5175

5176	5198	5219	5240
5177	5199	5220	5241
5178	5200	5221	5242
5179	5201	5222	5243
5180	5202	5223	5244
5181	5203	5224	5245
5182	5204	5225	5246
5183	5205	5226	5247
5184	5206	5227	5248
5185	5207	5228	5249
5186	5208	5229	5250
5187	52C9	5230	5251
5188	5210	5231	5252
5189	5211	5232	5253
5190	5212	5233	5254
5191	5213	5234	5255
5192	5214	5235	5256
5193	5215	5236	5257
5194	5216	5237	5258
5195	5217	5238	5259
5196	5218	5239	5260
5197			

TWO-CAR MOTOR LAVATORY UNITS

(Rebuild of 2-NOL)

Motor Saloon Brake Second, Driving Trailer Lavatory Composite.

(2-HAP)

5601	5603	5605	5606
5602	5604		

TWO-CAR NON-CORRIDOR SUBURBAN UNITS

(B.R. Standard design)

Motor Saloon Brake Second, Driving Trailer Second (part Saloon).

(2-EPB)

5701	5710	5719	5728
5702	5711	5720	5729
5703	5712	5721	5730
5704	5713	5722	5731
5705	5714	5723	5732
5706	5715	5724	5733
5707	5716	5725	5734
5708	5717	5726	5735
5709	5718	5727	5736

5737	5748	5759	5770
5738	5749	5760	5771
5739	5750	5761	5772
5740	5751	5762	5773
5741	5752	5763	5774
5742	5753	5764	5775
5743	5754	5765	5776
5744	5755	5766	5777
5745	5756*	5767	5778
5746	5757	5768	
5747	5758	5769	

* Fitted with Girling Disc Brakes

TWO-CAR MOTOR LAVATORY UNITS

(B.R. Standard design)

Motor Saloon Brake Second, Driving Trailer Lavatory Composite (part Saloon).

(2-HAP)

6001	6004	6007	6010
6002	6005	6008	6011
6003	6006	6009	

FOUR-CAR CORRIDOR BUFFET UNITS

(B.R. Standard design)

Gangwayed throughout

Motor Brake Second, Composite, Buffet, Motor Brake Second.

(4-BEP)

7001   7002

FOUR-CAR CORRIDOR UNITS

(B.R. Standard design)

Gangwayed throughout

Motor Brake Second, Composite, Second, Motor Brake Second.

(4-CEP)

7101	7102	7103	7104

WATERLOO AND CITY LINE MOTOR COACH NOS.

51	54	57	60
52	55	58	61
53	56	59	62

DIESEL MULTIPLE-UNIT COACH NUMBERS

(Descriptions under headings refer to type of unit in which vehicles are formed)

Motor Brake Second

(Twin units)

E50000	E50017	E50034
E50001	E50018	E50035
E50002	E50019	E50036
E50003	E50020	E50037
E50004	E50021	E50038
E50005	E50022	E50039
E50006	E50023	E50040
E50007	E50024	E50041
E50008	E50025	E50042
E50009	E50026	E50043
E50010	E50027	E50044
E50011	E50028	E50045
E50012	E50029	E50046
E50013	E50030	E50047
E50014	E50031	E50048
E50015	E50032	E50049
E50016	E50033	

Motor Brake Second

(W.R. 3-car Suburban)

W50050	W50064	W50078
W50051	W50065	W50079
W50052	W50066	W50080
W50053	W50067	W50081
W50054	W50068	W50082
W50055	W50069	W50083
W50056	W50070	W50084
W50057	W50071	W50085
W50058	W50072	W50086
W50059	W50073	W50087
W50060	W50074	W50088
W50061	W50075	W50089
W50062	W50076	W50090
W50063	W50077	W50091

Motor Second

(W.R. 3-car Suburban)

W50092	W50097	W50102
W50093	W50098	W50103
W50094	W50099	W50104
W50095	W50100	W50105
W50096	W50101	W50106

W50107	W50116	W50125
W50108	W50117	W50126
W50109	W50118	W50127
W50110	W50119	W50128
W50111	W50120	W50129
W50112	W50121	W50130
W50113	W50122	W50131
W50114	W50123	W50132
W50115	W50124	W50133

Motor Brake Second

(Twin units)

M50134	M50136	M50137
M50135		

Motor Lavatory Composite

(N.E. 4-car units)

E50138	E50143	E50148
E50139	E50144	E50149
E50140	E50145	E50150
E50141	E50146	E50151
E50142	E50147	

Motor Brake Second

(Twin units)

E50152	E50154	E50156
E50153	E50155	E50157

Motor Lavatory Composite

(Twin units)

E50158	E50160	E50162
E50159	E50161	E50163

Motor Brake Second

(Twin units)

E50164	E50166	E50167
E50165		

Motor Lavatory Composite

(Twin units)

E50168	E50170	E50171
E50169		

Motor Lavatory Composite

(N.E. 4-car units)

E50172	E50174	E50176
E50173	E50175	E50177

E50178	E50185	E50192
E50179	E50186	E50193
E50180	E50187	E50194
E50181	E50188	E50195
E50182	E50189	E50196
E50183	E50190	E50197
E50184	E50191	

Motor Brake Second
(Twin units)

E50198	E50211	E50223
E50199	E50212	E50224
E50200	E50213	E50225
E50201	E50214	E50226
E50202	E50215	E50227
E50203	E50216	E50228
E50204	E50217	E50229
E50205	E50218	E50230
E50206	E50219	E50231
E50207	E50220	E50232
E50208	E50221	E50233
E50209	E50222	
E50210		

Motor Lavatory Composite
(N.E. 4-car units)

E50234	E50238	E50242
E50235	E50239	E50243
E50236	E50240	E50244
E50237	E50241	E50245

Motor Brake Second
(Twin units)

E50246	E50252	E50256
E50247	E50253	E50257
E50248	E50254	E50258
E50250	E50255	E50259
E50251		

Motor Lavatory Composite
(Twin units)

E50260	E50264	E50267
E50261	E50265	E50268
E50262	E50266	E50269
E50263		

Motor Lavatory Composite
(N.E. 3-car units)

E50270	E50274	E50277
E50271	E50275	E50278
E50272	E50276	E50279
E50273		

Motor Brake Second
(N.E. 3-car units)

E50280	E50285	E50289
E50281	E50286	E50290
E50282	E50287	E50291
E50283	E50288	E50292
E50284		

Motor Brake Second
(Twin units)

E50293	E50295	E50296
E50294		

Motor Brake Second
(L.M. 3-car units)

M50303 M50304 M50305

Motor Lavatory Composite
(L.M. 3-car units)

M50321 M50322 M50323

Motor Brake Second
(Twin units)

SC50339	E50360	E50381
SC50340	E50361	E50382
SC50341	E50362	E50383
SC50342	E50363	E50384
SC50343	E50364	E50385
SC50344	E50365	E50386
SC50345	E50366	E50387
SC50346	E50367	E50388
SC50347	E50368	E50389
SC50348	E50369	E50390
SC50349	E50370	M50391
M50350	E50371	M50392
M50351	E50372	M50393
M50352	E50373	M50394
M50353	E50374	M50395
M50354	E50375	M50396
M50355	E50376	E50415
M50356	E50377	E50416
M50357	E50378	E50417
M50358	E50379	
E50359	E50380	

Motor Brake Second
(L.M. 3-car units)

M50420	M50422	M50423
M50421		

Motor Lavatory Composite
(L.M. 3-car units)

M50424	M50426	M50427
M50425		

Motor Brake Second
(L.M. 3-car units)

M50428	M50443	M50458
M50429	M50444	M50459
M50430	M50445	M50460
M50431	M50446	M50461
M50432	M50447	M50462
M50433	M50448	M50463
M50434	M50449	M50464
M50435	M50450	M50465
M50436	M50451	M50466
M50437	M50452	M50467
M50438	M50453	M50468
M50439	M50454	M50469
M50440	M50455	M50470
M50441	M50456	M50471
M50442	M50457	

Motor Lavatory Composite
(L.M. 3-car units)

M50480	M50495	M50510
M50481	M50496	M50511
M50482	M50497	M50512
M50483	M50498	M50513
M50484	M50499	M50514
M50485	M50500	M50515
M50486	M50501	M50516
M50487	M50502	M50517
M50488	M50503	M50518
M50489	M50504	M50519
M50490	M50505	M50520
M50491	M50506	M50521
M50492	M50507	M50522
M50493	M50508	M50523
M50494	M50509	

Motor Lavatory Second
(W.R. 3-car Cross-country)

W50647	W50664	W50680
W50648	W50665	W50681
W50649	W50666	W50682
W50650	W50667	W50683
W50651	W50668	W50684
W50652	W50669	W50685
W50653	W50670	W50686
W50654	W50671	W50687
W50655	W50672	W50688
W50656	W50673	W50689
W50657	W50674	W50690
W50658	W50675	W50691
W50659	W50676	W50692
W50660	W50677	W50693
W50661	W50678	W50694
W50662	W50679	W50695
W50663		

Motor Brake Composite
(W.R. 3-car Cross-country)

W50696	W50713	W50729
W50697	W50714	W50730
W50698	W50715	W50731
W50699	W50716	W50732
W50700	W50717	W50733
W50701	W50718	W50734
W50702	W50719	W50735
W50703	W50720	W50736
W50704	W50721	W50737
W50705	W50722	W50738
W50706	W50723	W50739
W50707	W50724	W50740
W50708	W50725	W50741
W50709	W50726	W50742
W50710	W50727	W50743
W50711	W50728	W50744
W50712		

Motor Lavatory Composite
(N.E. 3-car units)

E50745	E50746	E50747

Motor Lavatory Composite
(N.E. 4-car units)

E50748	E50750	E50751
E50749		

Motor Brake Second
L.M. 3-car units

M50752	M50758	M50764
M50753	M50759	M50765
M50754	M50760	M50766
M50755	M50761	M50767
M50756	M50762	
M50757	M50763	

Motor Lavatory Composite
(L.M. 3-car units)

M50785	M50791	M50797
M50786	M50792	M50798
M50787	M50793	M50799
M50788	M50794	M50800
M50789	M50795	
M50790	M50796	

Motor Brake Second
(W.R. 3-car Suburban)

W50818	W50826	W50834
W50819	W50827	W50835
W50820	W50828	W50836
W50821	W50829	W50837
W50822	W50830	W50838
W50823	W50831	W50839
W50824	W50832	W50840
W50825	W50833	

Motor Second
(W.R. 3-car Suburban)

W50871	W50879	W50887
W50872	W50880	W50888
W50873	W50881	W50889
W50874	W50882	W50890
W50875	W50883	W50891
W50876	W50884	W50892
W50877	W50885	W50893
W50878	W50886	

Motor Brake Second
(Twin units)

SC51108	SC51113	SC51118
SC51109	SC51114	SC51119
SC51110	SC51115	SC51120
SC51111	SC51116	SC51121
SC51112	SC51117	SC51122

Driving Trailer Lavatory Composite
(Twin units)

E56000	E56043	E56086
E56001	E56044	E56087
E56002	E56045	E56088
E56003	E56046	E56089
E56004	E56047	M56090
E56005	E56048	M56091
E56006	E56049	M56092
E56007	E56050	M56093
E56008	E56051	SC56094
E56009	E56052	SC56095
E56010	E56053	SC56096
E56011	E56054	SC56097
E56012	E56055	SC56098
E56013	E56056	SC56099
E56014	E56057	SC56100
E56015	E56058	SC56101
E56016	E56059	SC56102
E56017	E56060	SC56103
E56018	E56061	SC56104
E56019	E56062	M56105
E56020	E56063	M56106
E56021	E56064	M56107
E56022	E56065	M56108
E56023	E56066	M56109
E56024	E56067	M56110
E56025	E56068	M56111
E56026	E56069	M56112
E56027	E56070	M56113
E56028	E56071	E56114
E56029	E56072	E56115
E56030	E56073	E56116
E56031	E56074	E56117
E56032	E56075	E56118
E56033	E56076	E56119
E56034	E56077	E56120
E56035	E56078	E56121
E56036	E56079	E56122
E56037	E56080	E56123
E56038	E56081	E56124
E56039	E56082	E56125
E56040	E56083	E56126
E56041	E56084	E56127
E56042	E56085	E56128

E56129	E56144	SC56301
E56130	E56145	SC56302
E56131	M56146	SC56303
E56132	M56147	SC56304
E56133	M56148	SC56305
E56134	M56149	SC56306
E56135	M56150	SC56307
E56136	M56151	SC56308
E56137	E56170	SC56309
E56138	E56171	SC56310
E56139	E56172	SC56311
E56140	E56218	SC56312
E56141	E56219	SC56313
E56142	E56220	SC56314
E56143	SC56300	

Trailer Composite
(W.R. 3-car Suburban)

W59000	W59011	W59022
W59001	W59012	W59023
W59002	W59013	W59024
W59003	W59014	W59025
W59004	W59015	W59026
W59005	W59016	W59027
W59006	W59017	W59028
W59007	W59018	W59029
W59008	W59019	W59030
W59009	W59020	W59031
W59010	W59021	

Trailer Second
(W.R. 3-car Suburban)

W59032	W59036	W59040
W59033	W59037	W59041
W59034	W59038	
W59035	W59039	

Trailer Lavatory Second
(N.E. 4-car units)

E59042	E59045	E59047
E59043	E59046	E59048
E59044		

Trailer Lavatory Brake Second
(N.E. 4-car units)

E59049	E59052	E59054
E59050	E59053	E59055
E59051		

Trailer Lavatory Second
(N.E. 4-car units)

E59060	E59065	E59069
E59061	E59066	E59070
E59062	E59067	E59071
E59063	E59068	E59072
E59064		

Trailer Lavatory Brake Second
(N.E. 4-car units)

E59073	E59078	E59082
E59074	E59079	E59083
E59075	E59080	E59084
E59076	E59081	E59085
E59077		

Trailer Lavatory Second
(N.E. 4-car units)

E59086	E59088	E59090
E59087	E59089	E59091

Trailer Lavatory Brake Second
(N.E. 4-car units)

E59092	E59094	E59096
E59093	E59095	E59097

Trailer Lavatory Second
(N.E. 3-car units)

E59100	E59104	E59107
E59101	E59105	E59108
E59102	E59106	E59109
E59103		

Trailer Lavatory Brake Second

(N.E. 4-car units)

E59112   E59113

Trailer Lavatory Second

(L.M. 3-car units)

M59114   M59115   M59116

Trailer Lavatory Composite

(L.M. 3-car units)

M59132	M59148	M59164
M59133	M59149	M59165
M59134	M59150	M59166
M59135	M59151	M59167
M59136	M59152	M59168
M59137	M59153	M59169
M59138	M59154	M59170
M59139	M59155	M59171
M59140	M59156	M59172
M59141	M59157	M59173
M59142	M59158	M59174
M59143	M59159	M59175
M59144	M59160	M59176
M59145	M59161	M59177
M59146	M59162	M59178
M59147	M59163	M59179

Trailer Buffet Second

(W.R. 3-car Cross-country)

W59255	W59267	W59279
W59256	W59268	W59280
W59257	W59269	W59281
W59258	W59270	W59282
W59259	W59271	W59283
W59260	W59272	W59284
W59261	W59273	W59285
W59262	W59274	W59286
W59263	W59275	W59287
W59264	W59276	W59288
W59265	W59277	W59289
W59266	W59278	W59290

W59291	W59295	W59299
W59292	W59296	W59300
W59293	W59297	W59301
W59294	W59298	

Trailer Lavatory Second

(N.E. 3-car units)

E59302   E59303   E59304

Trailer Lavatory Second

(N.E. 4-car units)

E59305   E59306

Trailer Lavatory Second

(L.M. 3-car units)

M59307	M59313	M59319
M59308	M59314	M59320
M59309	M59315	M59321
M59310	M59316	M59322
M59311	M59317	
M59312	M59318	

Trailer Composite

(W.R. 3-car Suburban)

W59326	W59334	W59342
W59327	W59335	W59343
W59328	W59336	W59344
W59329	W59337	W59345
W59330	W59338	W59346
W59331	W59339	W59347
W59332	W59340	W59348
W59333	W59341	

Motor Brake Second

(S.R. Hastings)

S60000	S60008	S60016
S60001	S60009	S60017
S60002	S60010	S60018
S60003	S60011	S60019
S60004	S60012	S60020
S60005	S60013	S60021
S60006	S60014	S60022
S60007	S60015	S60023

Motor Brake Second
(S.R. Hampshire)

S60100	S60106	S60112
S60101	S60107	S60113
S60102	S60108	S60114
S60103	S60109	S60115
S60104	S60110	S60116
S60105	S60111	S60117

Trailer Lavatory Second
(S.R. Hastings)

S60500	S60512	S60524
S60501	S60513	S60525
S60502	S60514	S60526
S60503	S60515	S60527
S60504	S60516	S60528
S60505	S60517	S60529
S60506	S60518	S60530
S60507	S60519	S60531
S60508	S60520	S60532
S60509	S60521	S60533
S60510	S60522	S60534
S60511	S60523	S60535

Trailer Corridor First
(S.R. Hastings)

S60700	S60704	S60708
S60701	S60705	S60709
S60702	S60706	S60710
S60703	S60707	S60711

Driving Trailer Lavatory Composite
(S.R. Hampshire)

S60800	S60806	S60812
S60801	S60807	S60813
S60802	S60808	S60814
S60803	S60809	S60815
S60804	S60810	S60816
S60805	S60811	S60817

Motor Brake Second
(Twin units)

E79000	E79028	E79056
E79001	E79029	E79057
E79002	E79030	E79058
E79003	E79031	E79059
E79004	E79032	E79060
E79005	E79033	E79061
E79006	E79034	E79062
E79007	E79035	E79063
M79008	E79036	E79064
M79009	E79037	E79065
M79010	E79038	E79066
M79011	E79039	E79067
M79012	E79040	E79068
M79013	E79041	E79069
M79014	E79042	E79070
M79015	E79043	E79071
M79016	E79044	E79072
M79017	E79045	E79073
M79018	E79046	E79074
M79019	E79047	E79075
M79020	E79048	M79076
E79021	E79049	M79077
E79022	E79050	M79078
E79023	E79051	M79079
E79024	E79052	M79080
E79025	E79053	M79081
E79026	E79054	M79082
E79027	E79055	

Motor Lavatory Brake Second
(Inter-city units)

W79083	W79093	SC79103
W79084	W79094	SC79104
W79085	SC79095	SC79105
W79086	SC79096	SC79106
W79087	SC79097	SC79107
W79088	SC79098	SC79108
W79089	SC79099	SC79109
W79090	SC79100	SC79110
W79091	SC79101	SC79111
W79092	SC79102	

otor Brake Second
(Twin units)

M79118	M79129	E79140
M79119	M79130	M79141
M79120	M79131	M79142
M79121	M79132	M79143
M79122	M79133	M79144
M79123	M79134	M79145
M79124	M79135	M79146
M79125	M79136	M79147
M79126	E79137	M79148
M79127	E79138	M79149
M79128	E79139	

Motor Second
(N.E. 4-car units)

E79150	E79152	E79154
E79151	E79153	

Motor Lavatory Second
(Inter-city units)

SC79155	SC79160	SC79165
SC79156	SC79161	SC79166
SC79157	SC79162	SC79167
SC79158	SC79163	SC79168
SC79159	SC79164	

Motor Brake Second
(Twin units)

M79169	M79175	M79181
M79170	M79176	M79184
M79171	M79177	M79185
M79172	M79178	M79186
M79173	M79179	M79187
M79174	M79180	M79188

Motor Lavatory Composite
(Twin units)

M79189	M79191	M79193
M79190	M79192	

Driving Trailer Lavatory Composite
(Twin units)

E79250	E79255	E79260
E79251	E79256	E79261
E79252	E79257	E79262
E79253	E79258	
E79254	E79259	

Driving Trailer Lavatory Second
(Twin units)

E79263	E79273	E79283
E79264	E79274	E79284
E79265	E79275	E79285
E79266	E79276	E79286
E79267	E79277	E79287
E79268	E79278	E79288
E79269	E79279	E79289
E79270	E79280	E79290
E79271	E79281	E79291
E79272	E79282	

Trailer Lavatory Brake Second
(N.E. 4-car units)

E79325	E79327	E79329
E79326	E79328	

Trailer Lavatory Second
(N.E. 4-car units)

E79400	E79402	E79404
E79401	E79403	

Buffet Corridor First
(Inter-city units)

W79440	SC79443	SC79446
W79441	SC79444	SC79447
SC79442	SC79445	

Trailer Corridor First
(Inter-city units)

W79470	SC79475	SC79479
W79471	SC79476	SC79480
W79472	SC79477	SC79481
W79473	SC79478	SC79482
SC79474		

Motor Lavatory Composite
(Twin units)

E79500	E79503	E79506
E79501	E79504	E79507
E79502	E79505	

Motor Composite
(N.E. 4-car units)

E79508	E79510	E79512
E79509	E79511	

Driving Trailer Lavatory Composite
(Twin units)

M79600	E79623	M79652
M79601	E79624	M79653
M79602	E79625	M79654
M79603	M79626	M79655
M79604	M79627	M79656
M79605	M79628	M79657
M79606	M79629	E79658
M79607	M79630	E79659
M79608	M79631	E79660
M79609	M79632	E79661
M79610	M79639	M79662
M79611	M79640	M79663
M79612	M79641	M79664
E79613	M79642	M79665
E79614	M79643	M79666
E79615	M79644	M79667
E79616	M79645	M79668
E79617	M79646	M79669
E79618	M79647	M79670
E79619	M79648	M79671
E79620	M79649	M79672
E79621	M79650	M79673
E79622	M79651	M79674

M79675	M79679	M79682
M79676	M79680	M79683
M79677	M79681	M79684
M79678		

Motor Second
(4-wheel units)

M79740	M79745	M79748

Motor Brake Second
(4-wheel units)

M79742	M79744	M79750
M79743		

Trailer Second
(4-wheel units)

M79741	M79747	M79749
M79746		

Motor Brake Second
(Single units)

M79900	M79901

Railbus
(4-wheel unit)

SC79979

Experimental Unit

This unit is not in public service but is undergoing trials. The two coaches were converted from former L.M.S. steam-hauled Open Brake Thirds.

9821	9828

G.W.R. Railcars

W4W	W16W	W26W
W5W	W17W	W27W
W6W	W18W	W28W
W7W	W19W	W29W
W8W	W20W	W30W
W11W	W21W	W31W
W12W	W22W	W32W
W13W	W23W	W33W
W14W	W24W	W34W
W15W	W25W	W38W